PHYSICS OF PLANT ENVIRONMENT

NORTH-HOLLAND BOOKS

General Editors:

J. DE BOER, Professor of Physics, University of Amsterdam
H. BRINKMAN, Professor of Physics, University of Groningen
H. B. G. CASIMIR, Director of the Philips' Laboratories, Eindhoven

Monographs:

B. BAK, Elementary Introduction to Molecular Spectra
V. L. BONCH-BRUEVICH and S. V. TYABLIKOV, The Green Function Method in Statistical Mechanics
H. G. VAN BUEREN, Imperfections in Crystals
S. R. DE GROOT and P. MAZUR, Non-Equilibrium Thermodynamics
R. HOSEMANN and S. N. BAGCHI, Direct Analysis of Diffraction by Matter
H. JONES, The Theory of Brillouin Zones and Electronic States in Crystals
K. KUMAR, Perturbation Theory and the Nuclear Many Body Problem
H. J. LIPKIN, Beta Decay for Pedestrians
J. P. MARCHAND, Distributions, An Outline
A. M. L. MESSIAH, Quantum Mechanics, 2 vols
P. H. E. MEYER and E. BAUER, Group Theory, the Application to Quantum Mechanics
E. J. POST, Formal Structure of Electromagnetics
P. ROMAN, Theory of Elementary Particles
D. TER HAAR, Elements of Hamiltonian Mechanics
S. TOMONAGA, Quantum Mechanics

Edited Volumes:

P. M. ENDT and M. DEMEUR (editors), Nuclear Reactions, Vol. I
P. M. ENDT and P. B. SMITH (editors), Nuclear Reactions, Vol. II
FUNDAMENTAL PROBLEMS IN STATISTICAL MECHANICS. Proceedings of the NUFFIC International Summer Course in Science (Nijenrode, 1961)
SPACE RESEARCH, Vols. I-III. Proceedings of the 1st, 2nd and 3rd International Space Science Symposium, held respectively at Nice (1960), Florence (1961) and Washington, D.C. (1962)
J. G. WILSON and S. A. WOUTHUYSEN (editors), Progress in Elementary Particle and Cosmic Ray Physics, Vols. I-VII

PHYSICS
OF
PLANT ENVIRONMENT

EDITOR:

W. R. VAN WIJK

Professor of Physics, Agricultural University Wageningen, The Netherlands

CONTRIBUTORS:

A. J. W. BORGHORST   J. A. BUSINGER   W. J. DERKSEN   F. H. SCHMIDT

D. W. SCHOLTE UBING   D. A. DE VRIES   W. R. VAN WIJK

1963

NORTH-HOLLAND PUBLISHING COMPANY – AMSTERDAM

INTERSCIENCE PUBLISHERS, a division of

JOHN WILEY & SONS, INC. – NEW YORK

PUBLISHERS:

NORTH-HOLLAND PUBLISHING CO. – AMSTERDAM

SOLE DISTRIBUTORS FOR U.S.A.:

INTERSCIENCE PUBLISHERS, a division of

JOHN WILEY & SONS, INC. – NEW YORK

PRINTED IN THE NETHERLANDS

PREFACE

Physics of plant environment has originated from studies of the reaction of plants to their environment. In evaluating the effects of different climates on plant growth one is immediately confronted with questions concerning the physical state of the environment such as radiation, heat and water relations, diffusion, wind and turbulent exchange of matter. Modification of the micro-climate by tillage, drainage, irrigation, mulching, windshields, changing plant spacing etc. can to a considerable extent also be interpreted in terms of the physical state of the environment.

In the first chapter of this book some examples of a physical approach to a quantitative understanding of the response of plants to environmental conditions are briefly discussed. In the other chapters only the physics of the environment itself is treated. A discussion of plant reactions would have increased the size of the book beyond reasonable limits.

Basic concepts of meteorology and of soil physics are discussed in Chapter 2. The third chapter gives the fundamentals of temperature radiation and data on solar and terrestrial radiation as influenced by the state of the atmosphere and of the soil surface.

The fourth, fifth, sixth and seventh chapters deal with soil temperature, the distribution of heat between air and soil and the thermal properties of soils, in relation to its air and moisture content.

Periodic variations of the temperature as well as arbitrary temperature variations are discussed. The theory of periodic temperature variations in a soil consisting of two or three layers and its application to mulching and tillage are given.

Chapter 8 deals with the propagation of heat in the air near the ground and contains a brief discussion of evaporation in connection with the heat balance at the earth surface. Chapter 9 discusses the climate of a greenhouse in relation to the heat balance and gives some practical applications. Air pollution, its theory and some applications, forms the content of Chapter 10.

The book contains much material that has not been published in bookform before. As examples the distribution of heat between air and soil in Chapter 4, the treatment of heat impulses and arbitrary temperature variations by Laplace transforms in Chapters 5 and 8 and most of the quantitative applications to soils may be mentioned.

Our present knowledge of the physics of plant environment is far from complete. This is the reason why important processes such as the diffusion of soil air, and the transfer of heat and matter within a vegetative cover are not discussed. On the other hand flow of water in soils has not been included since excellent textbooks and comprehensive articles exist to which the reader is referred.

Physics of plant environment has for many years been a major field of research in the Laboratory of Physics and Meteorology of the Agricultural University at Wageningen, the Netherlands. This is reflected in the fact that the first eight chapters have been written by members of the staff or former members of the staff of this laboratory.

Several other staff members and former graduate students have also indirectly contributed to the book by carrying out research on special subjects. To some degree this applies also to the Agronomy Department of Iowa State University at Ames, Iowa and to the Arid Zone Research Centre of the University of Tunis.

I have highly appreciated the willingness of Dr. Businger, formerly of the Institute for Horticultural Engineering at Wageningen and Dr. Schmidt of the Royal Netherlands Meteorological Institute at de Bilt to write Chapter 9 and 10, respectively. The authors' thanks are due to Mrs Nancy Riddell for revising the English, to Miss C. W. Pitlo for typing and secretarial assistance, to Messrs Kleiss and Van den Brink for preparation of most of the figures and to the publishers, the North-Holland Publishing Company, Amsterdam, for the way in which they have co-operated during and after the preparation of the manuscript.

Part of this publication comes within the research programme of the Stichting voor Fundamenteel Onderzoek der Materie (Foundation for Fundamental Research on Matter – F. O. M.) and was made possible by financial support from the Nederlandse Organisatie voor Zuiver-Wetenschappelijk Onderzoek (Netherlands Organization for the Advancement of Pure Research – Z.W.O.).

The Editor is also highly indebted to Dr. P. J. Bruijn and Ir. H. Goedkoop Hzn. for checking the formulas and reading the proofs.

November 1962   W. R. VAN WIJK
Wageningen

CONTENTS

PREFACE VII

CONTENTS IX

FREQUENTLY USED SYMBOLS XV

1. INTRODUCTION, THE PHYSICAL METHOD

W. R. VAN WIJK

1.1 Scope of the present text 1

1.2 The placement of fertilizers 3

1.3 Water culture and pot experiments 5

1.4 Placement method and crop yield 7

1.5 The essential steps in the theoretical treatment 9

1.6 Tilth and soil temperature 10

1.7 Conclusions 12

1.8 Optimum depth of a water table in drainage 13

1.9 Contents of the book 16

2. THE ATMOSPHERE AND THE SOIL

W. R. VAN WIJK AND D. A. DE VRIES

2.1 Structure of the atmosphere 17

2.2 Composition of the air in the troposphere and in the stratosphere . . . 20

2.3 Pressure and wind 21

2.4 Temperature 23

2.5 Hydrostatic stability and the adiabatic lapse rate 25

2.6 Dynamic stability 29

2.7 Dry air 33

2.8 The barometric height formula 33

2.9 Adiabatic expansion 35

2.10 Air containing water vapor 37

2.11 Humidity of air 37

2.12 The wet adiabatic lapse rate 39

2.13 Properties of water 40

2.14 The saturation vapor pressure, capillary and osmotic phenomena . . . 42

2.15 The saturation vapor pressure over plane and curved surfaces 43

2.16 The saturation vapor pressure over a solution, osmotic pressure . . . 45

2.17 The influence of liquid pressure on the saturation vapor pressure . . . 47

2.18 Properties of soil, soil composition 48

2.19 Water movement in saturated soils 49
2.20 Water movement in unsaturated soils 51
2.21 The moisture sorption curve 53
2.22 Experimental methods, temperature measurement 55
2.23 Measurement of atmospheric humidity 57
2.24 The measurement of soil moisture 59

3. RADIATION

W. R. VAN WIJK AND D. W. SCHOLTE UBING

3.1 The nature of thermal radiation, definitions 62
3.2 Absorption and reflection of radiation 64
3.3 Kirchhoff's law, black body 65
3.4 Laws of Lambert, Stefan-Boltzmann and Wien 67
3.5 Planck's law for black body radiation 68
3.6 Black body radiation in a finite frequency interval 69
3.7 Summary of formulas on temperature radiation 70
3.8 Irradiance of the earth by the sun 71
3.9 Solar radiation at the top of the atmosphere 73
3.10 Extinction in a cloudless atmosphere, optical air mass, turbidity . . . 76
3.11 The influence of clouds, total global radiation 79
3.12 Empirical formulas for total global radiation 81
3.13 Reflection and absorption at the surface, photosynthesis, illumination . . 88
  3.13.1 Reflection 88
  3.13.2 Photosynthesis, absorption by plants 89
  3.13.3 Illumination 90
3.14 Terrestrial radiation 91
3.15 Net long wave radiation 92
3.16 Calculation of atmospheric and terrestrial radiation 94
3.17 The radiation balance of the earth 97
3.18 Instruments for radiation measurements 98

4. PERIODIC TEMPERATURE VARIATIONS IN A HOMOGENEOUS SOIL

W. R. VAN WIJK AND D. A. DE VRIES

4.1 The variation of surface temperature 102
4.2 The phenomenon of heat conduction, thermal conductivity . . . 103
4.3 The differential equation of heat conduction in one dimension . . 106
4.4 Harmonic variation of temperature with time 108
  4.4.1 Mathematical treatment of harmonic temperature variations, complex
        numbers 111
4.5 Combined diurnal and annual variation 112
4.6 Harmonic variation of the heat flux density, the energy balance . . 114

4.7   Periodic storage and release of heat 118
4.8   Comparison of the theory with observations 119
4.9   The influence of soil thermal properties on the temperature regime . . 121
4.10 The influence of surface roughness and of wind velocity on the temperature re-
      gime 127
4.11 The annual temperature variation 130
4.12 General periodic temperature variation, Fourier analysis 133
4.13 Calculation of the coefficients in a Fourier expansion 134
4.14 Example of the penetration of the harmonics into a soil 139
4.15 The correction of Lamont 139
4.16 Variation of the thermal diffusivity with time 140

5. GENERAL TEMPERATURE VARIATIONS IN A HOMOGENEOUS SOIL

W. R. VAN WIJK

5.1   Small deviations from periodicity 144
5.2   The transient term 144
5.3   Quick method for estimating the transient term 146
5.4   Example of the influence of the transient term 147
5.5   Sudden release of heat 149
5.6   Gradual release of heat 151
5.7   Initial and boundary conditions given 154
5.8   Use of Laplace transforms 156
5.9   Application to soils 159
5.10 Determination of λ and C 162
5.11 Penetration of frost, thawing 166
5.12 Some empirical data on soil temperature 169

6. SINUSOIDAL TEMPERATURE VARIATION IN A LAYERED SOIL

W. R. VAN WIJK AND W. J. DERKSEN

6.1   Examples of layered soils 171
6.2   Sinusoidal temperature variation in soil consisting of two layers . . 172
6.3   Derivation of the formulas in Table 6.1 174
6.4   The surface temperature 177
6.5   Temperature below the surface 180
6.6   Tillage, properties of a tilled soil 181
6.7   The diurnal variation on a tilled soil 183
6.8   Phase shifts, net long wave radiation 185
6.9   The annual variation on a tilled soil 187
6.10 The phase shift of the annual variation 188
6.11 Temperature below the surface 190
6.12 Comparison with experiment 190

6.13 Attempt to a quantitative comparison 192
6.14 Properties of a soil after tilth 195
6.15 Conclusions on thermal effects resulting from tilth 197
6.16 A sand layer on top of a peat soil 198
6.17 Dry upper layer 201
6.18 Other types of top layers 203
6.19 A soil consisting of three or more layers 206

7. THERMAL PROPERTIES OF SOILS

D. A. DE VRIES

7.1 Introduction 210
7.2 The heat capacity of soils 211
7.3 The thermal conductivity of soils 213
7.4 Theory of the thermal conductivity of granular materials . . . 214
7.5 The influence of moisture movement 218
7.6 Examples of calculations of the thermal conductivity 223
    7.6.1 Quartz sand 223
    7.6.2 Fairbanks sand 230
    7.6.3 Healy clay 232
    7.6.4 Fairbanks peat 233
    7.6.5 Concluding remarks. 235

8. TURBULENT TRANSFER IN AIR

W. R. VAN WIJK AND A. J. W. BORGHORST

8.1 Turbulence, mixing length 236
8.2 Equation of molecular exchange 238
8.3 Equations of turbulent exchange 240
8.4 Bowen's ratio 241
8.5 Some experiments on turbulence in the atmosphere 242
8.6 Constant thermal conductivity, sinusoidal variation 244
8.7 Advective air over a surface at constant temperature 245
8.8 Advective air, air temperature constant 247
8.9 Advective air, thermal diffusivity finite in both media 249
8.10 Exchange coefficient increases as $(z + z_0)$, wind profiles 250
8.11 Sinusoidal temperature variation 254
8.12 The heat wave 257
8.13 General temperature variation 259
8.14 Laplace transforms 261
8.15 Laplace transform for $\lambda = b(z + z_0)$ 262
8.16 An instantaneous change of heat flux density 263
8.17 Some references to microclimate 266

8.18 Water requirements of crops, transpiration 267
8.19 Evapotranspiration and potential evapotranspiration 270
8.20 Calculation of potential evapotranspiration 271

9. THE GLASSHOUSE (GREENHOUSE) CLIMATE

J. A. BUSINGER

9.1   Introduction 277
9.2   The energy budget of the glasshouse 278
9.3   The glasshouse temperature 279
9.4   The evaporation 281
9.5   Ventilation 282
9.6   The net radiation 285
9.7   The daylight coefficient f 286
9.8   The heat flux into the soil 288
9.9   The coefficients of convective heat transfer h_{in} and h_{ou} 288
9.10 Discussion of the greenhouse-effect 289
9.11 The natural glasshouse climate 290
9.12 The temperature 291
9.13 Air circulation 292
9.14 Climate control in the glasshouse, the glasshouse construction . . . 293
9.15 Heating of glasshouses 297
9.16 Heating systems 300
9.17 Air heating 300
9.18 Thin pipe heating 302
9.19 Heating with large pipes (4″) 303
9.20 Systems with large radiative part 303
9.21 Some remarks concerning the influence of the heating system on the climate . 304
9.22 Plant radiation 307
9.23 Ventilation 310
9.24 The ventilation required for conditioning the glasshouse 311
9.25 Methods of ventilation 312
9.26 Evaporation 313
9.27 Methods of water supply 317
9.28 Supply of CO_2 317
9.29 Automatic control of climate factors 318

10. ATMOSPHERIC POLLUTION

F. H. SCHMIDT

10.1 Introduction 319
10.2 Natural pollution 320
10.3 Artificial pollution 324

CONTENTS

10.4   Influence of air pollution on plants 326
10.5   Measuring methods for particulate pollution 330
10.6   Measuring methods for gaseous pollution 333
10.7   Diffusion of pollution in the atmosphere 334
10.8   Some numerical results 339
10.9   Modifications of the theory, stack height 343
10.10 Modifications of the theory, influence of the atmosphere 347
10.11 Influence of many sources 350

REFERENCES 356
LIST OF TABLES 374
SUBJECT INDEX 376
AUTHOR INDEX 379

FREQUENTLY USED SYMBOLS

Quantities of the same dimension are often represented by the same symbol. Suffixes are used to distinguish between such quantities, e.g. H^{net}, H_{so}, etc. This system has not rigorously been followed, however. Symbols which are in widespread use have been retained, e.g. K, a, v. The nature of the quantity is indicated, l is the length, t the time and m the mass.

A	area	$[l^2]$
C	volumetric heat capacity	$[cal\ l^{-3}\ °C^{-1}]$
D	damping depth	$[l]$
H	energy flux density	$[cal\ l^{-2}\ t^{-1}]$
K	exchange coefficient	$[l^2\ t^{-1}]$
L	heat of evaporation for 1 g water	$[cal\ m^{-1}]$
M	molecular weight	$[\ \ ]$
N	number	$[\ \ ]$
Q	energy	$[cal]$
R	gas constant	$[cal\ °C^{-1}]$
V	volume	$[l^3]$
a	thermal diffusivity	$[l^2\ t^{-1}]$
b	factor $\lambda_a(z + z_0)^{-1}$	$[cal\ l^{-2}\ t^{-1}\ °C^{-1}]$
c	specific heat	$[cal\ l^{-3}\ °C^{-1}]$
d	thickness of a layer, distance	$[l]$
h	coefficient of heat transfer	$[cal\ l^{-2}\ t^{-1}\ °C^{-1}]$
k	von Karman's constant	$[\ \ ]$
l	length	$[l]$
p	pressure	$[m\ l^{-1}\ t^{-2}]$
r	parameter	$[\ \ ]$
t	time	$[t]$
u	velocity in the x direction	$[l\ t^{-1}]$
v	velocity	$[\ \ ]$
w	velocity in the z direction	$[l\ t^{-1}]$
Γ	temperature lapse rate	$[l^{-1}\ °C]$
Θ	absolute temperature	$[°K]$
γ	psychrometer constant	$[m\ l^{-1}\ t^{-2}\ °C^{-1}]$
η	dynamic viscosity	$[m\ l^{-1}\ t^{-1}]$
ϑ	temperature	$[°C]$
λ	thermal conductivity	$[cal\ l^{-1}\ t^{-1}\ °C^{-1}]$
v	kinematic viscosity	$[l^2\ t^{-1}]$

ϱ	density; reflection factor	$[m\ l^{-3}]; [\quad]$
τ	shearing stress	$[m\ l^{-1}\ t^{-2}]$
φ	phase shift, angle	$[\quad]$
ω	radial frequency	$[t^{-1}]$

SUFFIXES

A	amplitude	m	mineral fraction
a, ai	air	max	maximum
ad	adiabatic dry; average daily	net	netto
ay	average yearly	o	at the surface; constant value
b	boundary	ou	outside
cl	clay	p	constant pressure
con	convection	pe	peat
d	dry; daily	s	saturation; solid material
dew	dew point	sa	sand
ev	evaporation	sh	short-wave
gl	glasshouse	so	soil
h	homogeneous	sw	solid material with water
i	initial	v	constant volume
in	inside	ven	ventilation
l	layered soil	w	water, water vapor
lo	long wave	y	yearly
		z	at depth z

CHAPTER 1

INTRODUCTION, THE PHYSICAL METHOD

W. R. VAN WIJK

*Laboratory of Physics and Meteorology of the Agricultural University Wageningen,
The Netherlands*

1.1. Scope of the present text

Application of the fundamental laws of natural science combined with the quantitative methods of reasoning of mathematical physics have led to spectacular developments in science and technology. In this book we attempt to describe the way in which similar methods can be applied to a range of problems encountered in agriculture and biology.

The essential characteristic of such an analytical or physical approach is that it leads to a quantitative theory of the studied phenomena, expressable in mathematical language. In doing so generalizations can be made from a limited amount of experimental data, i.e. the theory can be applied to circumstances differing from those encountered in the original experiments. This can rarely be done when a problem is approached in a purely empirical way.

In addition the analytical method can often help in considerably reducing the required number of experiments. In this connection it may be useful to point out that the application of mathematical statistics to the design and interpretation of experiments does not change their empirical character. Although these techniques can also serve to reduce the necessary number of experiments, they differ essentially from the physical methods referred to here.

Generally it is necessary to introduce drastic simplifications and schematizations in an agricultural problem to make it amenable to a mathematical analysis. Objections are sometimes raised that such simplifications restrict or even preclude the applicability of mathematical physics to agriculture. However, this need not be the case. The very purpose of the mathematical physical treatment is to isolate the essential characteristics of the problem and to abstract them from the less essential ones. The understanding gained from the study of a simplified problem will be very helpful in the interpretation of the complicated actual data. In some cases the mathematical treatment itself can be gradually extended to less simplified cases.

As an illustration the subject of soil temperatures may serve. An immense number of measurements has been published. Although the soil is far from homogeneous, the theory of heat conduction in a homogeneous medium enables a qualitative and often a semiquantitative interpretation of the observations. It explains, for instance, why the annual temperature variation penetrates into the soil much deeper than the diurnal variation; it accounts for the differences observed in soils of different constitution such as sand, clay or peat. It also explains the high maximum and low minimum temperatures that can occur at the surface of a dry soil and permits one to estimate how these extremes will be modified when the moisture content is changed. In some cases a further refinement can be obtained by taking into account the variation in composition or structure of the soil, e.g. when the soil consists of a number of horizontal layers with different thermal characteristics, or when these characteristics change gradually with depth.

The foregoing remarks are not meant to belittle the importance of ad hoc experiments as a means of arriving in a short time at the answer to a given practical problem. It is also recognized that the empirical method has often led to important results. However, it is our opinion that there exists a much greater scope for the application of physical methods in agricultural science than found in present day practice.

In the agricultural sphere physical methods have so far found application mainly in soil physics, soil chemistry, agrometeorology, and in agricultural engineering which deals principally with agricultural machinery and the techniques of agricultural operations. However, in analogy to chemical or mechanical engineering the term agricultural engineering might well be used in a more comprehensive sense, so that it includes all operations influencing agricultural production by physical means or through the action of physical factors. It is for agricultural engineering in this comprehensive sense that physical methods are particularly valuable, since they allow one to view the results of agricultural engineering operations in advance.

It is clearly impossible to give a comprehensive treatment of the application of physics in agriculture and biology in a text book of normal size. Accordingly we have chosen to deal principally with the physics of plant environment, i.e. the physics of the soil and air layers near the surface of the earth.

One of the major aims of agricultural practice must be to use and/or modify the natural environment in such a manner that the production of economically important plants is promoted. Obvious examples are soil cultivation, water management and the planting of shelterbelts, all of which have a pronounced influence on the physical conditions encountered by a growing crop. An understanding of the physics of plant environment is therefore a prerequisite for a guided modification of this environment.

Many problems of fundamental importance to our understanding of plant environment involve a consideration of the energy balance of the earth's surface. An equally important group of phenomena arises from a consideration of the water cycle. Excellent texts on flow of water in saturated soils exist (e.g. GUSTAFSSON [1946], or articles of Childs, of Kirkham *et al.* in LUTHIN [1957]).

The theory of flow of water in unsaturated soils is, however, still in a state of development (see e.g. PHILIP [1958]). Radiation, heat transfer in soil, transfer of heat and moisture in the air near the ground and spreading of impurities in this layer are considered in detail in this book. These phenomena are largely responsible for the microclimate near the ground. Although these matters are treated in texts on micrometeorology, additional emphasis is given here to the phenomena which affect crops. The reader will note that this leads to a different treatment than that when an explanation of the microclimate is the aim.

A discussion of macrometeorology falls outside the scope of this book, although the weather has a dominant influence on plant growth and on many agricultural operations. A common meeting ground for agronomists and meteorologists is obviously most desirable where crop production is studied in relation to weather. It is hoped that this text will help to promote co-operation between workers in agronomy and meteorology.

The following three sections of this introductory chapter contain by way of example a brief discussion of a few applications of the physical method to agricultural problems.

1.2. The placement of fertilizers

The first example deals with a problem that arose from agronomic practice, viz. the influence of the placement of fertilizers in bands as compared with broadcasting. This problem lends itself easily to schematization. With broadcast fertilizers it is reasonable to assume that the fertility does not change in a horizontal plane. The difference in environment caused by the placement is that the soil then consists of vertical slices of alternately low and high fertility. The other environmental factors are assumed to be the same in both cases. The problem was treated by VAN WIJK and DE WIT [1951] and DE WIT [1953].

From the introduction of de Wit's thesis we quote the following parts in which the history of the methods of applying fertilizers is briefly reviewed.

"Generally the fertilizers are broadcast over the surface of the soil before or after ordinary cultivation operations. Until some 40 years ago, this procedure was the only one practicable in Western Europe because the seed of common crops was broadcast also. Where the seed is drilled in rows, however, it is feasible to place the fertilizers in bands some distance from the seed. This practice has become common in regions where extensive cropping is practised and where the seed is drilled in widespaced rows. Drilling fertilizers and seed in one operation results in a saving of both fertilizer and labour. Under favourable conditions up to 90 per cent of the fertilizer has been saved by proper placement in these countries (e.g. U.S.A., Russia) . . ."

"Until World War II the American and Russian investigations did not receive much attention in Western Europe, since it was the general opinion, that important savings were possible only in regions where extensive cropping was practised. When it became necessary to restrict the use of fertilizer during the war, more economical use of fertilizers for grain crops was obtained in England by means of localized fertilizer placement . . . It appeared that on soils seriously deficient in phosphate, more than 50 per cent of the fertilizer could be saved by drilling seed and fertilizer together (combined drilling). The farmers adopted this method rapidly . . ."

In the literature many successful experiments of row placement are reported. Considerably higher yields have been obtained using the same amount of fertilizer per acre than with broadcasting. But there are also experiments in which broadcasting gave a higher yield. The question is not new and although field experiments have been carried out for approximately half a century no quantitative correlation between yield and placement method has been detected.

The essence of the physical approach to this problem was to establish the proper basis of comparison for the different methods of fertilizer application. Comparison at equal amounts of fertilizer per acre is a logical procedure from an economic viewpoint; it is illogical from a physical point of view since the response of the soil and the plant to different quantities of fertilizer per unit area of fertilized soil may and generally will, vary. Thus the first step is to study the behavior of plants in a soil on which a fertilizer is broadcast and in a soil on which the fertilizer is placed in bands such that the quantity of fertilizer per unit of fertilized area is the same in both cases (see Fig. 1.1). The quantity of fertilizer per acre is then proportional to the width of the fertilized band.

Under these conditions one can simplify the problem to the comparison of the behavior of a plant of which the root system is in contact with a nutrient solution containing a certain fertilizer, or combination of fertilizers with the behavior of a plant of which only a part of the root system is in contact with the same solution.

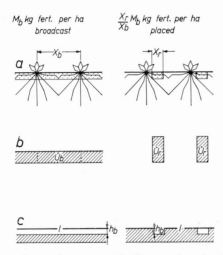

Fig. 1.1. Comparison of row placement of fertilizer to broadcasting (DE WIT [1953]).
a. X_b = distance between the crop rows. X_r = width of the fertilizer band. M_b kg fertilizer per ha broadcast and $(X_x/X_b)M_b$ kg fertilizer per ha placed.
b. $\check{U}_b$ = uptake rate from broadcast fertilizer, $\check{U}_r$ = uptake rate from placed fertilizer.
c. Line l indicates the level of availability of a particular nutrient other than the one applied, h_b represents the intensity of an unfavorable effect of the application of M_b kg of the fertilizer per ha on this level of availability. In many cases h_b equals zero.

Since water infiltrates the top soil of arable land predominantly in a vertical direction one may safely assume that the horizontal displacement of the fertilizer is small in comparison with its displacement in a vertical direction. Hence, at equal depths the concentration of the nutrient solution resulting from the broadcast fertilizer will be the same as that resulting from the fertilizer in row placement.

1.3. Water culture and pot experiments

Experiments on uptake of fertilizer from nutrient solutions in water cultures are known in which some of the roots were kept outside the solution, and also pot experiments were published in which only a portion of the soil in the pot received fertilizer. These investigations showed that less fertilizer was taken up by the plant if only part of the root system was in contact with the nutrient solution, but the rate at which the fertilizer was taken up by an incompletely exposed root system was higher than would follow from the proportion of exposed root surface. For instance, the amount of fertilizer taken up in a certain interval of time by a plant of which only 50 per cent of the roots were in contact with the nutrient solution was 75 per cent of the uptake of the fully exposed root system. The ratio of the uptakes was 50 per cent when only 20 per cent of the root surface was exposed.

Various types of fertilizer and various kinds of crops were found to give the same ratio of uptake as a function of exposed fraction of the root system. The ratio proved also to be independent of the concentration of the nutrient solution. The last mentioned property makes it possible to develop the theory for a soil solution the concentration of which varies greatly with depth and time.

The fraction of the root system of a field crop which is in contact with the fertilizer solution in case of row placement is equal to the ratio of the width of the fertilizer band to the distance between the plant rows. The uptake of

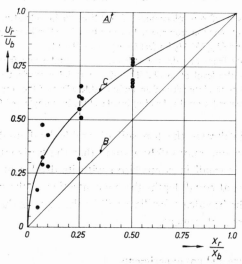

Fig. 1.2. The compensation function (DE WIT [1953]). The relationship between the ratio of the uptake rates from placed (U_r) and broadcast (U_b) fertilizer and the ratio between the width of the fertilizer band (X_r) and the distances between crop rows (X_b). Line A is to be expected if the rate of uptake from the fertilizer is independent of the fertilized area. Line B is to be expected if the rate of uptake is directly proportional to the fertilized area. Curve C represents the actual relationship.

the fertilizer in row placement can be calculated from a curve which is constructed from the waterculture and pot experiments. This curve is shown in Fig. 1.2 together with the experimental data. It can be expressed mathematically to a sufficient degree of accuracy by the relation

$$\dot{U}_r/\dot{U}_b = (X_r/X_b)^{0.44}. \tag{1.1}$$

X_r and X_b represent the widths of the fertilizer band and the distance between plant rows respectively (see also Fig. 1.1); $\dot{U}_r$ and $\dot{U}_b$ are the corresponding rates of fertilizer uptake (amount of fertilizer taken up per unit time).

It will be clear that more fertilizer is taken up per unit of root surface per unit time the smaller the exposed surface becomes. It is for this reason that de Wit has termed the function $(X_r/X_b)^{0.44}$ the *compensation function*.

We shall now apply these results to the uptake of fertilizer by a field crop and deduce the influence of placement on crop yield.

1.4. Placement method and crop yield

The actual rate at which fertilizer is taken up in the course of the growing season depends on many factors. However, the *ratio* of the actual uptakes in row placement to broadcasting is not dependent on those factors, as the analysis of the experiments which we have just discussed has shown; it depends to a first approximation only on the ratio X_r/X_b.

In those cases in which the total uptake of fertilizer is small compared with the total amount applied (phosphates are often an example of this situation), the ratio $\dot{U}_r/\dot{U}_b$ does not change with time and the total uptake in row placement can be calculated if that quantity is known for broadcasting or conversely. If it is further known how the yield is influenced by the amount of fertilizer which is applied in one method, e.g. in the most common method of broadcasting, one can calculate what yield would have been obtained for placement in bands.

For instance, let it be assumed that of a certain nutrient which is broadcast at a rate M_b kg/ha, U_b kg/ha is taken up. Then in a row placement in which $X_r = 0.5 X_b$, $0.75 U_b$ will be taken up from $0.5 M_b$ kg/ha. The entire rate-uptake curve can now be constructed for this placement method by multiplication of the uptake of the nutrient from broadcast fertilizer by 0.75 and plotting the result at a fertilizer rate of $0.5 M_b$. The curves in Fig. 1.3 have been constructed in this way. For the construction of the curves with $X_r = 0.25X_b$ and $X_r = 0.125X_b$ the compensation factors $U_r/U_b = 0.55$ and 0.41 respectively have been used. It is now possible to compare the uptakes in different placement methods in the common practical way, i.e. at equal quantities of fertilizer applied per unit area.

One reads from Fig. 1.3 that at $0.5\,M_b$ the highest uptake corresponds to a band width $X_r = 0.5X_b$ but that at $X_r = 0.25X_b$ the uptake is still higher

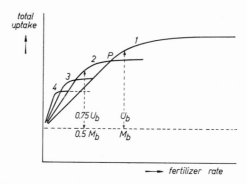

Fig. 1.3. The relationship between fertilizer rate and total uptake for different methods of application (DE WIT [1953]). Curve 1 for broadcast fertilizer, $X_r/X_b = 1$; curve 2, $X_r/X_b = 0.5$; curve 3, $X_r/X_b = 0.25$; and curve 4, $X_r/X_b = 0.125$ for placed fertilizer, calculated by means of the compensation function. P = point of intersection between the curves 1 and 2. The point of intersection P is sometimes situated in the flat part of the curve for broadcast fertilizer.

than in broadcasting; the last mentioned method of fertilizing in turn gives a higher uptake than placement in still smaller rows for which $X_r = 0.125X_b$.

It is obvious that with low application rates the increase in uptake from fertilizer increases with decreasing width of fertilizer band, but this is not true with high application rates. This important influence of the band width was not realized before; it has explained some puzzling results in row placement experiments in which the band width was unintentionally altered.

Analogous results were obtained with fertilizers of which a large fraction is taken up during the growing season or that are leached out considerably. In that case the concentration changes and the uptake rates vary during the growing season. Nitrogen fertilizers are an example of this type.

The last step is the comparison of the yields. Since crop yield depends on many other factors besides fertilization, one can only predict the yield which an arbitrary placement method will give in a certain year if the relationship between yield and total uptake of fertilizer is known for one fertilizer pattern, e.g. for broadcast fertilizer. The total uptake can be read from Fig. 1.3 for a different placement method and the corresponding yield found from the yield-uptake curve. Experience has shown that the place where a certain quantity of a nutrient is taken up does not influence its use by the plant. This is the probable explanation for the fact that in most cases the relationship between uptake and yield has been found to be independent of the fertilizer pattern. It is what one would expect if the fertilizers are taken

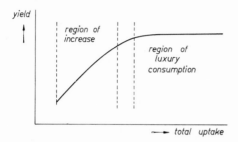

Fig. 1.4. Relation between yield and total uptake, of fertilizer (DE WIT [1953]). The curve represents the most common type of relationship between nutrient uptake and yield. The portion of the curve in which the yield increases markedly with increasing uptake is called the region of increase and the portion of the curve in which there is little or no increase in the yield with increase in uptake is called the region of luxury consumption. The relationship is in many cases independent of fertilizer pattern.

up independently. An exception to this behavior will occur when the availability of a fertilizer is decreased by the presence of some other nutrient (cf. Fig. 1.1c). The yield corresponding to a given quantity of the fertilizer nutrient absorbed by the plant may then be greater with placed fertilizer than with broadcast fertilizer. The most common type of relationship between yield and uptake is shown in Fig. 1.4.

De Wit has also discussed several other possible relationships and constructed nomograms to find directly the yield for placed fertilizer from the yield for broadcast fertilizer and the fertilizer rate.

1.5. The essential steps in the theoretical treatment

We have discussed this example at some length because it shows very clearly how the physical approach can lead to an understanding of apparently contradictory experimental data, thereby rendering them considerably more useful for practical application. The first important step is to realize which are the primary factors involved in the problem under consideration. They were in this case the exposed surface of the roots and the fertilizer uptake and not the yield.

Empirical relationships had to be used; the compensation curve is a case in point. This is due to the fact that the reaction of a plant to a change of external conditions can mostly not be predicted from a few principles of general validity.

It will often happen that experiments must be carried out to obtain such a relationship when one is studying a problem using the physical approach, or it may be that some constants or factors in a formula must be determined. But since a general understanding of the problem is then already obtained, this can serve as a guide for the design of the experiments and one can concentrate upon the factors which are most important. This is not so in the "purely empirical method" where often many factors are influencing the results and the relative importance of these factors may vary from year to year to an unknown degree.

1.6. Tilth and soil temperature

As a second example we shall consider the question of how the microclimate of the soil is affected by tilth. A major factor in microclimate is the *temperature regime of the soil and that of the lower air layer*. Many field experiments have been carried out in which the soil temperature was measured before and after tillage. The results seemed to be contradictory. Whilst some investigators reported an increase in soil temperature due to tillage others have observed a decrease and some did not find an effect at all.

In a Report of the Joint Committee on Soil Tilth of the American Society of Agronomy and the American Society of Agricultural Engineers [1945] it is said:

"... there has been very little done in the way of improving our situation with regard to measuring soil tilth and its effect on plant growth. We believe the reason for this is that there is very little enthusiasm among workers for the present methods of approach to the tilth problem that we are now making. It seems that it is going to be necessary for us to make some new approaches ..."

An important step to a new approach was made by the committee in the preparation of a critical evaluation of the relation of soil physical conditions to plant growth (SHAW [1952]).

A theoretical investigation into the influence of tilth on soil temperature was published by VAN DUIN [1956]. Here we shall give the gist of his argument and quote some of his results.

Tillage establishes a loose upper layer of soil with physical properties that are different from those of the undisturbed soil. The effect of tilth on the temperature regime is primarily a consequence of the change in thermal properties of this upper layer. Since heat transfer in the soil is mainly a process of heat conduction the mathematical physical theory of heat conduction can be applied to this problem. Here we shall in particular discuss the theoretical results for the case of periodic temperature variations as they are observed, for instance, in the annual and diurnal cycles.

The physical characteristics that govern heat conduction in a medium are thermal conductivity and volumetric heat capacity. The first step is to investigate how these two magnitudes are influenced by tillage. This was done by van Duin on the basis of experimental data on the porosity of a soil before and after tillage.*

As in the previous example one must be careful in selecting a basis of comparison. Apart from the thermal characteristics of the soil, the soil temperature depends on the amount of heat that enters or leaves the soil surface. The source of heat is solar radiation which on reaching the soil surface is partly reflected and for the major part absorbed in a very thin layer of soil. This energy is used for heating the soil and the air and also as latent heat for the evaporation of water. In addition the soil surface emits radiation of long, invisible wave lengths.

The energy balance equation of the surface can thus be written as

$$(1 - \varrho_{sh}) H_{sh} = H_{lo}^{net} + H_{so} + H_{ai} + H_{ev} , \qquad (1.2)$$

where H_{sh} is the incoming short-wave radiation (from sun and sky), ϱ_{sh} the reflection coefficient for this radiation, H_{lo}^{net} the net outward flow of long wave radiation, H_{so} the heat flow into the soil, H_{ai} that into the air and H_{ev} the heat consumed in evaporation.

All quantities are expressed as energy per unit of horizontal surface and per unit time (e.g. cal cm^{-2} min^{-1} or W cm^{-2}), except ϱ_{sh}, which is dimensionless.

In comparing the tilled soil with the undisturbed soil the factors which are assumed to be the same for both must be carefully ascertained. Evaporation, for instance, has a large cooling effect. Consequently one may arrive at a quite different conclusion about the influence of tillage on soil temperature when evaporation is different for the tilled and the undisturbed soil than under conditions of equal or negligible evaporation.

---

* See Chapter 4 for the definition of thermal conductivity and diffusivity and for the way in which they are related to the composition of the soil.

It is reasonable to make a comparison for equal meteorological conditions and equal surface cover when the evaluation of the thermal consequences of tillage in general is aimed at. In early spring, when the temperature in the upper soil layer is of most importance, bare soil and equal or negligible evaporation rates are likely to occur. The incoming short-wave radiation, H_{sh}, will then be the same for the tilled and the undisturbed soil, as it is determined by solar altitude and the state of the atmosphere. Further the reflectivity, ϱ_{sh}, of both soils can be taken as equal. The other terms in (1.2) will be different; tillage increases the heat resistance of the upper soil layer and thereby decreases the heat flux into the soil, though in general it increases the surface temperature. These facts again influence the heat flux to air, H_{ai}, and the net long wave emission, H_{lo}^{net}. Thus the thermal effects caused by tillage are rather complicated, which explains the often controversial statements found in the literature.

On the basis of certain simplifying assumptions VAN DUIN [1956] calculated the effect of tillage on each of the heat fluxes in (1.2). Once the heat flux at the surface, H_{so}, and the thermal properties of the soil are known, the temperature can be calculated from the theory of heat conduction as a function of depth and time.

For purely periodic variation of H_{so} it can be shown that the amplitude of the temperature variation decreases with depth, both in the undisturbed soil and in the tilled soil; the rate of decrease being greatest in the latter case. On the other hand the calculated amplitude at the surface is somewhat greater for the tilled soil, despite the fact that the amplitude of H_{so} is smaller than in the case of the undisturbed soil.

The damping of the temperature fluctuations with depth depends also on the period of the variations, the ones with the shorter period decreasing more rapidly. The diurnal variation for instance, becomes imperceptible at the depth of 30 to 60 cm, depending on the thermal characteristics of the soil. For the annual cycle this depth is $\sqrt{365} \approx 19$ times as large, so that it penetrates to about 600 to 1200 cm.

1.7. Conclusions

From his theoretical results van Duin could explain many contradictory observations. His principal conclusions were as follows.

The amplitude of the *annual variation* of surface temperature is very little affected by tilth, i.e. the calculated change in surface temperature is of the order of 0.1 °C for a moderate climate as in western Europe. For the *diurnal temperature variation* on a cloudless day the calculated change in surface amplitude is several degrees centigrade. This means that the maximum temperature will be several degrees higher and the minimum temperature a similar amount lower at the surface of the tilled soil. The danger of night frost is thus increased by tilth, a prediction that is in agreement with experience. The increase in diurnal variation due to tillage may have a noticeable influence on the germination of those kinds of seeds that are sensitive to extremes of temperature.

When the temperature varies in a nonperiodical manner the rate of change of temperature with time is of importance. After the onset of an interval of exceptionally warm weather, such as may occur in spring, the upper layers of the tilled soil will warm up more rapidly than those of the undisturbed soil, which can be a factor favoring germination. However, in the long run the differences between the two soils will tend to even out. The theoretical treatment shows clearly that it is futile to look for general rules such as that a tilled soil is warmer in summer and cooler in winter than an undisturbed soil. Observed temperature differences will depend *inter alia* upon the variation of incoming radiation with time, on the depth of tillage and on the depth of measurement. The tilled soil can be warmer at the surface than the undisturbed soil, but cooler below a certain depth.

It also follows from the analysis that a complete interpretation of experimental data is only possible when temperature measurements are taken at various depths, both in the undisturbed and the tilled soil. In the latter, temperatures should be measured at not less than two depths, both in the tilled layer and in the underlying undisturbed layer. A comparison of temperature measurements at one depth in the tilled and the undisturbed soil can only be of *ad hoc* value. In those, unfortunately scarce, instances where sufficient data were given to enable a quantitative estimate of the soil temperatures to be made, satisfactory agreement of theory and experiment was obtained. This gives further confidence in the applicability of the theory, which is based on various simplifying assumptions.

A problem which from a physical point of view is identical with that discussed here is the question of how a mulch influences temperature.

1.8. Optimum depth of a water table in drainage

The optimum depth at which a water table should be kept in a drainage project has been the subject of investigations for many decades. Trial field experiments in several parts of the world including the Netherlands gave

different results in different years. Furthermore, the results were dependent
upon the type of soil and upon the kind of crop involved. No general
conclusion as to the best depth of drainage could be reached from these experiments. Yet a theoretical analysis has led to a quantitative understanding of
the phenomena involved and consequently to definite suggestions about the
most suitable depth of the water table in a drainage operation (WESSELING
and VAN WIJK [1955]; these authors also in LUTHIN [1957]).

The primary objective of drainage is to remove a permanent or temporary
surplus of water from the upper soil layers so that plant roots do not suffer
from bad aeration. This requirement sets a limit for the minimum depth of
the water table below the surface. Obviously, this depth depends *inter alia*
on the extension of the root zone and thus turns out to be different for
different crops. It depends also on the prevailing weather. In a wet growing
season and in a period when evapotranspiration is low a deeper water table
will give better yields, than in a dry season and with high evapotranspiration, provided that other factors are not limiting crop yields. These effects
have to be taken into account for the interpretation of the experiments. It
also becomes clear that advice concerning the minimum depth of the water
table which will secure adequate aeration of the roots can only be given in a
statistical sense. It must be based upon a knowledge of the frequency of the
occurrence of wet and dry seasons. It is impossible to guarantee that a
certain water table will never prove to be too shallow but one can infer from
a long series of weather data that it will be satisfactory, say in 9 out of
10 years.

On the other hand deep drainage can also cause yield depression. In the
arid, semiarid and temperate zones rainfall is usually insufficient to meet
the transpiration requirement of crops during their growing season. Under
those conditions crops must rely on water storage and water transport in the
soil for part of their water needs. With increasing depth of the water table
both the water storage at the beginning of the growing season and the
upward rate of water movement in the soil decrease.

Clearly the optimum depth of the water table should be such that it
secures on the one hand a satisfactory aeration of the root zone and on the
other hand a sufficient storage of water in this zone and/or adequate transport of water towards the roots.

It follows that this optimum depth does not only depend on meteorological
conditions, which govern both rainfall and transpiration requirements, but
also on the rooting habits of the crop and on the physical properties of the
soil that determine the transport of water and air. Sometimes the two

requirements cannot both be satisfied. This may particularly be so for a crop with a shallow root system, as the storage capacity of the root zone is low. In general the aeration requirement then prevails and supplementary irrigation must be applied in dry years.

In a theoretical analysis the water requirements and the rates of water and air movement in the soil must be calculated. For these problems the reader is referred to the literature quoted. Here it will suffice to state that the transpiration requirement of crops can be estimated from standard meteoro-

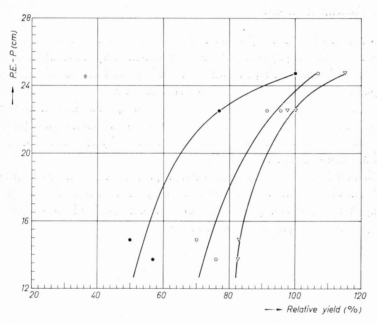

Fig. 1.5. Relation between relative yield of summergrain crops and P.E. — P (potential evaporation minus precipitation) at the experimental field "Nieuw-Beerta" (WESSELING–VAN WIJK [1957]).

    ● = water table at a depth of 40 cm.
    ○ = water table at a depth of 60 cm.
    ▽ = water table at a depth of 90 cm.

The yield is expressed in per cent yield of the plot with the water table at a depth of 120 cm. The dryer the year, the greater the difference P.E. — P. With increasing value of P.E. — P. the relative yields of the plots with a high water table increase rapidly. The soil was a clay soil with such a high water storage capacity that water stress did not occur even at a depth of the water table of 120 cm. This explains why yield at 90 cm water table always exceeds that of a higher water table. No clear picture emerges when relative yield is plotted as a function of water table depth.

logical data from the energy balance equation, which is solved for H_{ev}.

On the basis of an analysis along these lines Wesseling was able to explain field observations very satisfactorily, as is exemplified in Fig. 1.5. A criterion of practical importance in the design of a drainage installation can be formulated as follows: "What is the optimum depth of water table likely to be in eight out of ten years?" This optimum depth can then be calculated on the basis of meteorological records for the location in question, the physical properties of the soil and the rooting habits of the crop.

1.9. Contents of the book

While this introductory chapter was meant to discuss and illustrate the application of the physical method of approach in agricultural science and biology, subsequent chapters will treat various subjects out of the physics of plant environment in a more systematic manner.

Chapter 2 deals with properties of the atmosphere, the soil and water which will be of use in further chapters. The fundamental radiation phenomena are treated in Chapter 3, while heat transfer by conduction in the soil is dealt with in Chapters 4, 5 and 6.

Chapter 7 gives a survey of the thermal properties of soils. Heat transfer and transfer of matter in the air near the ground is treated in Chapter 8. Chapter 9 deals with glass house climate and the book concludes with Chapter 10 on the physics of air pollution.

CHAPTER 2

THE ATMOSPHERE AND THE SOIL

W. R. VAN WIJK and D. A. DE VRIES

Laboratory of Physics and Meteorology of the Agricultural University Wageningen,
The Netherlands

Plant environment is determined to a large extent by physical properties of the atmosphere and the soil, and by physical processes occurring in these media. The purpose of this chapter is to provide some basic information regarding the physical characteristics of air and soil, and regarding some common physical phenomena that are related to these characteristics. Because water plays an important role in many of these processes, its properties are also dealt with in this chapter.

The present discussion is concise by necessity. For a more comprehensive treatment we refer to hand- and textbooks on meteorology and soil physics listed in the bibliography.

2.1. Structure of the atmosphere

Atmosphere is the name given to the gaseous shell surrounding the earth. An outer boundary cannot strictly be defined since the density of the gas decreases roughly exponentially with height. The greatest height at which atmospheric, optical and electrical phenomena (e.g. aurora) have been observed is of the order of 1000 km.

A schematic representation of the vertical structure of the atmosphere is given in Fig. 2.1. Several atmospheric layers can be distinguished.

The *troposphere* is the layer in which the phenomena that give rise to "the weather" are most pronounced. It extends from the surface up to an average height of about 18 km above the equator and of 8 to 9 km above the poles. In the troposphere strong vertical air motions occur as a consequence of the heating of the air at the earth's surface. The greater height of the troposphere above the equator is due to the more intense heating at the lower geographic latitudes. The average height of the upper boundary of the troposphere, the so-called tropopause, varies with the season. In the troposphere the temperature normally decreases with height at a rate varying between about 0.3 °C per 100 m to 1.0 °C per 100 m, depending on the temperature and the humidity of the air.

The decrease of the temperature Θ with height z is called the *lapse rate* Γ; thus

$$\Gamma = -\delta\Theta/\delta z. \tag{2.1}$$

Lapse rates differing from normal may occur in the transition layer between two air masses of different origin, above a layer of cloud or dust, or close to

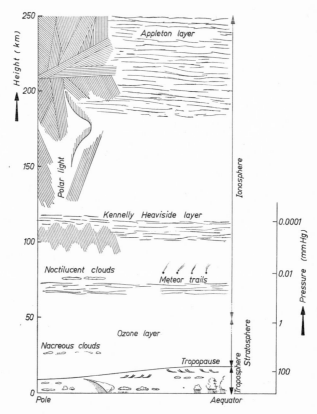

Fig. 2.1. Schematic representation of the vertical structure of the atmosphere. (VAN WIJK and DE VRIES [1952].)

the ground. If warmer air is overlying cooler air the temperature increases with height in the transition zone. This phenomenon is called *inversion*, and the layer in which Θ increases with height is termed an inversion layer. In such a layer the lapse rate is negative. In Fig. 2.2 temperature and humidity are shown as a function of height.

The temperature regime close to the ground differs markedly from that at a greater height because of the fact that very large positive and negative values of the lapse rate often occur. For instance, in the air at 1 cm above a bare soil surface at Poona, India, a lapse rate of $2 \times 10^4 \,°C \, m^{-1}$ was reported by RAMDAS [1951]. Inversions are also frequently found in the lowest air layer. The height of the air layer with an abnormal lapse rate depends on such factors as radiation and wind speed; it varies during the course of a day

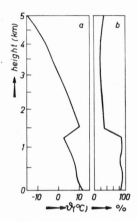

Fig. 2.2. Temperature (*a*) and humidity (*b*) in the troposphere as function of height. Data for 10–24–1959 at de Bilt. Warm air is overlying colder air causing an inversion at 1.2 km height.

and a year. Sometimes there is a sharp transition from this layer to a layer with a normal lapse rate, as in the example of Fig. 2.3; under other conditions the situation of the higher air layers is approached more gradually.

The singular behavior of the air near the ground and its importance for humans, animals and plants has given rise to the development of a special branch of meteorology that deals with the phenomena occurring in this layer. A large amount of data are discussed by GEIGER [1961] in his book "The climate near the ground". Theoretical aspects of the physics of the surface layer have been treated by SUTTON [1953].

Above the troposphere lies the *stratosphere*, a region extending to approximately 50 km, in which mainly strong horizontal winds prevail. The temperature remains nearly constant with height up to 25 km at higher latitudes. At low geographic latitudes (30°) the temperature in the stratosphere decreases slowly with height. It increases again above 25 km and reaches a maximum value of approximately 75 °C at a height of 50 km. This is due to the absorption of ultraviolet radiation by ozone present in the stratosphere.

Above 70 km the temperature decreases rapidly but it rises again at a greater height. Most of this information has recently been obtained from measurements with high altitude rockets.

Above 50 km ionization of the air molecules or of the atoms of its constituents becomes increasingly important. The layers above this limit are referred to by the collective name *ionosphere*. A discussion of ionospheric phenomena falls outside the scope of this book.

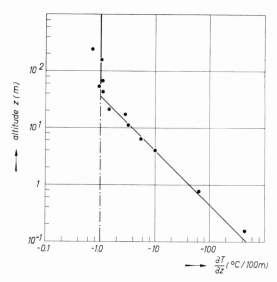

Fig. 2.3. Abnormal lapse rate in the air near the ground. An abnormal high lapse rate occurs below 40 m height. Note the sharp transition to the normal lapse rate. The data are average values for western and central Europe in the month of June. (After K. BROCKS [1948].)

2.2. Composition of the air in the troposphere and in the stratosphere

The chemical composition of the air is practically constant with height in the troposphere and it does not vary systematically over the earth, provided that water and impurities are left out of consideration. Local variations at low heights may occur due to particular circumstances. Owing to respiration in the soil, the carbon dioxide content may for instance be increased near the earth's surface, or the oxygen content may show an increase in the neighborhood of a forest as a consequence of a high assimilation rate.

The volumetric composition of dry air* in the troposphere is given in Table 2.1.

TABLE 2.1

Composition of the atmosphere

	Per cent by volume	molecular weight
nitrogen	78.09	28
oxygen	20.95	32
argon	0.93	40
carbon dioxide	0.02–0.04	44
helium		
neon		
krypton	0.01	
xenon		
ozone		
	100.00	29.0

Water is always present in the vapor state, but it can occur also in the liquid state as cloud drops, and in the solid state, e.g. as snow or hail particles. The total amount of water is in the range of 0.1 g to 40 g per kilogram of dry air. This small amount of water is responsible for most of the weather phenomena. The water concentration varies greatly with height and changes in course of time.

In addition to the components which have been mentioned, small quantities of other substances may be present as a *pollution*. Near towns or industrial centers sulphur dioxide, soot and dust can be present to such an extent that the ultraviolet part of the solar spectrum is markedly reduced in intensity. This may even happen in the visible region of the spectrum. Small concentrations of sulphur dioxide and fluorine compounds of the order of a few parts per million by weight have been found to cause severe damage to certain horticultural crops and to some flowers.

2.3. Pressure and wind

Air pressure is caused by the weight of the column of air above an observer. It is by definition the force exerted per unit of area. Thus, in an atmosphere

---

* The word "dry" is used here in its chemical meaning, i.e. the component water is absent. In the meteorological sense dry means that only water vapor but no liquid or solid water are present.

that is at rest the air pressure at any point is equal to the weight of a vertical air column with a cross section of unit area that extends from the chosen point to the upper boundary of the atmosphere. Air pressure therefore decreases continually with height, approximately in an exponential manner as can be seen from the pressure scale in Fig. 2.1. A theoretical explanation of this behavior is given in section 2.7.

As a consequence of the force exerted by the higher air layers on the lower ones the greater part of the mass of air is concentrated in the lower layers. It follows from the pressure distribution shown in Fig. 2.1 that approximately three quarters of the total mass of air are contained in the troposphere and nearly all of the remaining quarter in the stratosphere. Only slightly more than 0.01 per cent constitutes the ionosphere.

A great variety of units in which pressure is measured is in use. In the c.g.s.-system which is based on the centimeter, the gram mass and the second, the unit of pressure is dyne $cm^{-2} = g\ cm^{-1}\ sec^{-2}$. The air pressure at sea level is approximately 10^6 dyne cm^{-2}. The latter is called bar in the meteorological literature; actual pressures and their variations are mostly expressed in the unit millibar $= 10^3$ dyne cm^{-2} (abbreviation: mbar). As the mercury barometer has been the instrument most commonly used for accurate pressure determinations for many centuries, the pressure exerted by a column of mercury of unit height (usually mm or inch) is still frequently used as a unit. The temperature of the column is standardized at 0 °C and the geographic latitude, which also has an influence on weight, at 45°. The unit 1 mm of mercury thus defined is called torr in honor of Torricelli, the inventor of the mercury barometer.

The average atmospheric pressure at sea level has been called one atmosphere (abbreviated atma); its precise definition in the above mentioned units is:

$$1\ atma = 760\ mm\ Hg = 1013.2\ mbar.$$

Surface pressure depends on the condition of the atmosphere above the observer; hence it changes with the weather. In most cases the surface pressure (reduced to sea level) ranges from 970 mbar to 1050 mbar. Extremes are 887 mbar measured in the Pacific Ocean and 1075 mbar in Siberia. Apart from the irregular variation due to atmospheric motions the surface pressure shows seasonal and diurnal variations. The former are most pronounced over extended continents due to the seasonal heating and cooling of the air. The diurnal variation is a 12-hourly oscillation with two maxima (at approximately 10 h and 22 h) and two minima (at 4 h and 16 h). The amplitude of this oscillation ranges from about 2 mbar in the tropics to a fraction of a mbar at high latitudes.

Wind is primarily caused by horizontal pressure differences. If the pressure on the right hand face of a cube of air exceeds that on the left, the cube is subjected to a force from right to left. It will be accelerated and its velocity will increase until the force due to pressure differences is compensated for by forces which come into action when the air is moving, i.e. friction and inertia forces (the centrifugal force and Coriolis force). When the forces acting on the cube of air balance, the wind speed remains constant.

A theoretical analysis shows that in the stationary state the horizontal velocity is determined by the horizontal gradient. The latter can be expressed as dp/dx, where the x-direction coincides with the direction of maximum pressure change. A general picture of the pressure distribution is obtained from weather maps. Lines of constant pressure or *isobars* are drawn on such maps with equal pressure differences (usually of a few millibars) between successive isobars. The horizontal gradient for a given location is found by dividing the pressure difference between successive isobars near the location by their shortest distance. For example, if the distance between two isobars is 500 km and they differ by 5 mbar the pressure gradient is $5 \times 10^3/5 \times 10^7 = 10^{-4}$ dyne cm^{-3}.

2.4. Temperature

The temperature in the lower 30 km of the atmosphere is known with a reasonably degree of accuracy from measurements using balloons and aircraft as instrument carriers. Above that level incidental measurements have been made using rockets or, quite recently, satellites, but the experimental information is incomplete as yet. In addition theoretical relations are used for estimating the temperature of layers above the stratosphere on the basis of pressure data.

Excluding the air layer near the ground, which will be discussed in detail in later chapters, the average temperature in the troposphere decreases with height to approximately $-55\,°C$ at the top of the troposphere in the middle latitudes, and remains nearly constant in the stratosphere. In low latitudes the average temperature at the top of the troposphere is approximately $-80\,°C$ and it increases slightly with height in the stratosphere. A similar behavior has been found in polar regions, but here the top of the troposphere is approximately at $-50\,°C$.

The slight rise of temperature with height in the lower part of the strato-

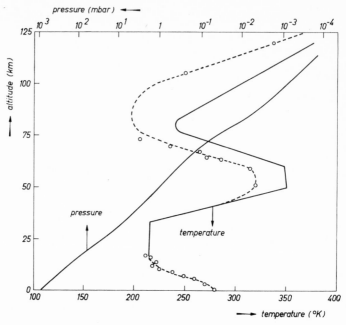

Fig. 2.4. Temperature and pressure as functions of altitude. (After BEST *et al.* [1947].) The full drawn line for the temperature is calculated. The dotted line has been drawn to fit the measurements (open circles).

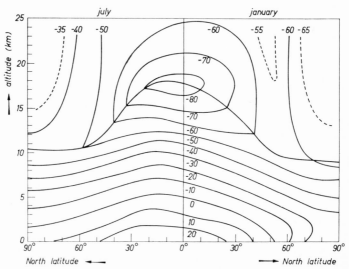

Fig. 2.5. Temperature distribution in the troposphere and the lower stratosphere for the northern hemisphere. (After VON PALMEN [1934]).

sphere is followed by a rapid increase in temperature from approximately −55 °C at 30 km to about 75 °C at 40 km height. This temperature rise is a result of the absorption of ultraviolet radiation by ozone. The absorption is so strong that the maximum temperature occurs at a height of 50 km, whereas the ozone concentration has its maximum (of 0.0004%) at 25 km. At still greater heights the temperature decreases again until at about 80 km a minimum value of −75 °C is reached.

The temperature and the pressure as functions of altitude are represented in Fig. 2.4. The temperature distribution in the troposphere and the lower stratosphere for the northern hemisphere are given in Fig. 2.5.

2.5. Hydrostatic stability and the adiabatic lapse rate

When a parcel of air ascends, the pressure of its surroundings decrease and as a consequence it will expand; conversely a descending air parcel is compressed. An expanding air parcel exerts mechanical work on the surrounding atmosphere. If this energy is not compensated for by heat exchange with the surroundings, its temperature will decrease to such an extent, that the difference in the parcels internal energy before and after the expansion is equivalent to the mechanical work. If the parcel is compressed the work exerted by the atmosphere on it causes a rise in temperature. A theoretical calculation of these temperature changes is given in section 2.9.

In a discussion of heat exchange in the atmosphere by vertical air movements the change of temperature of the moving air parcels with height must be taken into account. This has led to the introduction of the concept of *potential temperature*, which is the temperature that a mass of dry air would obtain if it were brought from its initial pressure to a standard pressure of 1000 mbar in a so-called *adiabatic* way, i.e. without exchanging heat with its surroundings. Vertical air movements are often rapid enough for the idealization of adiabatic movement to be valid to a sufficient degree of approximation. It will be shown in section 2.9 that the potential temperature can be found from

$$\Theta_{po} = \Theta(1000/p)^{R/C_p}, \tag{2.2}$$

where R is the gas constant (1.99 cal gmole^{-1} °C^{-1}) and C_p the molar heat* of air at constant pressure ($C_p = 6.97$ cal gmole^{-1} °C^{-1}).

---

* The molar heat is the specific heat multiplied by the molar weight of a substance.

It will further be shown in section 2.9 that the temperature change in a parcel of dry air, moving vertically in an adiabatic way, is approximately 1 °C for a difference in height of 100 m. A decrease of atmospheric temperature with height of this amount is called the *dry adiabatic lapse rate* and will be denoted by Γ^{ad}. According to this definition the potential temperature in an atmosphere with a dry adiabatic lapse rate is constant with height and no heat is transported by ascending or descending air parcels, because their temperature is equal to that of their surroundings at any height.

Because of the small temperature changes connected with adiabatic movements over heights of 10 m or less, the difference between potential and actual temperature can often be ignored in the lowest 10 m of air.

The possibility of vertical air movement in an atmosphere will now be discussed in more detail. If a rising air parcel is slowed down and eventually returns to its initial position the air layers at different heights do not easily mix; an existing stratification tends to persist as can sometimes be seen from the horizontal spread of the smoke of a fire, or of water droplets in a cloud or fog. The atmosphere is stable in respect to the ascending air. If on the other hand an ascending parcel is accelerated, an existing stratification will rapidly be dissolved once the process of mixing has been initiated by some incidental cause. The atmosphere is unstable in that case; strong vertical air currents can develop. When they penetrate to a sufficient height cloud formation occurs and convective clouds appear.

Consider an atmosphere at rest. Let the lapse rate in the vicinity of a point A have the value $\Gamma_A = -(\partial\Theta/\partial z)_A$. If a parcel of air, initially at rest at A, rises adiabatically its temperature decreases by an amount Γ^{ad} per unit of height, provided that no water vapor condenses during the rise as will be assumed for the present. Thus the rising parcel will become cooler than its surroundings if Γ_A is smaller than Γ^{ad}. The motion is then slowed down by the action of gravity, because the cooler air has the higher specific weight. A descending parcel will become warmer than the surrounding atmosphere and its motion will also be counteracted by buoyancy. The atmosphere at A is stable for vertical motion of air when $\Gamma_A < \Gamma^{\mathrm{ad}}$.

When on the other hand $\Gamma_A > \Gamma^{\mathrm{ad}}$, a parcel of air will be accelerated when it is displaced in a vertical direction. The atmosphere is now unstable and, for reasons which are discussed below, it is called *absolutely unstable*.

Note that in this discussion two types of temperature variation appear which should not be confused. One is the change of temperature with height in the atmosphere (assumed to be at rest), the other is the change in temperature of a parcel owing to a vertical displacement without exchange of heat.

Further it has been tacitly assumed that the parcel is so small that its movement does not lead to perceptible changes in its surroundings.

The discussion must be modified when condensation of water vapor or
evaporation of water droplets takes place in the moving parcel of air.

The quantity of water vapor that can be present in air under atmospheric

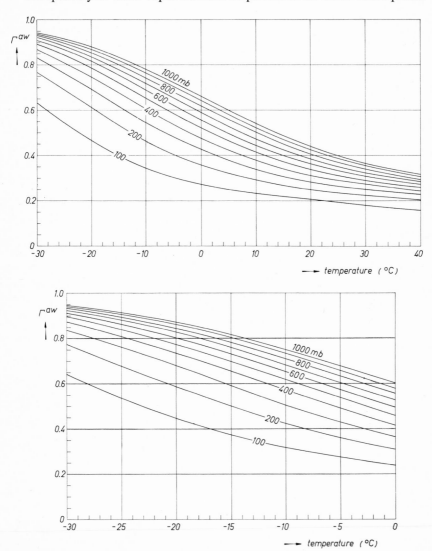

Fig. 2.6. Wet adiabatic lapse rate as a function of temperature and pressure: a. over water
b. over ice. (After KIEFER [1941]).

conditions is relatively small. At 30 °C the saturation vapor pressure of water is approximately 32 mm Hg (42.7 mbar). Thus only 4% of the pressure of one atmosphere at the earth's surface is caused by water in this case. The molar percentage is also approximately 4 and the weight percentage 3. Though 30 °C is not an extremely high temperature, especially near the surface, it is rather uncommon that air is saturated with water at that or a higher temperature. As at a lower temperature the saturation pressure is smaller, the molar concentration of water vapor is generally less than 0.04. The influence of such a low water content on the properties of air is small and thus air containing water vapor behaves in many respects as dry air to a good degree of approximation. This is no longer so if part of the vapor condenses, as the heat of condensation of even a fraction of a milligram of water in one gram of air can cause a noticeable increase in its temperature.

Therefore, when condensation (or sublimation) occurs the temperature of an ascending parcel does not decrease as rapidly with height as when all water remains in the vapor state. Conversely a descending parcel in which water droplets (or ice particles) evaporate does not attain as high a temperature as a parcel in which no liquid (or solid) water is present, both descending over the same distance.

It will be shown in section 2.9 that the dry adiabatic lapse rate $\Gamma^{\mathrm{ad}} = g/c_p$, with g the acceleration of gravity (981 cm sec^{-2}) and c_p the specific heat of air (1.0 × 10^7 erg g^{-1} °C^{-1}). The lapse rate of a parcel of air which contains water droplets or ice particles (so called "wet air") is termed the *wet adiabatic lapse rate*, Γ^{aw}. The quantity Γ^{aw} is always smaller than Γ^{ad} because of the heat liberated at condensation or sublimation in the ascending air. No simple expression for Γ^{aw} can be given (section 2.12); it depends in a rather complicated way on temperature and pressure, as can be seen from Fig. 2.6.

Repeating the argument concerning the stability for wet air, one arrives at the conclusion that an atmosphere is stable if $\Gamma < \Gamma^{\mathrm{aw}}$ and unstable if $\Gamma > \Gamma^{\mathrm{aw}}$. It is again assumed that no heat is exchanged between the parcel and its surroundings and that the latter are not affected by the motion.

Summarizing the results of this section the following criteria for hydrostatic stability are found:

$\Gamma < \Gamma^{\mathrm{aw}}$, atmosphere absolutely stable;

$\Gamma = \Gamma^{\mathrm{aw}}$, atmosphere in neutral equilibrium for wet air, stable for dry air;

$\Gamma^{\mathrm{aw}} < \Gamma < \Gamma^{\mathrm{ad}}$, atmosphere conditionally unstable, i.e. unstable for wet air, but stable for dry air;

$\Gamma = \Gamma^{\mathrm{ad}}$, atmosphere in neutral equilibrium for dry air, unstable for
     wet air;

$\Gamma > \Gamma^{\mathrm{ad}}$, atmosphere absolutely unstable.

2.6. Dynamic stability

The criteria for stability given in the previous section were derived for an atmosphere at rest. The influence of air movement on stability will be discussed in this section.

It may seem plausible that the stability for small vertical displacements is not influenced by the presence of a horizontal field of flow, i.e. a flow pattern in which the vertical component of the air velocity is zero everywhere. Hence one would expect no spontaneous vertical air movements to originate with this "*laminar*" flow type in a stable or a neutral atmosphere.

Reynolds was the first to demonstrate that under certain conditions the laminar flow type is not stable. Without apparent cause the laminar flow changes into a *turbulent* one, which is characterized by irregular movements in all directions superposed on the average field of flow.

Atmospheric motion is almost invariably of the turbulent type. Much attention has therefore been devoted to the study of atmospheric turbulence. The irregular vertical motions are largely responsible for the transport of matter, heat and momentum in the lower air layers. These phenomena will be discussed in later chapters. Here the basic factors which cause turbulence to originate or subside will be outlined briefly.

First a hypothetical case of laminar flow will be considered to illustrate the mechanism of friction in laminar flow. Let a quantity of fluid be bounded by two horizontal solid surfaces, $z = 0$ and $z = h$, and let the lower surface be at rest, while the upper one has a constant velocity U in the x-direction (see Fig. 2.7). Furthermore the fluid is supposed to adhere to the solid at the

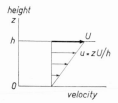

Fig. 2.7. Laminar flow. A tangential force $\tau = \eta \, du/dz$ must be exerted per unit area to move the upper plate with the constant velocity U.

boundaries. Experience shows that under steady conditions the velocity at a height z is in the x-direction with a magnitude $u = zU/h$.

A tangential force must be exerted on the upper plate to overcome friction in the fluid and experience shows that this force is proportional to the velocity gradient $du/dz = U/h$. The force per unit area, τ, can therefore be written as

$$\tau = \eta \, du/dz, \tag{2.3}$$

where η is a quantity characteristic of the fluid called the *coefficient of dynamic viscosity*, or briefly *dynamic viscosity*.

Considering a vertical column of fluid of unit cross section with its upper face in the upper solid boundary and its lower face at a height z, it can be seen that the lower face must experience a tangential force τ to the left, since all forces on the column must balance. In other words the fluid layers situated below a plane of unit area exert a so-called *shearing stress*, τ, on the layers above this plane. The upper layers, on the other hand, exert a stress τ on the lower ones (according to the principle of action equals reaction). In general the viscous shear stresses in laminar flow are proportional to the velocity gradient with η as a factor of proportionality.

The frictional force per unit of volume can be easily found in case the flow is in the x-direction with a velocity $u(z)$ depending on z only. For a volume element of unit horizontal cross section and vertical thickness dz the sum of the forces on the upper and the lower face is

$$\tau(z + dz) - \tau(z) = \frac{\partial \tau}{\partial z} \, dz = \eta \, \frac{\partial^2 u}{\partial z^2} \, dz. \tag{2.4}$$

The frictional force per unit of volume thus equals $\eta \, \partial^2 u/\partial z^2$ in this case (partial derivatives are written because u may depend on the time as well). The general expression for the component in the x-direction of the viscous force per unit of volume in an incompressible fluid is $\eta(\partial^2 u/\partial x^2 + \partial^2 u/\partial y^2 + \partial^2 u/\partial z^2)$.

Apart from these frictional or viscous forces the fluid experiences forces due to pressure differences and inertia. The inertial force per unit of volume can be expressed as $\varrho \, \partial u/\partial t$.

Introducing a characteristic length d and a characteristic velocity U the expression for the viscous and the inertial forces can be written as

$$\frac{\eta U}{d^2} \left(\frac{\partial^2 u'}{\partial x'^2} + \frac{\partial^2 u'}{\partial y'^2} + \frac{\partial^2 u'}{\partial z'^2} \right) \quad \text{and} \quad \frac{\varrho U^2}{d} \frac{\partial u'}{\partial t'},$$

where the dashed symbols are dimensionless, viz $u' = u/U$, $x' = x/d$,

$y' = y/d$, $z' = z/d$, $t' = Ut/d$. The ratio between the inertial force and the viscous force is therefore proportional to the so-called *Reynolds number*

$$\text{Re} = \frac{\varrho Ud}{\eta} = \frac{Ud}{\nu},$$ (2.5)

where $\nu = \eta/\varrho$; ν is termed the *kinematic viscosity*.

At low values of Re the frictional forces are predominant and experience shows that the flow is laminar. Reynolds has demonstrated that the laminar flow type is no longer stable at high values of Re, but changes into the turbulent one. For a theoretical discussion of the transition from laminar to turbulent flow we refer to the literature on the subject (e.g. LIN [1955]; SCHLICHTING [1958]).

In the preceding discussion the action of gravity has been kept out of consideration, i.e. the argument holds for an atmosphere that is in neutral equilibrium ($\Gamma = \Gamma^{\text{ad}}$). In a stable atmosphere the development of turbulent motion will be counteracted by gravity, in an unstable atmosphere vertical movements will be promoted. When Γ is much smaller than Γ^{ad} the counteracting influence of gravity becomes so strong that no turbulent motion can develop, or that existing turbulency subsides.

L. F. Richardson was the first to investigate theoretically the influence of gravity on turbulent motion. He compared the work done against gravity with the energy that sustains the turbulent movements. The ratio of these two quantities is propertional to the so-called *Richardson number*:

$$\text{Ri} = \frac{g\,\partial\Theta^{\text{po}}/\partial z}{\Theta(\partial u/\partial z)^2}.$$ (2.6)

The Richardson number is positive in a stable atmosphere, because here $\partial\Theta^{\text{po}}/\partial z$ is greater than zero, and negative in an unstable atmosphere. No turbulence will develop at sufficiently large values of Ri. The limiting or critical value of Ri at which there is just no turbulence has been the subject of many experimental and theoretical investigations. Values ranging from 0.04 to 0.5 have been proposed, while Richardson originally assumed unity as the critical value (e.g. OBUCHOV, [1946]; SUTTON, [1953]; SCHLICHTING [1958]).

Apart from its use as a stability criterion the Richardson number is often applied as a dimensionless parameter in the theory of turbulent motion in a non-neutral atmosphere. As such various other parameters were proposed by LETTAU [1949] and by BUSINGER [1954]. Businger arrived from a dimensional analysis of the equations of motion at the following parameter:

$$\text{Sn} = \frac{g z_0 H_{ai}}{\varrho c_p \Theta u_*{}^3}, \tag{2.7}$$

where z_0 (the so-called *roughness height*) depends on the aerodynamic prop-
erties of the surface, and $u_* = (\tau_0/\varrho)^{\frac{1}{2}}$ is the so-called *friction velocity* (τ_0 is
the value of τ at the surface). In the lower air layers Sn changes only slowly
with height, whereas Ri increases rapidly with height. It must be understood
that the value of Sn can not be used as a criterion for the subsidence of
turbulence.

Unstable conditions correspond with comparatively large negative values
of Ri and large positive values of Sn. PRIESTLEY [1956] showed that strong
free convection (i.e. air movement and heat transfer under the influence of
buoyancy) occurs at Ri < -0.035. Large values of $-$Ri and Sn occur on
days with strong surface heating (large $-\partial\Theta^{po}/\partial z$ and H_{at}) and light winds
(small $\partial u/\partial z$ and u_*).

It has already been mentioned that very large negative temperature
gradients are found quite close to the surface. It is not uncommon that under
these conditions the density decreases with height. The problem of the
stability of shallow layers of air heated from below was investigated by
BÉNARD [1901], RAYLEIGH [1916] and others (see also BRUNT [1944] and
SUTTON [1953]). It was shown that equilibrium can be maintained when the
so-called *Rayleigh number* (Ra) does not exceed a critical value. The condition is

$$\text{Ra} = \frac{g d^4 \, \Gamma}{\Theta a v} \leqslant \frac{27 \pi^4}{4}, \tag{2.8}$$

where d is the depth of the layer, a the thermal diffusivity of air and g the
acceleration of gravity*. With $\Theta = 293\,°\text{K}$, $a = 0.21\,\text{cm}^2/\text{sec}$, $v = 0.15\,\text{cm}^2/$
sec and $g = 981\,\text{cm/sec}^2$ this leads to: $\Gamma \leqslant 6.2\, d^{-4}\,°\text{C/cm}$. For an air layer
with a depth of 1 cm this leads to a critical value of $6.2\,°\text{C/cm}$ or $6.2 \times 10^4\,°\text{C}$
/100 m. When the critical value is exceeded a cell-like pattern of free convec-
tion is established.

The consideration of the influence of gravity on the stability of motion

---

* The Rayleigh number bears a close resemblance to the Grashof number which is used in
engineering calculations.
One has for a perfect gas

$$\text{Gr} = g d^3 \varDelta \Theta / \Theta v^2$$

in which g is the acceleration by gravity, d a characteristic length, $\varDelta\Theta$ the temperature
difference between the wall of a heat exchanger and the gas, $1/\Theta$ the volumetric expansion
coefficient of the gas and v its kinematic viscosity.

must be modified when there is an appreciable heat transfer by radiation from one part of the fluid to another (TOWNSEND [1958]). Radiative heat transfer tends to reduce temperature differences and thus increases the critical value of the Richardson number below which turbulence is possible.

2.7. Dry air

In this section we shall discuss some physical properties of dry air and some processes that take place in this medium.

Air can be considered as a perfect gas with a satisfactory degree of accuracy for most problems. This implies that pressure, volume and temperature of a given mass of air are interrelated by Boyle-Gay Lussac's law. This law applied to one gram molecule (gmole) of air can be written

$$pV = R\Theta, \tag{2.9}$$

in which R is the universal gas constant and Θ the absolute temperature. If p and V are expressed in dyne cm^{-2} and cm^3 respectively and Θ in °K, $R = 8.31 \times 10^7$ erg gmole^{-1} °K^{-1} = 1.99 cal gmole^{-1} °K^{-1}.

If applied to one gram the right hand side of (2.9) must be divided by the molecular weight of the gas, being 29.0 for air, since the volume, V_a, now is that of 1 gram instead of M gram. The equation then reads

$$pV_a = R_a\Theta, \tag{2.10}$$

where $R_a = R/M = 2.87 \times 10^6$ erg g^{-1} °K^{-1}.

The density or specific mass of dry air, $\varrho_a{}^d = V_a{}^{-1}$, can be calculated from (2.10); thus at 273 °K and a pressure of 1000 mbar the density of dry air (free of water) is 1.276×10^{-3} g cm^{-3}. It follows from (2.10) that the density at p mbar and Θ °K is

$$\varrho_a{}^d = 1.276 \frac{p}{1000} \frac{273}{\Theta} \text{ g cm}^{-3}. \tag{2.11}$$

2.8. The barometric height formula

Once the density is known as a function of pressure and temperature the decrease of pressure with height in an air column under hydrostatic equilibrium can be calculated.

First we shall ignore the variation of density with temperature, in other words we shall calculate the pressure for an isothermal atmosphere. Let the pressure at height z be p. At the height $z + dz$ the pressure is lower than at z, owing to the fact that the weight of the air comprised between those two heights exerts a pressure on the air below z but not on the air above $z + \mathrm{d}z$. The mass of air between the two heights is per unit of surface $\varrho\,\mathrm{d}z$, its weight is $g\varrho\,\mathrm{d}z$, with g the acceleration of gravity. Hence,

$$\mathrm{d}p = -g\varrho\,\mathrm{d}z, \tag{2.12}$$

or, according to (2.9)

$$\mathrm{d}p/p = -(gM/R\Theta)\mathrm{d}z. \tag{2.13}$$

Integration between the limits $z = 0$ and z gives the result

$$p(z) = p_0\,\exp[-(gM/R\Theta)z], \tag{2.14}$$

in which p_0 is the pressure at $z = 0$, e.g. the earth's surface. Equation (2.14) is known as the *barometric height formula*.

If the temperature is no longer assumed to be constant one obtains from (2.13)

$$p(z) = p_0\,\exp\left(-(gM/R)\int_0^z \Theta^{-1}\mathrm{d}z\right). \tag{2.15}$$

A linear variation of temperature with height, i.e. $\Theta = \Theta - \Gamma z$, gives the result

$$p(z) = p_0\left(\frac{\Theta_0 - \Gamma z}{\Theta_0}\right)^{gM/\Gamma R}, \tag{2.16}$$

were Θ_0 is the absolute temperature at $z = 0$ and Γ the lapse rate.

The relation between (2.14) and (2.16) becomes clear when the latter is written as

$$p(z) = p_0\,\exp\left[\frac{gM}{\Gamma R}\ln\left(1 - \frac{\Gamma z}{\Theta_0}\right)\right] \tag{2.17}$$

and a series expansion for the natural logarithm is applied.

$$p(z) = p_0\,\exp\left[-\frac{gM}{\Gamma R}\left(\frac{\Gamma z}{\Theta_0} + \frac{\Gamma^2 z^2}{2\Theta_0{}^2} = \ldots\right)\right]. \tag{2.18}$$

Proceeding to the limit $\Gamma = 0$ leads immediately to (2.14).

The variation of density with height follows from (2.11). Taking the logarithm of both sides and differentiating with respect to z one obtains with (2.10) and (2.12)

$$\frac{1}{\varrho}\frac{\mathrm{d}\varrho}{\mathrm{d}z} = \frac{1}{p}\frac{\mathrm{d}p}{\mathrm{d}z} - \frac{1}{\Theta}\frac{\mathrm{d}\theta}{\mathrm{d}z} = -\frac{gM}{R\Theta} + \frac{\Gamma}{\Theta}. \tag{2.19}$$

The density does not change with height when $\mathrm{d}\varrho/\mathrm{d}z = 0$, or when

$$\Gamma = gM/R. \tag{2.20}$$

With $g = 981$ cm sec^{-2}, $M = 29$ g/gmole and $R = 8.31 \times 10^7$ erg $°K^{-1}$ gmole^{-1}, the numerical value of Γ becomes 3.42×10^{-4} °C/cm or 3.42 °C/ 100 m. At still greater values of Γ the density increases with height.

2.9. Adiabatic expansion

In this section a number of formulas pertaining to adiabatic processes of dry air will be derived.

The work performed by a volume of expanding air on the surrounding atmosphere is $p\,dV$ if the volume increases from V to $V + dV$ and p is the average pressure during the expansion. It is assumed that the expansion is so slow that the pressure in the expanding air is practically equal to the environmental pressure at any moment. Let the change of internal energy U of the expanding air be dU and let the heat supplied to it be dQ. Application of the principle of conservation of energy leads to

$$dQ = dU + p\,dV. \qquad (2.21)$$

For a perfect gas it can be shown that U is independent of V, hence at constant volume ($dV = 0$)

$$dQ = dU = C_v\,d\Theta, \qquad (2.22)$$

where C_v is the molar heat at constant volume. For air the specific heat at constant volume c_v is 0.17 cal g^{-1} $°K^{-1}$.

Further according to (2.9)

$$p\,dV + V\,dp = R\,d\Theta. \qquad (2.23)$$

Substituting (2.22) and (2.23) in (2.21) leads to

$$dQ = (C_v + R)\,d\Theta - V\,dp. \qquad (2.24)$$

Hence, at constant pressure ($dp = 0$)

$$dQ = (C_v + R)\,d\Theta = C_p\,d\Theta, \qquad (2.25)$$

where $C_p = C_v + R$ is the molar heat at constant pressure. Thus $C_p = 6.97$ cal gmole^{-1} $°K^{-1}$ and the specific heat at constant pressure, $c_p = 0.24$ cal g^{-1} $°K^{-1} = 1.00 \times 10^7$ erg g^{-1} $°K^{-1}$.

Now for an adiabatic expansion $dQ = 0$, thus it follows from (2.24) and (2.25) that

$$d\Theta = \frac{V\,dp}{C_p} = \frac{R\Theta\,dp}{pC_p} \qquad (2.26)$$

and substituting for dp/p from (2.13)

$$\Gamma^{ad} = -\frac{d\Theta}{dz} = \frac{gM}{C_p} = \frac{g}{c_p} \tag{2.27}$$

with $g = 981$ cm sec^{-2} the *dry adiabatic lapse rate* is found to be 0.98×10^{-4} °C cm^{-1} or 0.98 °C per 100 m.

Integration of (2.26) leads to the relation between temperature and pressure for adiabatic expansion (or compression) of a perfect gas

$$\Theta p^{-R/C_p} = \text{constant} \tag{2.28}$$

and using (2.9)

$$pV^{\varkappa} = \text{constant} \tag{2.29}$$

with $\varkappa = C_p/C_v = 1.40$. Equation (2.29) is known as *Poisson's law*.

It will be noted that in the derivation of (2.27) for the dry adiabatic lapse rate it was assumed that the pressure changes are so slow that no noticeable pressure difference exists between the expanding air and its environment, while on the other hand the assumption $dQ = 0$ implies that the expansion takes place so quickly that heat exchange can be ignored. That it is possible to comply with both demands follows from a quantitative comparison between the propagation rate of a pressure disturbance and the transport rate of heat. The first is so much faster than the second, pressure being propagated with the velocity of sound ($\approx 3 \times 10^4$ cm sec^{-1}), that the displacement of a piston or of a virtual wall dividing the air parcel from its environment can be slow in regard to one process and fast to the other.

To conclude this discussion on the properties of dry air numerical values of some physical parameters are given in Table 2.2 for use in later chapters.

TABLE 2.2

Physical properties of water-free air

Temp. ϑ (°C)	Dyn. visc. η (g cm^{-1} sec^{-1}) $\times 10^{-4}$	Therm. cond. λ (cal cm^{-1} sec^{-1} °C^{-1}) $\times 10^{-5}$	Kin. visc. ν (cm^2 sec^{-1})	Therm. diff. a (cm^2 sec^{-1})
−20	1.615	5.45	0.1173	0.165
−10	1.667	5.63	0.1259	0.177
0	1.718	5.80	0.1346	0.189
10	1.768	5.97	0.1437	0.202
20	1.818	6.14	0.1529	0.215
30	1.866	6.30	0.1623	0.228
40	1.914	6.46	0.1720	0.242

2.10. Air containing water vapor

For most purposes water vapor in the atmosphere can be considered as a perfect gas as long as the air is not saturated. That the perfect gas law applies to water vapor with a good degree of approximation, even if it is close to saturation, is a consequence of the relatively small saturation vapor pressures that occur. A small pressure is associated with a large specific volume and a relatively small interaction between neighboring molecules.

The presence of water vapor can be taken into account by application of (2.9) to a mixture of perfect gases. The total pressure of such a mixture is equal to the sum of the pressures which each component would exert if it occupied the total volume alone. Its molecular weight and density are simply calculated as the arithmetic mean corresponding to the molar ratios of the gases in the mixture. Similarly the specific heats c_v and c_p are found by addition of the specific heats of the components, each multiplied by its fraction by weight in the mixture.

2.11. Humidity of air

Several methods are in use to express the amount of water vapor in air. The most common humidity variables are discussed in this section.

Absolute humidity is the density of the water vapor in the atmosphere, $\varrho_w (\text{g cm}^{-3})$. Since the density of a perfect gas at a given temperature is proportional to its partial pressure, the absolute humidity can be expressed in terms of partial pressure p_w. Applying (2.9) to water vapor ($M = 18$), one obtains

$$p_w = R\Theta/V_w = R\Theta/\varrho_w/18. \tag{2.30}$$

Expressing p_w in mbar and Θ in °K one has

$$\varrho_w = 2.17 \times 10^{-4} p_w/\Theta, \tag{2.31}$$

and for p_w in mm Hg

$$\varrho_w = 2.90 \times 10^{-4} p_w/\Theta. \tag{2.32}$$

For instance, at 17 °C (290 °K) one obtains $\varrho_w = 10^{-6} p_w$ g cm^{-3} when p_w is expressed in mm Hg. As a rule of thumb the number of grams of water vapor per cubic meter of air can be equated to the vapor pressure in mm Hg.

Relative humidity, h, is the ratio of the partial pressure of water vapor p_w to the saturation pressure, p_w^s, at the air temperature, hence

$$h = p_w/p_w^s. \tag{2.33}$$

It is often expressed as a percentage instead of a fraction, thus a relative humidity of 80 per cent means $p_w = 0.80\,p_w^s$.

A statement such as "h is low" only expresses the fact that p_w is small in respect to p_w^s at the prevailing air temperature Θ. It does not refer to the absolute value of p_w. If, for instance, Θ varies, h will vary as well though p_w may remain constant.

Specific humidity q is the mass of water vapor per unit mass of moist air, thus

$$q = \varrho_w/\varrho = M_w\,p_w/M_p, \tag{2.34}$$

where ϱ_w is the density of moist air, $M_w = 18$ is the molecular weight of water, M that of moist air and p is the total air pressure. For practical purposes one can equate M to the molecular weight of dry air $M_a = 29.0$.

Mixing ratio w is the mass of water vapor per unit mass of water free air, thus

$$w = \frac{\varrho_w}{\varrho - \varrho_w} = \frac{0.622\,p_w}{p - p_w}. \tag{2.35}$$

Since p_w is only a small fraction of p the mixing ratio differs very little from the specific humidity. The mixing ratio is often expressed as g of water vapor per kg of dry air. The magnitude of w must then be multiplied by 1000.

Dew point temperature or *dew point* Θ_{dew} is the temperature at which air with a given moisture content becomes saturated. Hence, Θ_{dew} is the temperature at which the saturation vapor pressure equals the actual vapor pressure p_w.

If the air is cooled below its dew point condensation can occur. When minute water droplets or dust particles which may serve as condensation nuclei are absent, condensation often takes place at temperatures that are appreciably lower. The air is then called supersaturated; this is not a state of equilibrium and condensation does occur immediately at the introduction of condensation nuclei.

Below 0 °C the name *frost temperature* or *frost point* is often used instead of dew point.

It has already been argued that the value of the mixing ratio is less than 0.04 under most atmospheric conditions. As a consequence many physical properties of moist air do not differ markedly from those of dry air. A notable exception forms the absorption characteristics for infrared radiation as will be shown in the following chapter.

The density of moist air, for instance, can be written as

$$\varrho = \frac{29(p - p_w)}{R\Theta} + \frac{18p_w}{R\Theta} = \frac{29p}{R\Theta}\left(1 - 0.378\frac{p_w}{p}\right), \tag{2.36}$$

or $\varrho = 29p/R\Theta'$, with $\Theta' = \Theta(1 - 0.378\,p_w/p)^{-1}$.   (2.37)

Θ' is called the *virtual temperature*; it is the temperature of dry air with the same density of moist air, both being at the pressure p. Θ' does not differ by more than a few per cent from Θ.

The specific heat is also influenced little by the presence of water vapor. For instance if the air is saturated at 30 °C the specific heat at constant pressure, $c_p = 0.246$ cal g^{-1}°C^{-1}, whereas the specific heat of dry air is 0.238 cal g^{-1}°C^{-1}.

The dry adiabatic lapse rate $\Gamma^{ad} = g/c_p$ (equation (2.27)) is therefore only slightly affected by the presence of water vapor. This holds no longer true when condensation occurs. A discussion of the wet adiabatic lapse rate is given in the next section.

2.12. The wet adiabatic lapse rate

A theoretical calculation of Γ^{aw} can also be based on the application of the principle of energy conservation as expressed by (2.21). The quantities U and V in this equation now must pertain to air containing water vapor and liquid or solid water. The term dU in (2.21) therefore contains changes in internal energy due to variation of both sensible and latent heat.

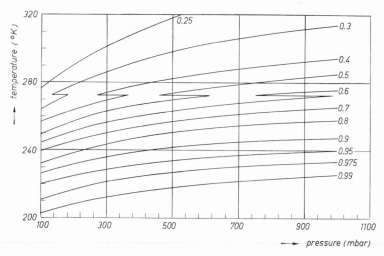

Fig. 2.8. Saturated adiabatic lapse rate (figures alongside the lines in °C per 100 m) as a function of temperature and pressure. The break in the continuity at 273 °K corresponds to the transition ice–liquid water. (After D. BRUNT [1933]).

BRUNT [1933] derived for the wet adiabatic lapse rate the following expressions

$$\Gamma_{\text{aw}} = \Gamma_{\text{ad}} \frac{1 + f_1(\Theta, p)}{1 + f_2(\Theta, p)} \tag{2.38}$$

with

$$f_1(\Theta, p) = \frac{18 L p_{\text{w}}^{\text{s}}}{R \Theta p},$$

$$f_2(\Theta, p) = \frac{0.622}{c_p\, p} \left[p_{\text{w}}^{\text{s}} \left(c_{\text{liq}} + \frac{\mathrm{d}L}{\mathrm{d}\Theta} \right) + L\, \frac{\mathrm{d}p_{\text{w}}^{\text{s}}}{\mathrm{d}\Theta} \right],$$

where L is the heat of evaporation for 1 g of water and c_{liq} the specific heat of liquid water.

2.13. Properties of water

The physical properties of water in the solid, liquid, or gaseous state which are of particular importance in subsequent discussions are density, specific heat, heat of vaporization and melting, surface tension, viscosity and saturation vapor pressure. These are given in Tables 2.3, 2.4 and 2.5. In addition the diffusion coefficient of water vapor in air in relation to temperature is presented in Table 2.6.

TABLE 2.3

Physical properties of ice

Temp. ϑ (°C)	Spec. heat c_p cal g^{-1} °C^{-1}	Therm. cond. λ (cal cm^{-1} sec^{-1} °C^{-1}) $\times 10^{-3}$	Heat of subl. (cal g^{-1})	Heat of fus. (cal g^{-1})	Density ϱ (g cm^{-3})
−20	0.468	5.81	677.9	69.0	0.920
−10	0.485	5.54	677.5	74.5	0.919
0	0.503	5.35	677.0	79.7	0.917

The absorption and emission characteristics of water vapor for temperature radiation are also of great importance, since they affect the heat exchange by radiation in the atmosphere and thus the temperature of the air and the soil. These properties are discussed in Chapter 3 in connection with the theory of radiation.

TABLE 2.4

Physical properties of liquid water

Temp. ϑ (°C)	Density ϱ (g cm⁻³)	Surf. tens. γ (g sec⁻²)	Dyn. visc. η (g cm⁻¹ sec⁻¹ $\times 10^{-2}$)	Heat of vap. L (cal g⁻¹)	Spec. heat c (cal g⁻¹ °C⁻¹)	Therm. cond. λ (cal cm⁻¹ sec⁻¹ °C⁻¹ $\times 10^{-3}$)
—10	0.99794	—	—	603.0	1.02	—
— 5	0.99918	76.4	—	—	—	—
0	0.99987	75.6	1.7921	597.3	1.0074	1.34
4	1.00000	—	—	—	—	—
5	0.99999	74.8	1.5188	594.5	1.0037	1.37
10	0.99973	74.2	1.3077	591.7	1.0013	1.40
15	0.99913	73.4	1.1404	588.9	0.9998	1.42
20	0.99823	72.7	1.0050	586.0	0.9988	1.44
25	0.99708	71.9	0.8937	583.2	0.9983	1.46
30	0.99568	71.1	0.8007	580.4	0.9980	1.48
35	0.99406	70.3	0.7225	577.6	0.9979	1.50
40	0.99225	69.5	0.6560	574.7	0.9980	1.51
45	0.99024	68.7	0.5988	571.9	0.9982	1.53
50	0.98807	67.9	0.5494	569.0	0.9985	1.54

TABLE 2.5

Physical properties of saturated water vapor

Temp. ϑ ($^{\circ}$C)	Vapor pressure $p_w{}^s$		Density $\varrho_w{}^s$	
	Over water	Over ice	Over water	Over ice
	(mm Hg)		(g cm^{-3})	
			($\times 10^{-6}$)	($\times 10^{-6}$)
-20	0.941	0.774	1.074	0.883
-15	1.434	1.24	1.61	1.39
-10	2.15	1.95	2.36	2.14
-5	3.16	3.01	3.41	3.25
0	4.58	4.58	4.85	4.85
5	6.53	—	6.80	—
10	9.20	—	9.40	—
15	12.78	—	12.85	—
20	17.52	—	17.30	—
25	23.75	—	23.05	—
30	31.82	—	30.38	—
35	42.20	—	39.63	—
40	55.30	—	51.1	—
45	71.90	—	65.6	—
50	92.50	—	83.2	—

TABLE 2.6

The diffusion coefficient of water vapor in air

Temp. ϑ ($^{\circ}$C)	-20	-10	0	10	20	30	40
Diff. coeff. D (cm^2 sec^{-1})	0.197	0.211	0.226	0.241	0.257	0.273	0.289

2.14. The saturation vapor pressure, capillary and osmotic phenomena

The saturation vapor pressure of water given in the previous section (Table 2.5) refers to the equilibrium pressure of pure water vapor over a plane surface of pure liquid water. The equilibrium vapor pressure is different when the surface between the two phases is curved, when the liquid phase is subjected to a pressure different from the pressure exerted by the vapor alone, or when the water contains substances in solution. Although the quantitative influence of these factors on the value of the vapor pressure is often small, their effect on plant development can be appreciable. The physical background of these phenomena will be discussed in the next section.

2.15. The saturation vapor pressure over plane and curved surfaces

Saturation vapor pressure refers to a state of equilibrium between a gaseous phase and a liquid or a solid phase. From the viewpoint of kinetic theory this equilibrium is a dynamic one; on the average the same number of molecules leave the gas phase per unit of time to enter into the liquid or the solid phase as conversely. In the dense phases the molecules are so closely packed that they are continually inside the sphere of attraction of neighboring molecules. In the gas phase on the other hand, at pressures of one atmosphere or less, the average distance between molecules is so large that they only influence each other during collisions.

A molecule near the boundary in the liquid or solid state can escape the attraction of its neighbors when its thermal velocity is sufficiently high. The fraction of molecules possessing a thermal velocity sufficient for escape increases rapidly with increasing temperature; this explains the exponential shape of the vapor pressure versus temperature curve.

The attraction experienced by a molecule near the boundary depends also on the curvature of the liquid (or solid)-gas interface. Let us, for instance, consider the concave surface in Fig. 2.9a. The shaded molecule is attracted by more surrounding molecules than would be the case with a plane surface. Hence, at the same temperature the equilibrium vapor pressure over the concave surface will be lower than over a plane surface. Over a convex surface, on the other hand, a higher vapor pressure must be expected owing to the smaller number of attracting molecules in the denser phase (Fig. 2.9b).

The attraction experienced by molecules near the surface of a liquid also exhibits itself in the phenomenon of surface tension. The pressure above a concave surface will be calculated by considering the rise of water in a

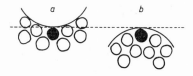

Fig. 2.9. Saturation vapor pressure above a concave (a) and a convex (b) surface. The "black" molecule is in the attraction spheres of more molecules near a concave surface than near a plane surface, hence a lower vapor pressure. The converse holds true near a convex surface.

capillary tube with a circular cross section, a phenomenon that also depends on surface tension. If the wall of the tube is completely wetted (contact angle zero) the liquid-vapor boundary is a hemisphere with radius r, equal to the radius of the capillary*.

When equilibrium is established the saturation vapor pressure above the concave surface must be equal to the vapor pressure at height z outside the

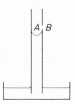

Fig. 2.10. Saturation vapor pressure above a concave surface. The saturation pressure in the capillary tube at A is equal to that outside the tube at the same height (point B).

capillary (see Fig. 2.10). If this were not so, piercing a hole through the wall slightly above the concave surface would cause a continuous transport of water vapor from the inside to the outside if the outside pressure were lower, or in the opposite direction if the outside pressure were higher and no equilibrium would be possible.

The vapor pressure at a height z above the plane surface is according to (2.14),

$$p_w^s(z) = p_w^s(0) \exp\left(-\frac{M_w g z}{R\Theta}\right), \tag{2.39}$$

where M_w is the molecular weight of water, thus $M_w = 18$.

As the column of water in the capillary is suspended from the water film on the inner wall one has, with γ the surface tension,

$$-2\pi r\gamma = \pi \varrho_w^l r^2 z g \qquad \text{or} \qquad z = -2\gamma/g\varrho_w^l r, \tag{2.40}$$

where ϱ_w^l is the density of liquid water. The minus sign arises from the fact that the curvature of a concave surface conventionally is considered to

---

* The rigorous theory shows that the surface is not strictly hemispherical, but the deviations from the spherical form decrease with decreasing r. A molecule traversing the boundary remains at the same distance from the walls of the capillary on the average. Thus the vapor pressure is not influenced by the presence of these walls. The argument is therefore applicable to a concave surface in general and independent of the material of the solid walls, provided that the contact angle is zero.

be negative ($r < 0$). Substituting for z in (2.27) one obtains

$$p_w^s(r) = p_w^s(0) \exp\left(\frac{2M_w\gamma}{\varrho_w^l rR\Theta}\right), \tag{2.41}$$

where $p_w^s(r)$ denotes the vapor pressure over a surface with curvature r and $p_w^s(0)$ that over a plane surface (curvature zero). For water at $15\,°\text{C}$ one obtains with $\gamma = 73.4$ g sec^{-2}

$$z = -0.150/r, \tag{2.42}$$

where z and r are both measured in cm. Values of the ratio $p_w^s(r)/p_w^s(0)$ calculated from (2.41) are given in Table 2.7.

Equations (2.41) to (2.42) also hold for a convex surface, as can be seen from a similar reasoning applied to a capillary that is not wetted (contact angle $= \pi$). In that case r is positive, according to the convention on the sign of curvature, and z is negative (capillary depression). The ratio $p_w^s(r)/p_w^s(0)$ is the inverse of that for a concave surface with the same radius of curvature; it is therefore greater than unity.

2.16 The saturation vapor pressure over a solution, osmotic pressure

The relation between the saturation vapor pressure of a solution and that of pure water is given by Raoult's law, which states that the ratio of the two is equal to the molar concentration of the solvent. If 1 mole of the solution contains c_{liq} moles of solute (the index liq indicates that the concentration in the liquid phase is taken), then one has

$$\frac{p_w^s(c_{\text{liq}})}{p_w^s(0)} = 1 - c_{\text{liq}} \tag{2.43}$$

where $p_w^s(c_{\text{liq}})$ represents the vapor pressure at concentration c_{liq}.

Raoult's law follows from thermodynamics (see GUGGENHEIM [1950]); it holds rigorously for a component which is nearly pure, thus for water in dilute watery solutions. The gas phase is supposed to obey the laws of a perfect gas and the liquid molar volume is ignored in respect to the molar volume in the gas phase. For dilute watery solutions ($c_{\text{liq}} \ll 1$) at atmospheric temperatures (2.43) holds to a good degree of approximation.

In calculating c_{liq} for electrolytes one has to count different ionic species as separate solutes. For instance, if 1 mole of water contains 0.01 moles of a salt that is completely dissociated in two ionic species one has $c_{\text{liq}} = 0.02/1.02 = 0.0196$. The saturation vapor pressure of the solution is 98.04 per cent of that for pure water according to Raoult's law.

Equation (2.43) is also related to the osmotic pressure of a solution. If the solution is poured into a tube which is closed at its lower end by a semi-permeable membrane (permeable to the solvent only) and the tube is placed in pure water, water is sucked into the tube and a pressure head is built up until equilibrium is established. The hydrostatic pressure at equilibrium (see Fig. 2.11) is called the osmotic pressure of the solution. The diameter of the tube must be so great that the capillary rise can be ignored.

Let z be the hydrostatic head and c_{liq} the molar concentration of the

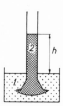

Fig. 2.11. Osmotic pressure. The hydrostatic pressure in the salt solution is higher than in pure water at the other side of the semipermeable membrane.

solutes in the equilibrium state. Again one concludes that the vapor pressure inside the tube must be equal to that outside the tube at the same height, thus:

$$\frac{p_w{}^s(c_{\text{liq}})}{p_w{}^s(0)} = 1 - c_{\text{liq}} = \exp\left(-\frac{M_w g z}{R\Theta}\right). \qquad (2.44)$$

Expanding the exponential function and ignoring the second and higher powers of its argument, which is allowed for small values of the latter, one obtains:

$$c_{\text{liq}} R\Theta = M_w g z. \qquad (2.45)$$

The osmotic pressure, p_{osm}, is equal to $\varrho_w{}^l g z$, thus:

$$p_{\text{osm}} = \frac{\varrho_w{}^l c_{\text{liq}} R\Theta}{M_w} = \frac{R\Theta}{V_{\text{liq}}}. \qquad (2.46)$$

Here $V_{\text{liq}} = M_w/\varrho_w{}^l c_{\text{liq}}$ is the molar volume of the solutes in the liquid phase, since c_{liq} moles of solute are contained in $M_w/\varrho_w{}^l$ cm^3 of solvent. The osmotic pressure is thus equal to the pressure that would be exerted by c_{liq} moles of a perfect gas in the same volume at the temperature of the solution. This result is known as *Van 't Hoff's law*.

2.17. The influence of liquid pressure on the saturation vapor pressure

In the previous discussions it has been assumed that the liquid was subjected to the pressure exerted by the vapor only. However, the actual pressure at the liquid-gas interface can be higher as well as lower than the saturation vapor pressure. The former case occurs, for instance, when air is present above the liquid, the pressure then being 1 atma, which is considerably higher than the saturation vapor pressure at normal atmospheric temperatures.

A pressure decrement can be caused by the application of a suction force to the liquid phase. A simple example is found in the case of water at a height z in a capillary tube (Fig. 2.10), where the suction is caused by the weight of the water column extending from the given height to the plane water surface outside the tube. Assuming, as before, that no air is present the hydrostatic pressure in the liquid at height z is then $p_w{}^s(0) - \varrho_w{}^l g z$. This quantity becomes negative for sufficiently great values of z; in that case the water is in a condition of strain.

Since at any height the liquid water must be in equilibrium with the vapor at the same height, it follows from (2.39) that

$$p_w{}^s(\Delta p_{\text{liq}})/p_w{}^s(0) = \exp(-gz/R_w\,\Theta) = \exp(\Delta p_l/\varrho_w{}^l\,R_w\,\Theta), \qquad (2.47)$$

where $R_w = R/M_w$, and $\Delta p_{\text{liq}} = -\varrho_w{}^l g z$ is the extra pressure to which the liquid is subjected. This expression holds for positive and negative values of Δp_{liq} (negative and positive z). It follows that the saturation pressure is increased by a positive pressure exerted on the liquid and decreased by suction ($\Delta p_{\text{liq}} < 0$). The effect is only appreciable for comparatively large

TABLE 2.7

Relative saturation vapor pressure at 15 °C

Radius of curvature r (cm)	Height of cap. rise z = —local press. head ψ (cm)	$p_w{}^s/p_w{}^s(0)$
10^{-1}	1.50	1.0000
10^{-2}	1.50×10	1.0000
10^{-3}	1.50×10^2	0.9999
10^{-4}	1.50×10^3	0.9989
10^{-5}	1.50×10^4	0.9890
10^{-6}	1.50×10^5	0.8954
10^{-7}	1.50×10^6	0.3305
10^{-8}	1.50×10^7	0.000016

absolute values of Δp_{liq} (see Table 2.7). For instance, at $\Delta p_{liq} = 1000$ mbar the increase of the saturation vapor pressure is approximately 0.1 per cent.

In soil physics it is customary to take atmospheric pressure as a datum level. In that case (2.47) holds as well, provided that Δp_{liq} is understood to be the difference between the hydrostatic liquid pressure and atmospheric pressure, and $p_w{}^s(0)$ to be the equilibrium vapor pressure over a plane surface of pure water subjected to a pressure of 1 atma. The pressure of soil water is of great importance for plant development, as will be illustrated subsequently.

A more unified treatment of the phenomena can be given on the basis of thermodynamical theory, using the concept of the Gibbs free energy. For such a treatment we refer to textbooks on thermodynamics (e.g. GUGGEN-HEIM [1950]) or to special treatises on the thermodynamics of soil moisture (e.g. EDLEFSEN and ANDERSON [1943]).

2.18. Properties of soil, soil composition

Soil consists of a solid phase, the so-called soil matrix, with inclusions of water and air.

The *solid phase* consists of particles of various sizes which usually form larger or smaller aggregates. The particles are mostly of mineral composition, but in addition the soil can contain a certain amount of organic matter. The size distribution of the particles defines the *soil texture*, their aggregation and the general geometrical configuration of the matrix defines the *soil structure*. Many physical properties of the soil are closely related to soil texture and structure, for instance the mechanical properties. The common classification of soils is based on soil texture, the so-called light soils being the coarse textured ones, whilst the heavy soils are fine-textured. For a discussion of the mechanical properties of soils and of the problems concerning soil texture and structure the reader is referred to treatises on soil physics and soil mechanics.

The volume between the aggregates and between the individual particles within aggregates is called the *pore space*. The pores are occupied by water or air. A distinction between *accessible pore space* and *blocked pore space* (or *blocked pores*) expresses the fact that part of the pore space can be filled with air or water while the soil as a whole remains intact, whereas the remaining (blocked) pores can only be filled or drained when the soil aggregates are destroyed.

The term *soil water* is used for the liquid phase which consists primarily of water, but which contains dissolved mineral substances (salts) and gases.

The gaseous phase is called *soil air*; it may have a composition different from atmospheric air. For instance, carbon dioxide is often present in a far larger quantity in the soil than in the atmosphere, owing to respiration of the root system and of the micro-flora and fauna in the soil.

For the scope of the present text the transport of heat and of water are the most important physical processes in the soil. Heat transfer and the related thermal properties of soils will be treated in later chapters. The remainder of this section will be devoted to a discussion of soil water movement. Movement of water through soils has long been recognized as a phenomenon that is of primary importance for plant growth. *Drainage*, by which excess of water is removed from the root zone, and infiltration (e.g. of rain or irrigation water), by which the water content of a soil is increased, have been studied by many soil physicists and the results of their investigations have found a widerspread application in practice. No other subject in agriculture has been treated so fully on a mathematical-physical basis as flow in saturated soils. Several excellent texts (e.g. GUSTAFSSON [1946]) and comprehensive articles (e.g. KIRKHAM [1957]; CHILDS [1957]) exist. The subject will only be treated cursorily in the present text. The discussion of soil properties related to water movement is limited to those that are encountered in the phenomena dealt with in subsequent chapters.

2.19. Water movement in saturated soils

The mathematical treatment of water movement in saturated soils, i.e. soils in which the pore space is completely occupied by water, is based on an empirical law discovered by DARCY [1856]. This law, in a generalized form, states that the flow rate of a liquid across a bed of granular material is proportional to the area and to the pressure gradient (see also MUSKAT [1936]), or

$$_{\text{vol}}\phi = -\frac{kA(\mathrm{d}p/\mathrm{d}s)}{\eta}. \tag{2.48}$$

Here $_{\text{vol}}\phi$ is the volumetric flow rate ($\text{cm}^3 \text{ sec}^{-1}$), A the area of the bed (cm^2), η the dynamic viscosity of the liquid ($\text{g cm}^{-1} \text{ sec}^{-1}$), $\mathrm{d}p/\mathrm{d}s$ the pressure gradient ($\text{g cm}^{-2} \text{ sec}^{-2}$) and k a proportionality factor (cm^2) depending on the geometry of the pore space. Any other set of self-consistent units may be used as well.

In a saturated soil the factor k is called the *saturated permeability*. The formulation of (2.48) has been chosen in such a manner that k is characteristic of the medium and does not depend on the properties of the fluid. Thus, in particular, k is the same for flow of water as for flow of air.* (Soils in which the pore geometry changes on wetting must be excepted.)

In soil physics the pressure is usually expressed as a pressure head, h, i.e. the pressure exerted by a column of water of height h, thus

$$p = \varrho_w{}^l g h. \tag{2.49}$$

The pressure gradient is proportional to the so-called hydraulic gradient, $i = dh/ds$, a dimensionless quantity. For the overall transmission velocity $v = {}_{vol}\phi/A$ one obtains from (2.48) and (2.49)

$$v = Ki. \tag{2.50}$$

This is the common form of Darcy's law. $K = k\varrho_w{}^l g/\eta$ is called the *hydraulic conductivity*. The dimension of both K and v is cm sec^{-1}. K not only depends on the geometry of the pore space, but it is inversely proportional to the kinematic viscosity, $v = \eta/\varrho_w{}^l$, of the soil water.

Equations (2.48) and (2.50) are restricted to laminar flow, which generally occurs with flow of water in soils. The critical value of the Reynold's number below which Darcy's law is applicable is about 5, thus

$$\mathrm{Re} = vd/v < 5, \tag{2.51}$$

with d the average diameter of the soil particles.

It will be noted that v is the average flow velocity across the bed. The average flow velocity of the fluid in the pores is greater, because only a fraction of the total cross section is available for fluid movement.

A simple case is that of laminar flow in a cylindrical tube of circular cross section. In that case the average flow velocity is given by Poiseuille's law, which in the present notation reads

$$v = \frac{r^2(dp/ds)}{8\eta} = \frac{\varrho_w{}^l g r^2 i}{8\eta}. \tag{2.52}$$

This expression is equivalent to (2.48) and (2.50), with $k = \frac{1}{8}r^2$ and $K = \varrho_w{}^l g r^2/8\eta$. It will be noted that the permeability is proportional to the area of the cross section of the flow channel.

By application of (2.52) the permeability of an array of parallel cylindrical

---

* The flow of air in bulk must not be confused with the process of exchange of carbon dioxide and oxygen between the soil and the atmosphere. This phenomenon is caused primarily by molecular diffusion (see Chapter 8).

pores with circular cross section can be easily calculated. The computation of the permeability of a real medium from the equations for fluid movement, though possible in principle, leads to great mathematical difficulties (see PHILIP [1957]). Existing formulas for calculating permeability or hydraulic conductivity are based on simplified models, or are of a semiempirical nature. A discussion of this subject will not be attemped here (see e.g. CARMAN [1956]; PHILIP [1957]; SCHEIDEGGER [1957]).

Because of the strong influence of the pore diameter the permeability depends strongly on soil texture and structure. Values of K ranging from about 0.1 cm/sec for coarse sands to 10^{-9} cm/sec for fine clays are found in nature (see Table 2.8).

TABLE 2.8

Hydraulic conductivity, K, of saturated soil (after GUSTAFSSON [1946])

Soil	range of K (cm/sec)
Gravel	$1.9 \times 10^{-2} - 1.6 \times 10^{-1}$
Coarse sand	$1.4 \times 10^{-4} - 3.3 \times 10^{-3}$
Sand	$1.9 \times 10^{-3} - 1.2 \times 10^{-1}$
Medium fine sand	$5.6 \times 10^{-4} - 8.3 \times 10^{-3}$
Not homogeneous gravel and sand	$2.8 \times 10^{-5} - 8.3 \times 10^{-4}$
Coarse moor sand	$1.9 \times 10^{-4} - 2.2 \times 10^{-4}$
Fine moor sand	$8.3 \times 10^{-6} - 1.9 \times 10^{-5}$
Moraine gravel	$8.3 \times 10^{-7} - 3.9 \times 10^{-5}$
Moraine sand	$8.3 \times 10^{-8} - 1.7 \times 10^{-5}$
Slight loamy sandy clay	$8.3 \times 10^{-8} - 2.2 \times 10^{-7}$
Slight loamy moraine sand	$2.8 \times 10^{-8} - 1.7 \times 10^{-7}$
Sandy clay loam	$2.8 \times 10^{-8} - 2.2 \times 10^{-7}$
Loam	$1.7 \times 10^{-9} - 1.7 \times 10^{-7}$
Heavy clay	$1.4 \times 10^{-9} - 2.5 \times 10^{-9}$

2.20. Water movement in unsaturated soils

When a saturated soil is drained, for instance by the application of a suction force, part of the pore space becomes filled with air instead of water. At low suction values the larger pores are emptied, but with increasing suction water is sucked out of other pores, and gradually also the narrower pores are emptied. (cf. equation (2.41)). The soil particles remain covered with thin water films and water also forms rings around the points of contact between particles.

The movement of water in unsaturated soils is also found to obey (2.48) and (2.50). But the unsaturated permeability and unsaturated hydraulic conductivity depend on the distribution of water within the pore space, and therefore on the moisture content. The value of K decreases rapidly with decreasing moisture content, because both the total cross section available for flow and the cross section of the individual flow channels become smaller.

The total pressure head, h, is composed of a local pressure head ψ and a position head in the field of gravity, z, thus*

$$h = \psi + z. \tag{2.53}$$

If atmospheric pressure is taken as a datum level, ψ is positive for local pressure above atmospheric pressure and negative for local pressure below atmospheric pressure. In the latter case ψ is called the soil moisture tension. The level from which z is counted is arbitrary; one may, for instance, take the water table as the zero level for z. Since in that case the pressure is atmospheric at $z = 0$, one has $h = \psi = 0$ for $z = 0$.

For hydrostatic equilibrium (no moisture movement) the gradient of h must be zero and thus $h = 0$ or $\psi = -z$ for all z. The local pressure head, ψ, is thus positive below the water table and negative above it.

In case there is no hydrostatic equilibrium, ψ can have any value *a priori*. In general ψ will depend on all three space coordinates, x, y and z. Water movement is governed by (2.50). The mathematical treatment of water movement in unsaturated soils is greatly complicated by the fact that K is a function of the moisture content. The reader is referred to papers by CHILDS and COLLIS-GEORGE [1950] and PHILIP [1958] for a treatment of this problem.

Drainage by gravity of an originally saturated soil proceeds increasingly slower in the course of time, until after a few days it becomes practically imperceptible, even in a period of several days or weeks. The water content after approximately five days of drainage by gravity is called the *field capacity* of the soil (WADLEIGH [1955]). Field capacity is a somewhat arbitrary property, because the moisture content attained after five days is not a true equilibrium value. It depends *inter alia* on the depth of the drained column and on the moisture characteristics of the soil.

The permeability becomes very small at low values of the moisture content, but it remains different from zero as long as the moisture content is not zero. In addition, water moves in the vapor phase as well as in the liquid phase. Vapor movement will be treated in Chapter 7 in connection with the thermal properties of soils.

---

* In hydraulic engineering ψ is called the pressure head and z the static head.

2.21. The moisture sorption curve

The soil moisture sorption curve expresses the equilibrium relationship between the water filled pore space and the local pressure or tension. The relationship can be established experimentally in several ways. The most direct way is by the application of a suction or a pressure to a soil sample. Another method consists of using the relationship between the saturation vapor pressure and liquid pressure (equation (2.47)). Some experimental details are given in the following section.

By way of example the moisture sorption curves of a clay soil and of a sandy soil are shown in Fig. 2.12. From the moisture sorption curve can be

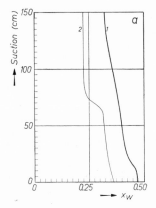

Fig. 2.12. Moisture sorption curves. The volumetric water content (cm³ of water per cm³ of soil) is indicated by x_w. 1. Heavy clay soil (RICHARDS [1931]). 2. Sandy soil at Wageningen, containing approx. 5% humus.

TABLE 2.9

Hydraulic conductivity (in cm/day) of unsaturated soils
(after RICHARDS and MOORE [1952])

Soil	Soil moisture tension $(-\psi)$							
	0	10	20	40	60	80	100	200
Superstition sand	158.16	31 20	15 60	8.88	0.576	0.494	0.4122	0.00288
Coachella loamy fine sand	57.6	19.58	10.37	4.47	3.00	1.91	0.456	0.01392
Pachappa fine sandy loam	35.52	12.24	11.57	10.32	7.20	4.08	2.292	0.0576
Milville silt loam	40.56	3.12	2.88	2.64	2.028	1.416	1.2136	0.1416
Chino silty clay loam	17.352	1.440	0.912	0.312	0.2328	0.1536	0.1128	0.0278
Preston clay	10.32	0.864	0.696	0.288	0.1248	0.0600	0.0328	0.00696

obtained information about the pore size distribution of the soil and therefore also concerning its hydraulic conductivity (see CHILDS and COLLIS
GEORGE [1950]).

The relationship between hydraulic conductivity and moisture tension for
a number of soils, as measured by Richards and Moore, is given in Table 2.9.
The particle size distribution of the various soils is shown in Table 2.10.
The influence of soil texture and of moisture tension (or moisture content)
on the saturated and unsaturated conductivities is clearly illustrated in these
data.

A knowledge of the soil moisture tension is of great importance for
agricultural practice, since the tension determines the energy needed by the
plant roots to extract water from the soil locally. Plants can only take up
water if the tension does not surpass a certain limit, the value of which
varies for different species. The soil moisture tension at which plants begin
to show wilting is for most species of the order of 10 to 20 atma. The actual

TABLE 2.10

Particle size distribution (in per cents by weight) of the soils in Table 2.9

Soil	Particle size (mm)		
	2.0–0.05	0.05–0.002	<0.002
Superstition sand	89.6	4.8	5.6
Coachella loamy fine sand	85.1	10.5	4.4
Pachappa fine sandy loam	59.4	32.9	7.7
Milville silt loam	24.9	60.3	14.8
Chino silty clay loam	5.8	58.1	36.1
Preston clay	1.5	52.9	45.6

value at which wilting sets in depends on a multitude of factors, such as
atmospheric conditions, root density and extension, the hydraulic conductivity and the moisture sorption curve (see PHILIP [1957]). As a rule of thumb
a tension of 16 atma is often used as a value above which plants will show
permanent wilting. The corresponding moisture content is called the wilting
point or permanent wilting percentage. At smaller moisture contents the
water is then assumed to be held so tightly by the soil, that it is no longer
available to plants. Dissolved salts have a similar effect as they increase the
osmotic tension of the watery solution outside the plant in respect to the
solution inside it. For a comprehensive discussion of the problems concerning wilting and the permanent wilting percentage the reader is referred to a
review article by SLATYER [1957].

2.22. Experimental methods, temperature measurement

In this paragraph the principal methods of measuring temperature, atmospheric humidity and soil moisture are briefly discussed. For more detailed information reference is made to the textbooks mentioned in the bibliography and to the specialized literature indicated in the text.

The most common instrument for measuring temperature is the liquid (for instance mercury) in glass thermometer. A thermometer actually indicates the temperature of the reservoir. A good thermal contact is, therefore, necessary between the reservoir and the object of which the temperature is to be measured. In other words the resistance for the transfer of heat between the reservoir and the object must be low. At the same time the exchange of heat between the reservoir and other objects must be eliminated as far as possible.

When a liquid in glass thermometer is placed in close contact with a solid or immersed in a liquid the conduction of heat between the thermometer bulb and its surroundings is usually sufficient for ensuring a reliable reading of the temperature of the medium near the reservoir. An example of the former case is a thermometer fitting in a hole in the soil. Small errors can arise from heat conduction along the stem of the thermometer and from the fact that part of the liquid thread may be at a temperature different from that of the bulb (thermometers are calibrated such that they read correctly when the entire thermometer is at the same, constant temperature). Soil thermometers should therefore not be placed in a metal casing. Radiation errors are negligible when a thermometer is placed in the soil. They are usually small when liquid temperatures are measured.

When placed in air, ventilation is generally needed to ensure sufficient thermal contact between the thermometer and its surroundings. In addition the thermometer should be shielded against solar and terrestial radiation, because air is largely transparent for both. Ventilation can be natural or artificial. In standard meteorological practice thermometers are housed in the so-called Stevenson screen, which allows natural ventilation and also acts as a radiation shield. Artificial ventilation is usually performed by a fan driven by a clockwork or electrical motor. A simple and cheap way of ventilating is by swirling the thermometer.

Apart from mercury, alcohol and toluene are used as thermometric liquids, particularly in maximum and minimum thermometers. The degree of accuracy attained with liquid in glass thermometers is in general a few tenths of a degree centigrade.

In bimetallic thermometers the sensitive element consists of two strips of metals with different thermal expansion coefficients which are firmly welded together. When the temperature changes the element is deformed and this deformation is used to move a pointer over a temperature scale. Linear or slightly curved elements and coils are commonly used. The degree of accuracy attainable is also a few tenths of a degree centigrade. Bimetallic thermo-meters can easily be made recording; they are frequently applied in thermo-graphs.

Electrical methods are based on the change of resistance with temperature or on the thermoelectric effect. They have many advantages for specialized work; for instance, they can be made distant reading and recording and can be used for measuring rapid changes in temperature.

Resistance thermometers consist of a thin wire, mostly platinum or nickel, often spiraled on a cylinder. A bridge circuit is generally used for measuring the resistance. The resistance of platinum and of most other pure metals increases by 0.4 to 0.5 per cent of its value for each degree centigrade rise in temperature at ordinary temperatures. The resistance versus tempera-ture relation shows very little change in the course of time, in particular for platinum wire. This makes the instrument especially suited for accurate measurements during prolonged periods.

A special type of resistance thermometer is the thermistor. This is a semiconductor that changes its resistance, R, with temperature according to the formula

$$R = B\,e^{a/\Theta} \tag{2.54}$$

where a and B are positive constants and Θ is the absolute temperature. The temperature coefficient is, therefore, found to be

$$(1/R)\,dR/d\Theta = -a/\Theta^2. \tag{2.55}$$

The resistance of a thermistor decreases rapidly with increasing temperature. The temperature coefficient is negative, its absolute value decreases with increasing temperature. At ordinary temperatures a value of $-0.05\,°C^{-1}$ is not uncommon. Hence, the effect of temperature on resistance is about ten times as great as with a metal wire. Thermistors can be made in various shapes, e.g. rods, plates, small beads. Because they are semiconductors their resistance is comparatively high, for instance 10^3 to 10^5 ohm for a thermistor of pinhead size. The resistance of a thermistor at a given temperature is more liable to change in the course of time than that of a pure metal. More frequent calibration is therefore desirable (Vos [1953]).

When two wires of different metals are welded together at two points and the welds are kept at different temperatures, an electric potential difference between the welds is established and electric current flows through the circuit formed by the two wires. This effect is called the thermoelectric or Seebeck effect. When this effect is used for temperature measurements, one of the welds is usually kept at a reference temperature while the other is placed in contact with the object in study. The thermoelectric potential difference, which is roughly proportional to the temperature difference between the two welds, is measured by a compensation method or the thermoelectric current is measured with a galvanometer placed in the circuit.

Combinations of metals frequently used at ordinary temperatures are copper-constantan which produces approximately 40 μV per degree centigrade temperature difference, iron-constantan with approximately 50 μV $^\circ$C^{-1} and chromel-constantan with approximately 60 μV $^\circ$C^{-1}.

In many applications the ends of the two wires constituting a thermocouple are connected directly to the measuring potentiometer. The temperature of the latter then serves as the reference temperature. Modern instruments contain built-in electrical compensation for changes of the temperature of the instrument.

With normal commercial or laboratory apparatus the degree of accuracy obtained in thermoelectric temperature measurements is about 0.2 $^\circ$C. When a degree of accuracy of 0.1 $^\circ$C or less is desired special apparatus and frequent calibration are needed.

The small dimension and consequently small heat capacity of thermocouples, thermistors and thin platinum wires render these elements suitable for the measurement of rapidly fluctuating air temperatures and of the temperature of small objects such as leaves or water droplets.

2.23. Measurement of atmospheric humidity

The most common instrument for measuring atmospheric humidity is the wet and dry bulb psychrometer. It consists of two thermometers one of which has its bulb covered by a wick that is kept wet by placing its lower end in a reservoir of distilled water. When air flows past the thermometers water is evaporated from the wick and as a result the wet bulb thermometer records a lower temperature than the dry one. From the simultaneous readings of both thermometers the various humidity parameters mentioned in section 2.11 can be deduced. This is usually done with the help of so-called psychrometric tables or graphs. The complete theory of the psychrometer is rather complicated and will not be treated here (see e.g. VAN DER HELD [1952]).

It is obvious that sufficient ventilation of the thermometers is essential. In meteorological practice special tables are used for the so-called "unventilated" psychrometers placed in a Stevenson screen. The method becomes unreliable when the air velocity is below approximately 2 m sec^{-1}. It is much more satisfactory to use artificial ventilation, as is done in the Assmann psychrometer and the sling psychrometer, in connection with the normal psychrometric tables.

Instead of conventional thermometers, thermocouples or thermistors are also used (MONTEITH [1954]). Particularly in a small volume of air, as between plant leaves, these modifications with their small sized temperature sensing elements are of practical interest. A vibrating thermocouple psychrometer has been described for use in still air (DE WIT [1954]).

In another method for measuring humidity a polished metal surface is cooled until water condenses on it. This is observed visually or by means of a photoelectric cell. The temperature of the surface at which condensation just appears is the dew point of the air. This method, which is straightforward in principle, requires much refinement in order to supply an accurate value of the dew point.

Further methods are based on the use of hygroscopic materials. The hair hygrometer and similar types make use of the fact that human hair, animal fibres (e.g. goldbeater's skin) or synthetic organic materials elongate with increasing relative humidity. There is generally some hysteresis, which means that the instrument does not exactly return to the same point of the scale when the humidity reaches the same value after going through a sequence of different (in particular low) values. Frequent calibration is desirable.

Changes in the electrical conductivity of films containing hygroscopic salts, like lithium chloride, are often used to measure relative humidity in connection with climate control and air conditioning apparatus. Hygrometers of this type are favored for recording instruments in technical applications and in radio-sondes for measuring the atmospheric humidity of the upper air layers.

The most direct use of hygroscopic material for humidity determination is by forcing a known quantity of air through a vessel containing it and determining the absorbed moisture by weighing. Sulphuric acid and phosphorus pentoxide are the chemicals most commonly used for this purpose.

Various methods have been critically discussed by PENMAN [1955].

2.24. The measurement of soil moisture

In agriculture both the quantity of water present in the soil and its tension are of importance. The former affects many soil properties, such as mechanical strength, thermal conductivity and diffusivity. It can be measured directly by determining the loss in weight of a soil sample on drying. It is often required to know the volumetric instead of the gravimetric moisture percentage. It is, therefore, of importance to take soil samples of a known volume with as little disturbance of the soil as possible.

Indirectly the moisture content of a soil can be determined by measuring some other physical property connected with it, such as the thermal conductivity or the moisture tension. However, most of these properties not only depend on the moisture content, but also on the distribution of moisture in the soil. As a consequence no unique relation exists between the moisture content and the measured quantity. The moisture sorption curve in particular shows a marked hysteresis for most soils. For a discussion of this phenomenon the reader is referred to the textbooks on soil physics.

Another difficulty encountered in work on soils is caused by the variation in composition, texture and structure from one place to another, even over distances of the order of ten centimeters. This inhomogeneity of natural soils makes it desirable to have at one's disposal experimental techniques for measuring soil properties *in situ* both locally and averaged over a considerable soil volume.

The scattering of fast neutrons (emitted by a radioactive source) by the hydrogen nuclei contained in water is nowadays widely used to measure the volumetric moisture content of a soil volume with a radius of the order of 10 cm (see e.g. BELCHER *et al.* [1950]; GARDNER and KIRKHAM [1952]; HOLMES [1956]; VAN BAVEL *et al.* [1956]).

Of the various methods used for measuring the volumetric moisture content of a small volume the thermal conductivity method is the most accurate (see DE VRIES [1958]).

Soil moisture tension below 1 atma can be measured in the field with a so-called *tensiometer* (RICHARDS [1942]). It consists of a porous cup filled with water and connected to a manometer. When the cup is placed in the soil it exchanges water with the soil in the liquid and vapor phase through its pores. At equilibrium the soil moisture tension is equal to that of the water in the cup; the latter can be read on the manometer.

At too high values of the tension air enters through the widest pores in the cup wall and the pressure in the cup becomes equal to that of the soil air.

The cup should, therefore, have narrow pores of uniform size. To ensure a sufficiently rapid response to changing tension the permeability for water of the wall should be as high as is compatible with demands of pore size and mechanical strength. A satisfactory type of cup is made, for instance, by a recently developed method of sintering small glass spheres of uniform size (NIELSEN and PHILIPS [1959]).

At tensions close to 1 atma the tensiometer usually breaks down owing to air entrance through joints or to the formation of air or vapor bubbles in the water of the system. Porous blocks of gypsum, nylon or fiberglas are frequently used in the field as a comparatively simple, though not very accurate, instrument for measuring moisture tension (and moisture content) above 1 atma. The electrical resistance measured between two electrodes embedded in the block depends on its water content, which varies with the moisture tension of the surrounding soil (the moisture content versus tension relation for the blocks also shows some hysteresis).

Blocks of various composition and structure are in use (see BOUYOUCOS [1952]; COLMAN and HENDRIX [1949]; CRONEY et al. [1951]).

In the laboratory cylindrical soil samples are often placed on a porous plate and suction is applied by reducing the air pressure below the plate. The equilibrium moisture content can be determined by weighing. This method can of course only be used for tensions up to 1 atma. At higher tensions the pressure gradient is reversed; the soil sample is placed on a porous membrane and an air pressure greater than 1 atmosphere is applied to a closed space above the membrane, while its lower face is at atmospheric pressure (pressure membrane apparatus, see RICHARDS [1947]).

The relation between saturation vapor pressure and tension (section 2.17) can also be used. However, in the region of most importance for plant growth, i.e. for tension values up to 20 atma the reduction of the saturation vapor pressure is 1 per cent or less. A high sensitivity is therefore needed. RICHARDS [1958] has recently succeeded in improving the wet and dry bulb psychrometer to such a degree of refinement that the equilibrium vapor pressure of a moist soil or a plant leaf can be measured in the region of 99 to 100% relative humidity. A chromel-constantan thermocouple is used to measure the drop in temperature of a water droplet due to evaporative cooling when brought into a cavity in the soil sample. The sample and the thermocouple are situated in a closed container, which is placed in a thermostat, kept at a constant temperature within limits of $\pm 5 \times 10^{-4}$ °C. The output of the thermocouple is measured with an accuracy of 0.01 μV. The difficulty of producing a water droplet of standard size was solved by dipping a thin silver cylinder (0.185 cm outer diameter, 0.149 cm inner diameter, 0.051 cm height) in water.

The equilibrium vapor pressure is not only affected by soil moisture tension, but also by the presence of solutes in the soil water. The result of a vapor pressure determination gives the combined effect of both phenomena and is only a measure of moisture tension when the effect of solutes is negligible. Plant roots must overcome the binding effects of moisture tension and dissolved substances in order to extract water from the soil.

The tensiometer, on the other hand, measures soil moisture tension only, provided that solutes can diffuse freely from the soil to the cup and *vice versa*. This is not so, for instance, when the exchange of water between the soil and the cup occurs entirely in the vapor phase.

CHAPTER 3

RADIATION

W. R. VAN WIJK and D. W. SCHOLTE UBING

Laboratory of Physics and Meteorology of the Agricultural University, Wageningen, The Netherlands

3.1. The nature of thermal radiation, definitions

Radiation is an important item in the energy balance of the atmosphere and the earth's surface. Its fundamental properties are discussed in the first part of this chapter. Numerical data concerning solar and terrestrial radiation are given subsequently. The chapter concludes with a survey of apparatus for radiation measurements for agrometeorological purposes.

All bodies emit radiant energy in the form of electromagnetic waves when they are at a temperature above absolute zero. The source of this *thermal radiation* or *temperature radiation* is the incessant molecular motion. During collisions, or more generally as a result of interactions between molecules, part of their energy is transformed into radiation. Conversely, radiation can be absorbed by the molecules and converted into kinetic and potential energy, thereby raising the temperature of the body. The emission and absorption of thermal radiation are governed by the temperature and the nature of the emitting or absorbing substance.

Molecules can also emit radiation when they are excited by impinging atomic particles, e.g. electrons, as is the case in a gas discharge or when they absorb short-wave radiation from external sources which causes fluorescense. In addition there are many other mechanisms of excitation. The laws applying to radiation produced by such processes are quite different from those applying to thermal radiation, because there is no equilibrium between the thermal motion of the molecules and the emitted radiation. A discussion of these phenomena falls outside the scope of this book.

Radiant energy is the energy travelling in the form of electromagnetic waves. It is denoted by the symbol Q and has the dimension of energy so that it is measured in joule, erg, calorie or an equivalent quantity.

The amount of radiant energy emitted, transferred or received per unit time is called *radiant flux* Φ. It has the dimension of energy per unit time. In physical literature the watt or the erg sec^{-1} are commonly used as units, in meteorology the unit cal min^{-1} is frequently employed.

The amount of radiant energy that is emitted or received may vary greatly with the direction of emission or observation. This, for instance, is the case for a sky which is partly covered by clouds. To take such variations into account in the calculations the concept of solid angle is introduced. If a body is viewed from a point of observation O, each straight line passing through O and intersecting the body is said to lie within the *solid angle*, ω, subtended at O by the body. Solid angles are dimensionless: they are expressed in steradians. A solid angle of one steradian (abbreviated sr) cuts out an area of 1 cm^2 on a sphere of radius 1 cm having its center in O, or more generally an area of R^2 on a sphere of radius R. The solid angle subtended by the entire sphere (also the entire space) is therefore $4\pi R^2/R^2 = 4\pi$ sr.

Radiant intensity J is the radiant flux per unit of solid angle, or $J = d\Phi/d\omega$; it is measured in W sr^{-1} or equivalent units.

Radiant flux density H $= d\Phi/dA$ is the flux per unit of surface; it is expressed as W m^{-2}, erg cm^{-2} sec^{-1}, cal cm^{-2} min^{-1}, or equivalent units. When it is desired to point out that the radiant flux is directed towards the surface of observation the term *irradiancy* or *irradiance* is used. If one wants to stress that the radiation is emitted by a source, the radiant flux density is sometimes called *radiancy or emittancy* (M).

Steradiancy B $= dH/\cos\vartheta \, d\omega = dJ/\cos\vartheta \, dA$, in which dH is the radiant flux density per unit of solid angle for a source of radiation in a direction that makes an angle ϑ with the normal on the surface of the source. The factor $\cos\vartheta$ arises from the fact that a surface element dA when viewed in the direction ϑ appears as an element $\cos\vartheta \, dA$ (see Fig. 3.1) The unit for steradiancy is W sr^{-1} cm^{-2} or an equivalent unit.

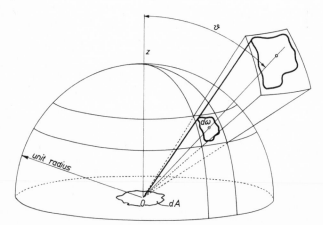

Fig. 3.1. Unit sphere for definition of steradiancy.

The amount of radiant energy contained in thermal radiation depends strongly on the wave length, λ, of the radiation that is emitted or received. It is often necessary to consider the energy, intensity, flux, etc. per unit of wave length interval. Such quantities are called *spectral* quantities. They will be indicated by the subscript λ, e.g. the spectral radiant intensity $J_\lambda = dJ/d\lambda$, the spectral radiant flux density $H_\lambda = dH/d\lambda$, the spectral radiant emittancy $M_\lambda = dM/d\lambda$, etc. The energy emitted per unit of surface and time in a wave length interval λ_1 to λ_2 is found by integrating M_λ with respect to λ between the limits of the interval, hence it is given by the expression

$$\int_{\lambda_1}^{\lambda_2} M_\lambda \, d\lambda.$$

The total emittance M is found by extending the integration over all possible wave lengths

$$M = \int_0^\infty M_\lambda \, d\lambda. \tag{3.1}$$

3.2. Absorption and reflection of radiation*

In an absorbing medium the radiant intensity decreases gradually in the direction of propagation. Let J be the intensity somewhere in the medium and let dx be an element of distance measured along the path of the rays in the direction belonging to J. The change in intensity along dx can then be written as

$$dJ = -aJ \, dx. \tag{3.2}$$

The quantity a defined by this equation is called the *absorption coefficient*, its dimension is that of an inverse length (e.g. cm^{-1}). The absorption coefficient is primarily a property of the medium; in most cases it varies with the wave length of the radiation, and it may also vary with the temperature and pressure of the medium, the degree of polarization of the radiation and the intensity itself.

If a is a constant, one obtains upon integrating (3.2) Bouguer-Lambert's exponential law of absorption

$$J = J_0 \exp(-ax), \tag{3.3}$$

where J_0 is the radiant intensity at $x = 0$.

---

* A reader not directly interested in radiation measurement or theory may omit reading sections 3.2 to 3.6 inclusive.

The *extinction coefficient* $\varkappa$ (cm^{-1}) is used instead of the absorption coefficient, if it is desired to stress that the depletion of radiant intensity is not only caused by true absorption, i.e. by the conversion of radiant energy into heat, but that it is also due to other causes as, for instance, scattering.

The *absorptance* or *absorption factor* α is the fraction of incident radiation intensity absorbed by a body; it is thus a dimensionless quantity and ranges between 0 and 1. The absorptance is also generally a function of the wave length.

The *reflection factor* ϱ is the fraction of incident radiation intensity that is reflected at the surface of a body. The *transmission factor* τ is the fraction of the incident intensity that is transmitted by the body. Both ϱ and τ are numbers ranging from 0 to 1. One has

$$\alpha + \varrho + \tau = 1. \tag{3.4}$$

This equation expresses the fact that the incident energy is divided into absorbed, reflected and transmitted energy.

3.3. Kirchhoff's law, black body

Kirchhoff's law (1898) states that for a small wave length interval and a given direction the ratio between radiant emittancy and absorptance is the same for all bodies at the same temperature, thus

$$M_\lambda / \alpha(\lambda) = f(\lambda, \Theta), \tag{3.5}$$

where f is a universal function of λ and Θ. The notation $\alpha(\lambda)$ has been used to point out that the value of the absorptance for the particular wave length should be taken.

The maximum value of $\alpha(\lambda)$ is unity. A body which absorbs all incident radiation, irrespective of its wave length or direction of incidence, is called a *black body*. Hence, for a black body $\alpha(\lambda) = 1$ for all values of λ, and $f(\lambda, \Theta)$ represents its spectral emittance.

A perfect black body does not exist, but many actual bodies can be considered as practically "black" for a certain range of wave lengths, i.e. $\alpha(\lambda) = 1$ for those wave lengths. The "color" black refers, of course, to blackness for visible radiation only. So, for instance, is the atmosphere "black" for the wave lengths indicated in Fig. 3.2 as being practically completely absorbed. A thin layer of liquid water can also be considered as "black" for radiation of wave lengths from 1 to 100 μ. Since the incident radiation is practically completely absorbed within a layer of a fraction of a millimeter thickness, one often says that a water surface is black also.

A surface painted a dull black reflects only a small percentage of visible radiation. For some applications it may be a sufficient approximation of a black body, as for instance in an instrument for the measurement of solar radiation. However, a far better approximation is a small hole in the wall

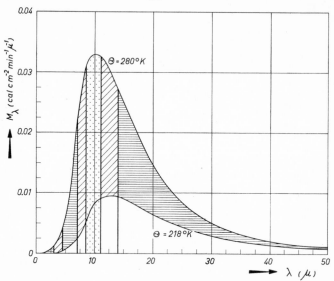

Fig. 3.2. Black body radiation at terrestial temperatures and absorption by water, carbon dioxide and ozone in the atmosphere. The curve for $\Theta = 280\,°K$ gives black body emission at the top of the troposphere. The curve $\Theta = 210\,°K$ represents black body radiation for the temperature of the stratosphere.

Horizontal hatching represents the region of complete absorption by water vapor, sloping hatching and the dotted area, partial absorption by water vapor and carbon dioxide. The dotted area indicates partial absorption by ozone.

of a hollow body. A beam of radiation that enters the hole and hits the inside wall is partly reflected to another part of the wall, where again a fraction is absorbed and so on. After a number of reflections very little radiant energy is left and the chance that some of it is reflected outwards through the hole is exceedingly small.* For similar reasons a dense vegetative cover in which part of the leaves are seen on edge when viewed from above is much darker, i.e., has a lower reflection factor, than the surface of a single leaf.

---

* The following simple experiment will demonstrate this principle. The inside of a cigar box is painted white, the outside a dull black. A hole of approximately 1 cm diameter is drilled in the center of one of the side walls. The hole appears a more intensive black than the walls when the box is closed; it becomes white on lifting the lid.

The importance of the concept of the black body lies in the fact that its emittancy is a relatively simple universal function of λ and Θ. Kirchhoff's law provides the connection with real bodies.

3.4. Laws of Lambert, Stefan-Boltzmann, and Wien

Lambert's cosine law (1760) states that the radiant intensity emitted by a black body is proportional to the cosine of the angle between the direction of emission and the normal direction,

$$J(\vartheta) = J(0)\cos\vartheta. \tag{3.6}$$

Boltzmann (1884) derived from theoretical considerations that the total radiant emittancy of a black body, M, is proportional to the fourth power of its absolute temperature, a result which had previously been found empirically by Stefan (1879). The relation is known as *Stefan-Boltzmann's law*

$$M = \varepsilon\sigma\Theta^4, \quad (\varepsilon = 1 \text{ for a black body}) \tag{3.7}$$

and the constant σ as Stefan-Boltzmann's constant. Its value is 5.67×10^{-12} W cm^{-2} °K^{-4} for the energy radiated in the half space subtending a solid angle 2π.

For a plane surface the steradiance in the normal direction is $B_n = M/\pi$, a result that can be deduced from Lambert's law.

Wien (1896) derived from theoretical considerations that for a black body, M_λ and consequently also J_λ have a maximum value; the wave length for which this maximum occurs being inversely proportional to the absolute temperature

$$\lambda_{max}\Theta = 0.2898 \text{ cm}°\text{K}, \tag{3.8}$$

in which λ is expressed in cm and Θ in degrees Kelvin. This relation is known as *Wien's displacement law*.

Instead of the wave length the frequency, $v = c/\lambda$, can also be used as an independent variable, with c velocity of light (2.99774×10^{10} cm sec^{-1} in vacuo). Thus the emittance in the frequency range v to $v + \mathrm{d}v$ can be written as

$$\mathrm{d}M = M_v\mathrm{d}v, \quad \text{or} \quad M_v = \mathrm{d}M/\mathrm{d}v.$$

Now, as $\mathrm{d}v = -(c/\lambda^2)\mathrm{d}\lambda$, a wave length interval of unit length corresponds to a greater frequency interval for short wave lengths than for long wave lengths. As a consequence the maximum value of M_v for a black body does not occur at the frequency c/λ_{max}, but at a frequency $\nu_{max} = 0.5681\ c/\lambda_{max}$.

3.5. Planck's law for black body radiation

The study of black body radiation led Planck to the introduction of the energy quantum into physics. This was an entirely new idea at the time (1900); it subsequently proved to be of great fundamental importance and has given rise to the development of the quantum theory of radiation and of matter.

Using the assumption that absorption and emission of radiant energy can only take place in finite quantities (quanta) equal to $h\nu$, Planck obtained an expression for $B_{n\lambda}$ which is in excellent agreement with experience. The constant $h = 6.6252 \times 10^{-27}$ erg sec is Planck's constant; the energy quantum $h\nu$ increases proportional to ν and thus becomes greater with higher frequency or shorter wave length. The spectral steradiance in the normal direction, $B_{n\lambda}$, was found to be:

$$B_{n\lambda} = \frac{c_1 \lambda^{-5}}{\exp(c_2/\lambda\Theta) - 1},\tag{3.9}$$

in which $c_1 = 1.1907 \times 10^{-5}$ erg cm^2 sec^{-1} sr^{-1} and $c_2 = 1.438$ cm °K. Since the radiation emitted by a black body is unpolarized, the energy of linearly polarized radiation emitted is half that given by (3.9).

The spectral radiant emittance, M_λ, is obtained from (3.9) by applying Lambert's law and integrating over the solid angle. One obtains for a plane surface

$$M_\lambda = \frac{\pi c_1 \lambda^{-5}}{\exp(c_2/\lambda\Theta) - 1}.\tag{3.10}$$

The constants c_1 and c_2 can be expressed in the fundamental physical constants h, c and $k = 1.3802 \times 10^{-16}$ erg °K^{-1} (Boltzmann's constant). The relations are $c_1 = 2hc^2$ and $c_2 = hc/k$.

The counterpart of (3.9) for the steradiancy per unit of frequency interval is

$$B_{n\nu} = \frac{c_1 \nu^3}{c^4 [\exp(c_2\nu/c\Theta) - 1]} = \frac{2h\nu^3}{c^2 [\exp(h\nu/k\Theta) - 1]}.\tag{3.11}$$

Stefan-Boltzmann's law can be obtained by integrating (3.10) with respect to λ; the Stefan-Boltzmann constant turns out to be $\sigma = 2\pi^5 k^4/15c^2h^3$. Wien's displacement law can also be derived from (3.10) and λ_{max} is found to be equal to $ch/4.965k\Theta$. The curve H_λ versus λ for black body radiation at other temperatures than 280 °K may be found from Fig. 3.2 by multiplying the abscissa by $280/\Theta$ and the ordinate by $(\Theta/280)^5$.

3.6. Black body radiation in a finite frequency interval

For many applications the energy in a wave length interval of finite extension is required. Introducing the variable $x = c_2/\lambda\Theta = h\nu/k\Theta$ one obtains

$$\frac{\int_{\nu_1}^{\nu_2} M_\nu d\nu}{\int_0^\infty M_\nu d\nu} = \frac{\int_{\lambda_1}^{\lambda_2} M_\lambda d\lambda}{\int_0^\infty M_\lambda d\lambda} = \frac{15}{\pi^4} \int_{x_1}^{x_2} \frac{x^3 dx}{e^x - 1} = I(x_2) - I(x_1), \quad (3.12)$$

with

$$I(x) = \frac{15}{\pi^4} \int_0^x \frac{x^3 dx}{e^x - 1}. \quad (3.13)$$

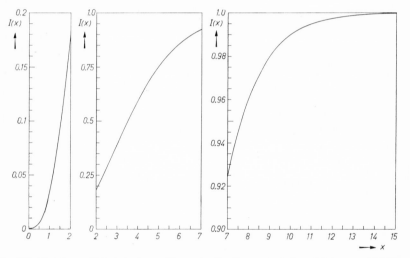

Fig. 3.3. Fraction of black body emittance in the frequency interval 0 to $\nu = (k\Theta/h)x$.

Numerical values of $I(x)$ can be read from Fig. 3.3. From (3.12) it follows that $I(x)$ is the fraction of black body emittance travelling in the frequency interval 0 to $\nu = (k\Theta/h)x$, or in the wave length interval $\lambda = (c_2/\Theta)x^{-1}$ to infinity. For $x = \infty$ the integral in (3.13) has the value $\pi^4/15$, so that $I(x) = 1$ in this case. The same fraction $I(x)$ holds for the radiant intensity, the radiancy, etc., travelling in the frequency interval 0 to ν.

Let us by way of example calculate the fraction of infrared radiation intensity for an incandescent lamp with a tungsten filament. It is assumed that the filament radiates as a black body at a temperature of 2580 °K. The filament is not a true black body but its spectral emittance is approximately the same as that of a black body at a somewhat lower temperature (cf. DE VOS [1953]). This temperature is called the radiant temperature of the body. Considering all radiation with a wave length superior to 0.75 μ as infrared radiation one finds the corresponding value of x to be 7.4, from which $I(x) = 0.94$ results. Thus only six per cent of the radiation is in the visible and ultraviolet regions. Taking the lower limit of the visible region as 0.40 μ the fraction of ultraviolet radiation is found to be less than 0.1 per cent.

For a radiant temperature of 6090 °K, which applies approximately to the sun's radiation, one obtains for $\lambda = 0.75$ μ the values $x = 3.14$ and $I(x) = 0.41$.

In this case 59 per cent of the total radiant intensity is in the visible and ultraviolet regions. The ultraviolet region alone ($x = 1.68$) contains 15 per cent of the total radiant intensity at this radiant temperature,* so that a fraction of 44 per cent is visible.

The spectral distribution of the infrared radiation is also very different at the two temperatures. For the incandescent lamp the maximum spectral intensity occurs at $\lambda_{max} = 1.12$ μ. This wave length is not active in photosynthesis.

It is important to recognize the different spectral composition of daylight and artificial illumination in biological experiments. BROUWER [1956] reported a five to ten times smaller transpiration of green leaves as compared to plants exposed to daylight, when the leaves were irradiated by an incandescent lamp, the total irradiance being the same in both cases. This was due to the effect of the spectral composition of the radiation on the opening and closing of the stomata. With the incandescent lamp most of the stomata were closed, whereas they were fully open in daylight.

3.7. Summary of formulas on temperature radiation

The spectral steradiance of a black body, i.e. the radiant energy emitted per unit of surface, unit of time, unit of solid angle in a direction perpendicular to the surface and unit of wave length interval is given by Planck's law

$$B_{n\lambda} = \frac{c_1 \lambda^{-5}}{\exp(c_2/\lambda\Theta) - 1},$$
(3.14)

---

* Most of the ultraviolet radiation is absorbed in the higher layers of the atmosphere.

with $c_1 = 1.1907 \times 10^{-5}$ erg cm^2 sec^{-1} sr^{-1} and $c_2 = 1.438$ cm °K. The spectral steradiancy of a black body in a direction which is at an angle ϑ with the normal direction is according to Lambert's law

$$B_\lambda(\vartheta) = B_{n\lambda} \cos\vartheta. \qquad (3.15)$$

The total steradiancy in the normal direction is found from (3.14) by integration with respect to λ. This yields

$$B_n = 1.807 \times 10^{-12} \Theta^4 \text{ W cm}^{-2} \text{ sr}^{-1}. \qquad (3.16)$$

From (3.15) it follows that

$$B(\vartheta) = B_n \cos\vartheta. \qquad (3.17)$$

The radiant emittance of a black body is found from (3.17) by integration with respect to the solid angle. This yields for a plane surface Stefan-Boltzmann's law

$$M = \pi B_n = \sigma\Theta = 5.67 \times 10^{-12} \Theta^4 \text{ W cm}^{-2}. \qquad (3.18)$$

For a body that does not radiate as a black body the spectral emittancy is reduced by the absorption factor (Kirchhoff's law), thus

$$M_\lambda = \alpha(\lambda) M_{b,\lambda}, \qquad (3.19)$$

where the emittancy of a black body is denoted by the subscript b.

Relations between frequently occurring units are

$$1 \text{ W} = 10^7 \text{ erg sec}^{-1} = 14.331 \text{ cal min}^{-1},$$
$$1 \text{ cal} = 4.1855 \text{ joule} = 4.1855 \times 10^7 \text{ erg.}$$

Many solid and liquid bodies and substances, among which are most electrical insulators and most natural surfaces, can be considered as grey bodies to a good degree of approximation (i.e. α is a constant) with a fairly high value of α, say $\alpha > 0.80$ for temperature radiation at atmospheric temperatures. For most natural surfaces α is even greater than 0.9 (see section 3.14). Electrical conductors on the other hand have much smaller α-values, i.e. of the order of 10^{-2} to 10^{-1}. They also exhibit large deviations from Lambert's law, whereas electrical insulators obey Lambert's law to a very good degree of approximation, except at ϑ-values close to $\frac{1}{2}\pi$ where $B_\lambda \ll B_{n\lambda}$. Since $\cos\vartheta$ is small anyway at these values of ϑ, these deviations have little influence on the total emittance.

3.8. Irradiance of the earth by the sun

As an example of the application of the laws of temperature radiation, the irradiance of the earth at the outer layers of the atmosphere, due to a spherical black body at the average sun's distance ($x = 1.4968 \times 10^{13}$ cm) and with the radius of the sun ($R = 6.965 \times 10^{10}$ cm), will be calculated in this section (BRUIJN [1960]). The geometrical situation is schematically shown in Fig. 3.4.

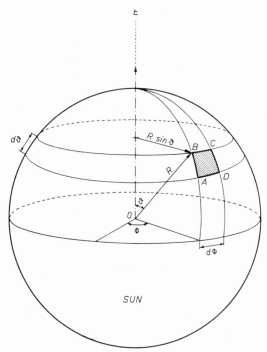

Fig. 3.4. Irradiance of the earth. The distance sun-earth is so great compared with the radius of the sun that:
1. All parts of the surface of the sun can be considered as being at the same distance from the earth.
2. The direction to the earth is parallel to $\overline{EO}$ for any point of the surface of the sun.
3. Half of the sphere is visible from the earth.

A terrestrial surface of 1 cm² which is perpendicular to the direction sun-earth ($\overline{OE}$), receives radiation from each point of the solar disc, travelling in a small solid angle $\Delta\omega = 1/x$. A surface element dA of the sun's surface contributes to the irradiance of the chosen unit area an amount (see equation (3.17)),

$$dH = B_n \cos\vartheta \, dA \, \Delta\omega, \tag{3.20}$$

where B_n is given by (3.16).

From Fig. 3.4 it can be seen that $AB = R\,d\vartheta$ and $AD = R\sin\vartheta\,d\phi$, where ϕ is the azimuth of A. Hence

$$dA = R^2 \sin\vartheta\,d\vartheta\,d\phi. \tag{3.21}$$

Thus for the total irradiancy one obtains:

$$H = \int_0^{2\pi} d\phi \int_0^{\pi/2} (R^2/x^2)\,B_n \cos\vartheta \sin\vartheta\,d\vartheta = \pi(R^2/x^2)\,B_n, \tag{3.22}$$

and according to (3.18)

$$H = (R^2/x^2)\sigma\Theta^4 = 1.23 \times 10^{-16}\,\Theta^4 \text{ W cm}^{-2}. \tag{3.23}$$

Inserting $\Theta = 5760\,^\circ\text{K}$ leads to $H = 0.135$ W cm$^{-2} = 1.94$ cal cm^{-2} min^{-1}. This quantity, i.e. the irradiancy of 1 cm^2 perpendicular to the sun's rays at the top of the atmosphere is known as the *solar constant*.

The spectral irradiancy as derived from the extrapolation of measurements of the solar spectrum to the outer boundary of the atmosphere is shown in Fig. 3.5 together with the spectral irradiancy that would result if the sun were a black body with a temperature of 5760 °K or 6090 °K. The former value yields the same total irradiancy as the actual solar spectrum, the latter leads to a curve with its maximum at the same wave length (i.e. 0.4775 μ) as that of the measured spectrum.

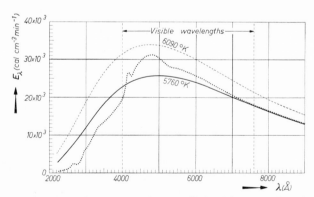

Fig. 3.5. Spectral irradiancy by the sun at the outer limit of the atmosphere (extrapolated) and by black bodies at 6090 °K and 5760 °K as a function of wave length.

3.9. Solar radiation at the top of the atmosphere

Approximately half of the solar energy that enters the atmosphere consists of visible radiation (light), most of the remaining energy is infrared radiation and a relatively small fraction is ultraviolet radiation. About 98% of the radiation energy is contained in the wave length interval 0.25 μ to 4 μ. Approximately 1% of the energy is contained in wave lengths below the lower limit and 1% in wave lengths above the upper limit .

The absolute temperature of the earth's surface is roughly 300 °K. The black body radiation corresponding to this temperature has its maximum spectral intensity at approximately 10 μ and 98% of its energy is contained in the wave length interval of 0.50 μ to 80 μ. Hence, the solar spectrum consists almost entirely of wave lengths that are shorter than those of the earth's spectrum. The solar radiation is, therefore, also called short-wave radiation, the temperature radiation of the earth and the atmosphere long wave radiation.

When the solar spectrum is observed in the troposphere, radiation with wave lengths below 0.29 μ is absent owing to the absorption by ozone in the stratosphere. Strong absorption lines, known as Fraunhofer lines, are due to selective absorption by atoms and molecules in the solar atmosphere and —to a lesser extent—in the terrestrial atmosphere. They are so narrow that they cannot be indicated on the wave length scale used in Fig. 3.5.

The irradiancy of a horizontal surface at the top of the atmosphere is proportional to $\cos \vartheta$, where ϑ is the angle between the incident solar rays and the direction normal to the surface. For this purpose the solar beam can be considered to consist of parallel rays. Hence

$$H_{\text{sh}}^{\text{top}}(\vartheta) = H_{\text{sh}}^{\text{top}}(0) \cos \vartheta. \tag{3.24}$$

The normal irradiancy, the so-called solar constant $H_{\text{sh}}^{\text{top}}(0)$ is subject to slight variations owing to the variable distance between the earth and the sun and to changes in solar activity. The first mentioned factor causes an annual fluctuation of -3.5% to $+3.4\%$ of the average value. The second factor can also cause deviations of a few per cent.*

The irradiancy of a horizontal surface depends on the solar altitude, i.e.

---

* From recent measurements at high altitudes the value $H_{\text{sh}}^{\text{top}}(0) = 2.00$ cal cm^{-2} min^{-1} seems more probable.

In the present text the older value of 1.94 cal cm^{-2} min^{-1} has been retained, since the matter is still in a state of flux. For most agricultural applications a few per cent difference in the value of the solar constant is of no consequence.

on geographical latitude ϕ and on the sun's declination δ. Assuming a constant value of $H_{sh}^{top}(0)$ one has (cf. Fig. 3.6)

$$H_{sh}^{top}(\vartheta) = H_{sh}^{top}(0) \left[\sin\phi \sin\delta + \cos\phi \cos\delta \cos 2\pi (t - t_0)/T\right]. \quad (3.25)$$

Here $T = 24$ hr is the period of rotation of the earth, t is the time (measured

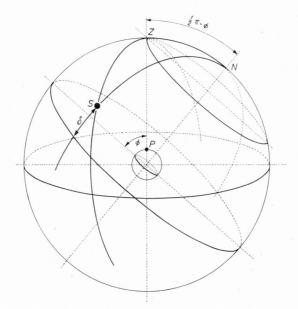

Fig. 3.6. Celestial globe.

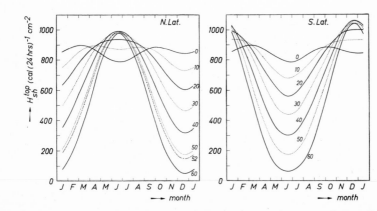

Fig. 3.7. Seasonal variation of solar irradiancy in the absence of an atmosphere at different latitudes. (After ANGOT [1907].)

in hours) and t_0 is a constant, which must be chosen such that $H_{sh}^{top}(0)$ has its maximum value at true noon. Thus $t_0 = 12$ hr if the difference between true noon and average noon is ignored.

Tables of the irradiancy at the top of the atmosphere are given in many handbooks (cf. Smithsonian Meteorological Tables [1951]); a graphical representation gives Fig. 3.7. These data are often referred to as "Angot's values" (ANGOT [1883]).

Equation (3.24) is only valid for positive values of $\cos\vartheta$. When the right hand side becomes negative one has $H_{sh}^{top}(\vartheta) = 0$. The interval of time that $\cos\vartheta$ is positive is the day length. It varies in the course of a year owing to the variation of δ. The latter is zero on March 21 and on September 23, it reaches a minimum value of $-23.4°$ on December 22 and a maximum value of $+23.4°$ on June 21. Graphs of day lengths can also be found in the Smithsonian Meteorological Tables.

For most agricultural applications one is interested in the total radiant energy received in periods of the order of a day or a month, rather than in momentary values. H_{sh}^{top} must then be integrated with respect to t over the period in question. In this manner one obtains the total solar irradiancy at the top of the atmosphere, or at the surface in the absence of an atmosphere, during a day, $_{day}H_{sh}^{top}$ (cal cm^{-2} day^{-1}), or a month, $_{mo}H_{sh}^{top}$ (cal cm^{-2} month^{-1}). If refraction of the rays is ignored this is also the irradiancy, at the surface for a completely transparent atmosphere. The actual irradiancy at any altitude will be different due to extinction in the atmosphere.

3.10. Extinction in a cloudless atmosphere, optical air mass, turbidity

Extinction of solar radiation is due to absorption, scattering and reflection. In this section the extinction in a cloudless atmosphere is discussed; the influence of clouds will be treated separately in the next section. The absorption and scattering of the normal atmospheric gases (excluding water vapor) will be discussed first; the influence of water vapor and atmospheric pollution afterwards.

In an atmosphere that is free of water vapor and solid, liquid, or gaseous pollution, the depletion of solar energy is mainly due to *molecular scattering*, and to a smaller extent to absorption in the ultraviolet region by ozone and in the red spectral region by oxygen molecules.

Scattering by molecules and by other transparent particles with dimensions that are small compared with the wave length of the radiation is proportional to the fourth power of the frequency (so-called Rayleigh-scattering, *vide* KRONIG [1959]). Scattering by larger objects, such as fine dust particles, follows a different law, but is still dependent on frequency. ALBRECHT [1951] found that a second power law agreed better with the observations than a fourth power law.

However this may be, the extinction coefficient in Bouguer-Lambert's law depends strongly on the wave length. Consequently the distribution of spectral intensity is changed after a solar beam has covered some distance in the atmosphere and the extinction becomes a rather complex function of the path length (cf. VOLZ [1954]).

The ratio of the path length for an angle ϑ with the vertical to that for zenith sun ($\vartheta = 0$), is called the *optical air mass m*. It is equal to $(\cos \vartheta)^{-1} = \sec \vartheta$. The depletion of solar radiant energy for different values of m is shown in Fig. 3.8.

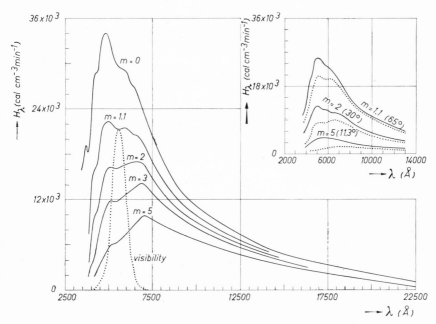

Fig. 3.8. Depletion of solar radiation. The curves in the main figure represent spectral radiant flux density on a surface perpendicular to the line sun–earth for different optical air mass. At the top of the atmosphere $m = 0$ (comp. Fig. 3.5). Atmospheric transmission is as observed in Washington D.C. for average clear sky. (After KIMBALL [1924].) The full drawn curves in the inserted figure represent spectral radiant flux density of direct and scattered radiation on a horizontal surface (spectral global radiation). The broken curves give the contribution of the direct rays. (After ALBRECHT [1951].)

The following semi-empirical equation relating irradiancy of the earth's surface by direct solar radiation $_{dir}H_{sh}(\vartheta)$ to optical air mass was given by Kastrow (see ALISOW, DROSDOW and RUBINSTEIN [1956])

$$_{dir}H_{sh}(\vartheta) = H_{sh}^{top}(\vartheta) \cdot (1 + Cm)^{-1}. \qquad (3.26)$$

The constant C is determined experimentally: it depends on the state of the atmosphere. In an example given by Alisow et al., the value of C is 0.106, from which one finds 0.45 for the ratio $_{dir}H_{sh}(\vartheta)/H_{sh}^{top}(\vartheta)$ for a solar altitude of 5°. Bouguer-Lambert's law based on the extinction coefficient for zenith sun following from (3.26) with $C = 0.106$ leads to 0.32, while the experimental value was 0.56.

The influence of the variable atmospheric constituents and atmospheric pollution is often taken into account by the introduction of a *turbidity factor*. It is a factor by which the actual optical air mass must be multiplied to obtain the apparent optical air mass of an atmosphere free of water vapor and pollution which would cause the same depletion. The turbidity factor is moderately insensitive to solar altitude. This property renders it suitable for characterizing the state of the atmosphere.

ALISOW et al. [1956] give the following ranges of turbidity factors, the value in the range depending on the season: for equatorial latitudes 3.4 to 6.7, for 8 metropolises 3.1 to 4.3, for low country in Europe and the U.S.S.R. 2.1 to 3.5, for mountains 1.8 to 2.7.

The extinction caused by water vapor is determined by the total amount of vapor encountered by the solar rays. This quantity can only be derived from soundings of the upper atmosphere. The humidity at screen height gives only a rough indication.

An atlas and tables giving average monthly data of solar irradiancy at the top of the atmosphere and at the earth's surface for the entire globe have recently been published (BERNHARDT and PHILLIPS [1958]). The atlas also contains data upon the separate effects of molecular scattering, turbidity and clouds. Similar maps were published by BLACK [1956] and BUDYKO [1956].

To illustrate the influence of water vapor and of dust some data are given in Table 3.1 for the depletion of direct solar irradiancy. The figures in columns 3 to 6 are fractions lost from the direct beam for a zenith sun ($m = 1$). The seventh column contains the turbidity factors for zenith sun, i.e. the factors obtained by dividing the values in column 6 by those in column 3. The turbidity factors for $m = 2$ (solar altitude = 60°) have been calculated from data not shown in the Table.

To illustrate the depletion in different wave length intervals some figures calculated by MOON [1940] are represented in Table 3.2. The increase in extinction with decreasing wave length is clearly demonstrated by these data.

Finally some of the results obtained by BERNHARDT and PHILLIPS [1958] are given in Table 3.3. These figures are averages for various months and latitudes.

TABLE 3.1

Depletion of solar radiation by various atmospheric constituents
(after H. H. KIMBALL [1927])

Location	Season	Dry air	Water vapor	Dust	Total	Turbidity factor $m = 1$	$m = 2$
Apia	winter	0.094	0.197	0.077	0.368	3.9	3.2
(Samoa)	summer	0.094	0.205	0.048	0.347	3.7	2.9
Washington	winter	0.094	0.081	0.087	0.262	2.7	3.30
(D.C.)	summer	0.094	0.165	0.103	0.362	3.85	2.13
Jungfraujoch (Switzerl.)	summer	0.066	0.037	0.020	0.123	1.86	1.58

TABLE 3.2

Normal spectral irradiancy (in cal cm^{-2} min^{-1}) at sea level in dependence of the optical air mass. (The data refer to a total vapor content of 2.0 cm of precipitable water, 0.28 cm path length through ozone at normal pressure and temperature and 300 dust particles per cm^3 near the ground.) [after MOON 1940]

wave length interval (μ)	optical air mass $m = 0$	$m = 1$	$m = 2$	$m = 3$	$m = 4$	$m = 5$
0.29–0.40	0.136	0.059	0.029	0.015	0.008	0.004
0.40–0.70	0.778	0.616	0.481	0.379	0.302	0.240
0.70–1.10	0.522	0.454	0.393	0.343	0.301	0.266
1.10–1.50	0.232	0.140	0.103	0.084	0.071	0.060
1.50–1.90	0.104	0.075	0.066	0.060	0.056	0.052
>1.90	0.168	0.019	0.014	0.011	0.010	0.009
total	1.940	1.363	1.086	0.892	0.748	0.631

3.11. The influence of clouds, total global radiation

Clouds exert a profound influence on the amount of short-wave radiation received at the earth's surface. The absorption in clouds is usually small, but dense clouds reflect a considerable fraction of the direct solar radiation. The

TABLE 3.3

Short-wave radiation received on a horizontal surface (in cal cm^{-2} day^{-1}) for various latitudes, months and atmospheric conditions [after BERNHARDT and PHILLIPS 1958]

	N. Lat.				S. Lat.			
	0	30	60	90	30	60	90	
January	600	350	50	—	715	685	730	
April	605	610	460	350	450	170	—	At the top of
July	560	670	640	690	320	40	—	the atmosphere
October	595	365	70	—	685	630	630	
January	520	290	30	—	630	580	580	Direct radiation
April	535	530	380	225	385	130	—	after correction
July	490	585	545	555	265	25	—	for Rayleigh
October	525	305	50	—	605	530	485	scattering
January	360	215	20	—	480	510	—	Direct radiation
April	365	420	320	—	280	110	—	for a turbid,
July	335	430	440	—	195	15	—	cloudless atmos-
October	360	220	25	—	470	470	—	phere
January	160	120	10	—	255	130	—	Direct radiation
April	160	230	130	—	140	30	—	for a turbid
July	145	240	155	—	90	10	—	atmosphere and
October	170	130	10	—	225	130	—	clouds
January	260	160	10	—	350	270	—	
April	260	310	150	—	210	70	—	Total global
July	240	340	275	—	150	20	—	radiation
October	270	230	60	—	290	190	—	

sides of such clouds, when illuminated by the sun's rays, therefore show a brilliant white color.

The reflection factor, i.e. the ratio between the reflected and the incoming radiation, of clouds depends largely on the type of cloud, as determined by its shape and thickness, the number of particles per unit volume, and the size and nature (water or ice) of these particles. Dense clouds can reflect more than 70 per cent of the incident solar radiation.

The absorption of short-wave radiation in clouds occurs mainly in the long wave region of the solar spectrum. A graph showing how reflection, absorption and transmission vary with cloud thickness is given in Fig. 3.9. It provides an approximate idea of the interception of solar radiation by clouds. The principal causes for the depletion of radiant flux density are refraction and subsequent reflection of light in the water droplets and scattering of light by very small droplets.

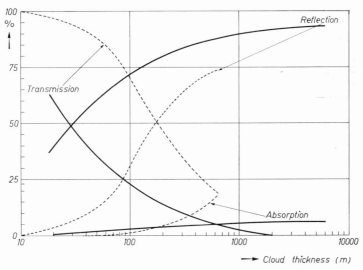

Fig. 3.9. Reflection, absorption and transmission of solar radiation by clouds as a function of cloud thickness.

——— Unspecified type of clouds. (After BERRY et al. [1945].)

– – – – Data for stratus clouds. (After NEIBURGER [1949].)

Total global radiation H_{sh} is the sum of the irradiancy of a unit of horizontal surface caused by direct solar radiation and diffuse short-wave radiation due to clouds, dust and molecular scattering from all parts of the sky. The ratio of diffuse to direct radiation varies greatly with optical air mass and the state of the atmosphere, in particular its content of clouds, water vapor, dust and other pollutants. Average values for different latitudes have been given in Table 3.3.

Graphs illustrating the diurnal and the monthly variation of H_{sh} at a number of selected locations are given in Fig. 3.10. Each curve represents the diurnal variation averaged for all days in the relevant month. The influence of solar altitude is clearly visible. A further interpretation of the graphs can be given in the light of data on the cloudiness for the various stations. The monthly averages of the daily totals are given in Table 3.4.

3.12. Empirical formulas for total global radiation

Total global radiation is generally an important term in the energy balance

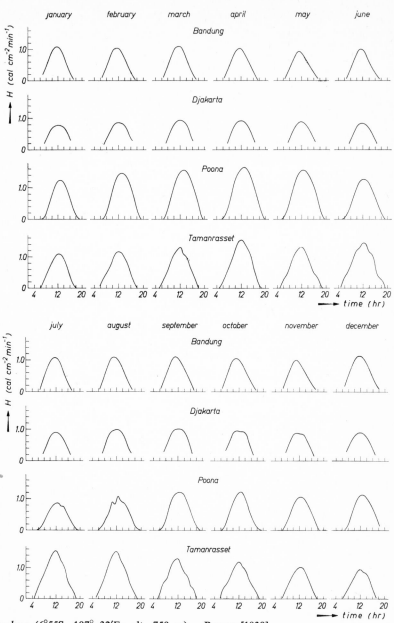

Bandung (6°55S, 107° 32′E; alt. 750 m) and Djakarta (6°10′S, 106°56E) after DEE and REESINCK [1952], Poona (18°31′N, 7353′E; alt. 500 m) after RAMAN [1938], Tamanrasset (33°7′N, 6°5′E; alt. 69 m) after Institut de Meteorologie et de Physique du Globe [1953].

Fig. 3.10. Monthly average of daily radiation at various meteorological stations (cal cm^{-2} min^{-1}).

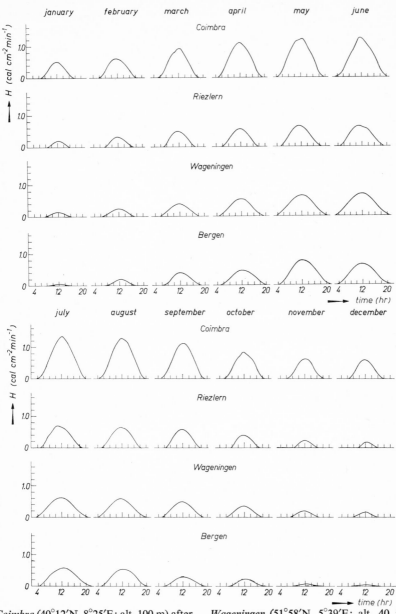

Coimbra (40°12′N, 8°25′E; alt. 100 m) after Instituto Geofisico. Coimbra Universidade [1940],

Riezlern (47°22′N, 10°10′E; alt. 2000 m) after HOELPER [1939],

Wageningen (51°58′N, 5°39′E; alt. 40 m) after DE VRIES [1955],

Bergen (60°22′N, 5°20′E; alt. 400 m) after SCHIELDRUP [1952].

Fig. 3.10. (*continued*)

TABLE 3.4

Monthly average of daily total global radiation at some selected meteorological stations

Average total global radiation in cal cm^{-2} day^{-1}

Location	J	F	M	A	M	J	J	A	S	O	N	D
Bandung; 6° 55′S, 107° 32′E, alt. 750 m	430	420	425	405	350	375	375	450	460	450	375	475
Djakarta; 6° 10′S, 106° 50′E, alt. 8 m	360	395	405	400	375	360	360	430	460	425	405	375
Poona; 18° 31′N, 73° 53′E, alt. 500 m	480	662	695	769	740	558	385	433	509	478	432	480
Tamanrasset; 33° 7′N, 6° 5′E, alt. 69 m	455	517	543	700	634	689	702	668	559	503	419	370
Coimbra; 40° 12′N, 8° 25′E, alt. 100 m	144	240	360	528	595	624	652	600	485	336	240	206
Riezlern; 47° 22′N, 10° 10′E, alt. 2000 m	51	98	178	225	290	309	328	297	227	134	66	39
Wageningen; 51° 58′N, 5° 39′E, alt. 40 m	46	92	178	280	370	402	360	320	225	135	55	39
Bergen; 66° 22′N, 5° 20′E, alt. 400 m	15	66	160	238	442	480	351	290	138	83	24	10
Ishigaki-jima; 24° 20′N, 124° 10′E, (island near Formosa)	260	252	369	358	482	416	553	500	509	406	325	283
Kumamoto; 32° 49′N, 130° 42′E	202	289	325	414	426	284	440	403	378	313	260	243
Tottori; 35° 31′N, 134° 11′E,	86	111	167	230	289	284	392	358	255	251	178	154
Akita; 39° 43′N, 140° 06′E	170	221	379	462	521	397	526	519	391	270	202	150

TABLE 3.5

Values of the constants α and β in the linear regression equation $H_{\mathrm{sh}} = H_{\mathrm{sh}}^{\mathrm{top}} (\alpha + \beta\, n/N)$

Location	Position	Period of obs.	Nr. of months	α	β	Correlation coefficient	Reference
Rothamsted	51.8 N, 0.4 W	1931–1940	84	0.18	0.55	0.79	PENMAN [1948]
Gembloux	50.6 N, 4.7 E	1939–1950	60	0.15	0.54	0.83	Anonymous
Versailles	48.8 N, 2.5 E	1935–1951	99	0.23	0.50	0.90	Anonymous
Mt. Stromlo	35.3 S, 149.1 E	1928–1939	144	0.25	0.54	0.79	RIMMER and ALLEN [1950]
Dry Creek	34.8 S, 138.6 E	1947–1950	48	0.30	0.50	0.95	I.C.I. ALKALI
Adelaide	35.0 S, 138.6 E	–	–	0.23	0.48	0.90	BLACK et al. [1955]
Deniliquin	35.5 S, 145.0 E	1956–1958	24	0.27	0.54		DE VRIES [1958]

of the earth's surface. Direct measurements of this quantity are made only in a comparatively few locations. For a cloudless atmosphere it can be estimated with some degree of confidence from the data given in the previous sections. When clouds are present a theoretical approach becomes too complicated for use in agricultural or meteorological practice, and recourse must be had to empirical formulas relating irradiancy to visual observations of the degree of cloudiness. It will be understood from the foregoing that these relations must be of a statistical character.

For a given latitude and a transparent atmosphere the total irradiancy received by a horizontal surface during a period of one day will again be denoted by H_{sh}^{top} (the so-called Angot value, *vide* Fig. 3.7). The relation between total global radiation (also for a period of one day) and cloudiness will be taken into account by an empirical quadratic regression formula

$$H_{sh} = H_{sh}^{top} (a - bm - cm^2). \tag{3.27}$$

Here m denotes the average fraction of the sky covered by clouds; a, b and c are constants which are to be determined statistically from series of simultaneous observations of H_{sh} and m. These constants are obviously dependent on the state of the atmosphere and the cloud type, so that they may vary with the location and also with the season at a given location.

BLACK [1956], treating a large amount of data from stations all over the world arrived at the following overall values: $a = 0.803$, $b = 0.340$, $c = 0.458$. These values were derived for m-values ranging from 0.1 to 0.9. Extrapolation to $m = 0$ leads to an average absorption factor of about 0.20 for a cloudless atmosphere.

The value of H_{sh} calculated from (3.27) must be interpreted as a statistical estimate of this quantity. If the constants are properly determined for a given location the standard deviation is approximately 25% when daily values are considered and approximately 5% when monthly averages are taken (cf. DE VRIES [1955]).

Total global radiation can also be related to the duration of bright sunshine, as measured by the Campbell-Stokes sunshine recorder (see section 3.18). Let the number of hours of bright sunshine during a day be denoted by n, and the day length in hours, i.e. the maximum possible value of n for the same day, by N. The quantity n/N is termed the relative duration of (bright) sunshine. Assuming a linear regression equation relating H_{sh} to n/N one has

$$H_{sh} = H_{sh}^{top} (\alpha + \beta \, n/N), \tag{3.28}$$

where α and β can be determined statistically from simultaneous measurements of H_{sh} and n/N. Some values found for several locations are given in Table 3.5. The standard deviation of the H_{sh}-values calculated from (3.28) is about the same as that for values found from (3.27) (see DE VRIES [1955], [1958a]).

Since $1 - n/N$ is the part of the day that solar radiation is intercepted by clouds one might expect that m is approximately equal to $1 - n/N$. This is indeed the case; at Wageningen monthly averages of $m + n/N$ range from 0.88 in December to 1.03 in August. The difference between the values for summer and winter are explained by the enhanced screening effect of the clouds at low solar altitudes.

The agreement between predicted and real values of H_{sh} can generally be improved by assuming H_{sh}/H_{sh}^{top} to be a quadratic function of n/N. For the desert of Mesopotamia, for instance, the graph of H_{sh} versus n/N is concave towards the n/N axis (WARTENA [1959]).

A formula that is frequently used instead of (3.28) is Ångström's formula

$$H_{sh} = H_{sh}^{nc}[\alpha + (1 - \alpha)n/N], \tag{3.29}$$

where H_{sh}^{nc} is the total global radiation at the surface when no clouds are present. The "constant" α varies with the state of the atmosphere and the

TABLE 3.6

Values of the constant α in Ångström's linear regression equation
$$H_{sh} = H_{sh}^{nc}[\alpha + (1 - \alpha)n/N]$$

Locality	Position	Altitude (m)	α	Reference
Bandung	7 °S, 107 °E	750	0.29–0.40	DEE and REESINCK [1951]
Stocksund	59 °N, 18 °E	57	0.21–0.26	ÅNGSTRÖM [1928]
Blue Hill	42 °N, 71 °W	195	0.27	HAURWITZ [1934]
Washington D.C.	39 °N, 77 °W	127		
Lincoln	41 °N, 97 °W	381	0.22	KIMBALL [1927]
Madison	41 °N, 89 °W	308		
Helsinki	60 °N, 25 °E	12	0.24	LUNELUND [1931]
Wageningen	52 °N, 6 °E	40	0.29	DE VRIES [1955]
Polar region	74 °N, 155 °E		0.54	MOSBY [1925]
Davos	47 °N, 10 °E	1600	0.48	PROHASKA [1943]
Ostalpen		1000	0.26	
Ostalpen		2000	0.33	SAUBERER [unpublished]
Ostalpen		3000	0.42	
Chogo Lungma	36 °N, 75 °E	4800	0.50	ÅNGSTRÖM and TRYSELIUS [1934]

type of clouds. At Wageningen, for instance, α ranged from 0.25 in February to 0.34 in August (DE VRIES [1955]). Average values for various locations are collected in Table 3.6.

For a critical survey of the above mentioned and other regression formulas for total global radiation the reader is referred to a thesis by SCHOLTE UBING [1959].

TABLE 3.7

Reflection factors of natural surfaces for total global radiation*

Surface	Per cent reflected
fresh snow	80–85
compressed snow	70
melting snow	30–65
dry salt cover	50
lime	45
quartz sand	35
granite	15
dark clay, wet	2–8
dark clay, dry	16
sand, wet	9
sand, dry	18
bare fields	12–25
wet plowed fields	5–14
grass, green	16–27
grass, dried	16–19
prairie, wet	22
prairie, dry	32
stubble fields	15–17
grain crops	10–25
pine, spruce wood	10–14
deciduous wood	16–37
yellow leaves (fall)	33–36
desert, midday	15
desert, low solar altitude	35
water ($\vartheta = 0$ to $30°$)	2
water ($\vartheta = 60°$)	6
water ($\vartheta = 85°$)	58

* References: ALLISOW *et al.*, [1956]; ÅNGSTRÖM [1925]; BERRY *et al.* [1954]; GEIGER [1961]; Smithsonian Meteorological Tables [1951].

3.13. Reflection and absorption at the surface, photosynthesis, illumination

3.13.1. REFLECTION

A considerable fraction of the short-wave radiation flux that reaches the surface of the earth is reflected. The remaining fraction is absorbed and changed into thermal energy of the absorbing matter.

Reflection factors for total global radiation are given in Table 3.7 for various natural surfaces. They vary greatly with the type of surface or surface cover. The variation in reflecting power explains to some extent the different temperature regimes that are associated with different types of surface. For instance, the extremely high reflection factor of snow is responsible for the persistence of a complete snow cover, once it has been established. On the other hand the moderating influence of an extended body of water on the climate is mainly due to its action as a reservoir of solar energy. This action is explained by the low reflection factor of a water surface at high and moderate solar altitudes and the absorption of short-wave radiation in a deep water layer.

The reflection factor for short-wave radiation of the earth as a whole, including the atmosphere, is called the *albedo* of the earth. Its value is approximately 0.43.

Reflection and absorption factors vary with the wave length but this fact is of minor importance for the heat balance of the surface.

At a soil surface short-wave radiation is absorbed in a very thin layer. In a body of water, on the other hand, part of the solar radiation can penetrate to great depths. Absorption coefficients of pure water for various wave length intervals are given in Table 3.8. About 30 per cent of the solar

TABLE 3.8

Absorption coefficient $\varkappa$ of solar
radiation in pure water

Wave length (μ)	$\varkappa$ (cm^{-1})
0.3–0.5	3.5×10^{-4}
0.7	5.8×10^{-3}
0.8	2.4×10^{-2}
0.9	6×10^{-2}
1.5	$\simeq 7$

radiation is absorbed in a water layer of 10 cm thickness (ZUIDHOF and DE VRIES [1940]).

Data on the penetration of solar radiation in sea water are given in Landolt-Börnstein's tables, Vol. III [1952].

3.13.2. PHOTOSYNTHESIS, ABSORPTION BY PLANTS

The energetic efficiency of photosynthesis is the ratio of the chemical energy stored in the synthesized organic matter to the radiant energy absorbed in the chlorophyll. This quantity reaches a maximum of 20 to 35 per cent in the red region of the spectrum, viz. for wave lengths of 0.6 to 0.7 μ (WASSINK [1956]). The efficiency decreases rapidly in the near infrared, where it is practically zero at 0.75 μ, and more gradually in the visible part of the spectrum, where the efficiency per quantum of absorbed radiation ($h\nu$) remains approximately constant. An energetic efficiency of about 16 per cent at 0.4 μ can be considered as a fair estimate for optimum conditions (GAASTRA [1958]).

When a vegetation is exposed to solar radiation under natural conditions

TABLE 3.9

Reflection and transmission characteristics of (green) leaves for short-wave radiation. After ÅNGSTRÖM [1925] and GEIGER [1961]

Wave length interval (μ)	Reflection factor (%)	Wave length interval (μ)	Transmission factor (%)
< 0.4	< 10	< 0.4	< 10
0.4–0.75	8–20	0.4–0.7	5–20
0.75–1.0	≃ 40	0.7–1.0	40–50

Type of leaf	Overall transm. factor (%)
Common hazel (Corylus avelana)	26
Dandelion (Taraxacum officinale)	28
Lilac (Seringa vulgaris)	26
Roses (Rosa)	25
Alder (Alnus vulgaris)	21
Common birch (Betula verrucosa)	26
Aspen (Populus tremula)	21

a considerable fraction of the energy is absorbed by inactive parts of the plant. The absorption by leaves depends on the type and the thickness of the leaf; some typical values of the absorption factors of individual leaves are given in Table 3.9.

The overall energetic efficiency, i.e. the ratio of the chemical energy stored to the total radiant energy per unit of surface is of the order of 1 to 3 per cent over the entire growing season for the common agricultural crops.

The overall energetic efficiency has recently attracted renewed interest. Technological progress enables one at present to eliminate unwanted properties in certain agricultural products. For instance, taste can be improved by extraction or distillation. This has opened the possibility of growing varieties that have a higher photosynthetic efficiency than the traditional ones, which were primarily selected on a basis of quality.

3.13.3. ILLUMINATION

The sensitivity of the human eye to radiation varies greatly with wave length. It shows a maximum at about 0.555 μ and is practically zero outside the region 0.4 to 0.7 μ. The intensity of illumination is determined by the impression of brightness experienced by the human eye of average sensitivity.

In photometry a black body at the temperature of melting platinum (2042.16 °K) is used as a standard light source. It has by definition a surface *brightness* of 60 candelas per cm^2 or 60 *stilb*, when viewed in a direction perpendicular to the surface. The *luminous intensity* (candlepower) of an arbitrary light source is expressed in *candelas* (c). Hence, a spherical light source with a surface area of 1 cm^2 and a constant surface brightness that is 1/60 times that of a black body at the platinum point has a luminous intensity of 1 candela.

A spherical light source of 1 candela is said to emit a *luminous flux* of 4π *lumen*. When 1 lumen (lm) falls on a surface of 1 m^2 the illumination is said to be 1 lux (lx). An alternative unit for measuring illumination is the phot; 1 phot equals one lumen per cm^2 and thus equals 10^4 lux.

Brightness impressions caused by light of two different colors can be compared by admitting them alternately in quick succession (e.g. ten times per second) to the eye. The brightness impression caused by parallel beams of light with equal spectral radiant flux shows a maximum at a wave length of 0.555 μ. Here a radiant flux of 1 W corresponds to a luminous flux of 680 lm. For light of other wave lengths this quantity has to be multiplied by a relative luminosity factor. Values of this factor are shown in Fig. 3.11.

Since the energy distribution in the solar spectrum varies with solar altitude and with the state of the atmosphere the illumination that corresponds to a given irradiancy varies also. An average value is (KIMBALL [1924]; REESINK and DE VRIES [1942])

$$1 \text{ cal cm}^{-2} \text{ min}^{-1} = 698 \text{ W m}^{-2} = 82 \times 10^3 \text{ lux}.$$

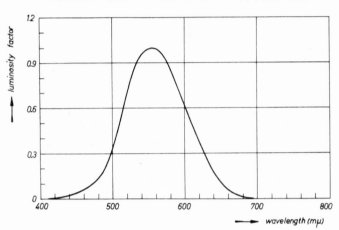

Fig. 3.11. Relative luminosity factor.

3.14. Terrestrial radiation

The earth emits radiation of a much longer average wave length than the radiation emitted by the sun. As regards its emission characteristics for this so-called long wave radiation the surface of the earth can to a good degree

TABLE 3.10

Absorption factors α of natural surfaces for long wave radiation

Surface	α
sand (dry-wet)	0.95–0.98
mineral soil (dry-wet)	0.95–0.97
peat (dry-wet)	0.97–0.98
firs	0.97
trees	0.96
grass	0.96–0.98
leaves	0.94–0.98
water	0.95
snow	0.97

of approximation be considered as a black body with a surface temperature of about 280 °K. It then follows from Planck's law that the terrestrial radiation is mainly contained in the wave length region of 4 to 50 μ with a maximum spectral intensity at approximately 10 μ (Fig. 3.2).

The high values of the absorption factors of natural surfaces given in Table 3.10 evince the black body character of the earth's surface for temperature radiation at normal temperatures.

The atmosphere is highly transparent to solar radiation but not to terrestrial radiation. The principal absorbing agents are clouds, water vapor and carbon dioxide.

The absorption by liquid water is particularly strong. A cloud of 50 m thickness is practically opaque for terrestrial radiation, even if it contains only 1 gram of liquid per cubic meter, which means that the total thickness of water in the cloud is only 0.05 mm. Clouds consisting of ice or snow particles are opaque for terrestrial radiation also. In most cases the radiation emitted by the top or the bottom of a dense layer of clouds can be considered as black body radiation belonging to the temperature of the upper or lower boundary.

Water vapor shows a strong absorption for most wave lengths occurring in the terrestrial spectrum, but in some regions the absorption is only slight. A region of partial transparency near 10 μ is of particular importance for the heat balance of the earth, since the maximum of the spectral emittance is near that wave length. This so-called *window* at 10 μ is to a large extent responsible for the cooling of the earth by radiant heat loss during a cloudless night. A region of weak absorption at 4 μ is less important owing to the small spectral emittance in this region.

Carbon dioxide also absorbs long wave radiation, but to a lesser extent than water vapor. It is partially transparent in the window at 10 μ.

A schematic graphical representation of the absorption of long wave radiation in the atmosphere is given in Fig. 3.2.

3.15. Net long wave radiation

The absorbing agents in the atmosphere also emit long wave radiation belonging to their temperatures and emission factors, according to Kirchhoff's law. Part of this temperature radiation reaches the earth's surface. The net loss of radiant energy of the surface is thus found by subtracting this back radiation of the atmosphere from the radiation emitted by the surface itself. It will be shown in section 3.17 that the atmospheric radiation is an important item in the energy balance of the earth's surface and of the earth as a whole.

The emission of the atmosphere can be calculated in principle, when the distribution of the emitting agents (i.e. liquid water, water vapor and carbon dioxide) and their emission characteristics are known. These calculations are very complicated and in practice graphical methods or empirical formulas are employed (section 3.16).

The influence of atmospheric radiation on the net radiation loss of the earth's surface is illustrated by the data of Table 3.11. Assuming an average

TABLE 3.11

Net radiation loss of the earth's surface under different cloud covers

Type of clouds	Net long wave emittance (cal cm^{-2} min^{-1})	Mean height of cloud base (km)
nimbo stratus	0.005–0.02	1.5
alto cumulus	0.01–0.04	3
cirrus	0.10–0.13	6
cloudless atmosphere	0.12–0.18	–
transparent atmosphere	0.50	–

temperature of 280 °K for the surface one finds for a transparent atmosphere an emittance of 0.5 cal cm^{-2} min^{-1} from Stefan-Boltzmann's law. If this figure is compared with the value for a cloudless atmosphere (0.12 to 0.18) it becomes clear how important the absorption and re-emission of water vapor and carbon dioxide are. The influence of clouds increases with decreasing height of the cloud base, owing to the increase of base temperature. It must be noted that the values of Table 3.11 are rough average figures, so that they do not apply generally.

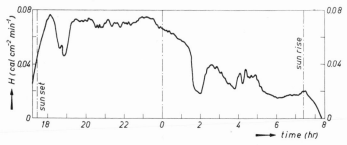

Fig. 3.12. Net radiation during a night with variable cloud cover. Observation at Wageningen, the Netherlands.

An actual recording of the net radiation during a night with variable cloud cover is presented in Fig. 3.12.

3.16. Calculation of atmospheric and terrestrial radiation

It will be clear from the foregoing discussion that for an accurate calculation of atmospheric radiation from a cloudless atmosphere the water vapor content and the temperature must be known as functions of height. These data are obtained from atmospheric soundings. The distribution of carbon dioxide with height can be considered to be constant in the troposphere.

Because of the complex nature of the absorption spectrum of water vapor the calculation of atmospheric radiation leads to complicated integrations. Numerical and graphical methods (so-called radiation charts) have been developed by various authors (e.g. ELSASSER [1942]; BRUINENBERG [1946]; DEACON [1950]), to facilitate the computation. The presence of clouds can be taken into account by considering them as black bodies. For the application of these methods the reader is referred to the literature on the subject.

In many cases no atmospheric soundings are available, but only standard meteorological observations at ground level. One must then have recourse to empirical formulas in which enter cloudiness, vapor pressure and air temperature at screen height. These formulas again have a statistical character.

The accuracy of the estimate derived from such a formula consequently depends on the deviation of the actual atmospheric situation from the average one for which the formula has been determined. The error, therefore, decreases generally as the period to which the formula is applied increases. Periods of approximately a week are often considered to give satisfactory results, say with an error of 10 per cent or less. SCHOLTE UBING [1959] even found good agreement for periods of one day by taking the variation of cloudiness during day and night into consideration.

Formulas for calculating the radiation emitted by a cloudless atmosphere towards the earth's surface are usually of the type

$$H_{\text{lo}}^{\text{atm}} = \sigma \Theta_{\text{ai}}^4 f(p_{\text{w}}). \tag{3.30}$$

Here Θ_{ai} is the absolute air temperature at screen height, $f(p_{\text{w}})$ an empirically determined function of the vapor pressure at screen height, and σ Stefan-Boltzmann's constant.

The most suitable form of $f(p_{\text{w}})$ has been the subject of a number of investigations. A much used form is the following, proposed by BRUNT [1932]

$$f(p_w) = a + b\sqrt{p_w}. \tag{3.31}$$

For England suitable values of the constants are $a = 0.44$ and $b = 0.066$ mbar$^{-\frac{1}{2}}$. As the value of these constants depends on the condition of the atmosphere other values have been found at various locations (see Table 3.12). Studies at Lake Hefner (Oklahoma) have revealed the variability of a and b at the same location for time-intervals of the order of one week (ANDERSON [1952]).

The following form of $f(p_w)$ proposed by Ångström (1915) is also frequently used

$$f(p_w) = a - b\,e^{-\gamma p_w}. \tag{3.32}$$

Values of the constants in this formula for various locations are presented in Table 3.13.

From observations at Lake Hefner, ANDERSON [1952] found that a simple linear regression equation

$$f(p_w) = a + bp_w \tag{3.33}$$

was of the same accuracy as the formulas of Brunt and Ångström.

For the range of vapor pressures of 2 to 30 mbar the difference between (3.31), (3.32) and (3.33) with proper values of the constants is less than 10%. This is also the accuracy of the estimate obtained from each of them when periods of a week or longer are considered.

Since the surface can be considered as a grey body with an emission factor ε close to 1 (*vide* Table 3.10), the net radiation loss of the surface for a cloudless atmosphere can be written as

$$H_{lo}^{net} = \varepsilon\sigma\,[\Theta_{ea}^4 - \Theta_{ai}^4\,f(p_w)], \tag{3.34}$$

where Θ_{ea} is the temperature of the surface. Since the absorption coefficient for atmospheric radiation is also equal to ε, H_{lo}^{atm} must be multiplied by it as well.

In western Europe and in locations with similar climates the *average value* of Θ_{ea} is approximately equal to the *average* of Θ_{ai} for periods of a day. Since Θ_{ea} cannot be easily measured directly, formula (3.34) is often used with the assumption $\Theta_{ea} = \Theta_{ai}$. However, this assumption cannot be applied in all climates, in particular not when there is a considerable net loss of sensible heat from the surface to the atmosphere, as is the case in arid and semiarid climates (see PHILIP [1957]; WARTENA [1959]).

Cloudiness is often taken into account by multiplication of the right hand side of (3.34) with a factor of the form $1 - vm$, where m is fractional cloudi-

TABLE 3.12

Values of the constants a and b (mbar^{-1}) in Brunt's formula $f(p_w) = a + b p_w^{\frac{1}{2}}$

Location	Position	Altitude (m)	a	b	References
Benson	32 °N, 1 °W		0.53	0.065	DINES [1927]
Upsala	60 °N, 18 °E	200	0.43	0.082	ASKLÖF [1920]
Bassour	37 °N, 3 °E	1160	0.48	0.058	ÅNGSTRÖM [1915]
Montpellier	43 °N, 1 °W	2859	0.60	0.042	BOUTARIC [1920]
Lindenberg	47 °N, 9 °E	40	0.34	0.110	ROBITZSCH [1926]
Poona	19 °N, 74 °E	564	0.55-0.62	0.038-0.029	RAMANATHAN and DESAI [1932]
Washington D.C.	39 °N, 77 °W	137	0.44	0.061	KIMBALL [1918]
Mt. Weather	37 °N, 78 °W	540	0.52	0.066	KIMBALL [1918]
Various Loc. in U.S.A.			0.53	0.062	
Mt. Whitney	36 °N, 118 °W	4420	0.50	0.032	ÅNGSTRÖM [1924]
Kanzelhöhe	47 °N, 14 °E	1500	0.47	0.063	ECKEL [1934]
Kew	52 °N, 0 °W	5	0.62	0.056	Observatory Staff
Lake Hefner	36 °N, 98 °W	363	0.34-0.62	0.029-0.082	ANDERSON [1952]
California	37 °N, 120 °W		0.66	0.039	GOSS and BROOKS [1956]

TABLE 3.13

Values of the constants a, b and γ (mbar^{-1}) in Ångström's formula $f(p_w) = a - b\,e^{-\gamma p_w}$

Location	Position	Altitude (m)	a	b	γ	References
Upsala	60 °N, 18 °E	200	0.81	0.24	0.119	ÅNGSTRÖM and ASKLÖF [1915]
Mt. Weather	37 °N, 78 °W	540	0.80	0.33	0.154	KIMBALL [1918]
Kanzelhöhe	47 °N, 14 °E	1500	0.71	0.24	0.163	ECKEL [1934]
Poona	19 °N, 74 °E	564	0.79	0.27	0.112	RAMANATHAN and DESAI [1932]
Lake Hefner	36 °N, 98 °W	363	0.71-0.81	0.24-0.33	0.04-0.074	ANDERSON [1952]
Europe	—	—	0.82	0.25	0.21	BOLZ and FALCKENBERG [1949]

ness and v is a statistically determined constant. So the complete empirical equation for the net long wave radiation loss of the surface becomes

$$H_{lo}^{net} = \varepsilon\sigma[\Theta_{ea}^4 - \Theta_{ai}^4 f(p_w)][1 - vm]. \tag{3.35}$$

It follows from Table 3.10 that v will be highly dependent on the type of clouds. Often $v = 0.9$ is used for low clouds and $v = 0.2$ for cirrus clouds. An average value proposed by PENMAN [1956] is $v = 0.8$.

Because the emittance of the surface does not depend on the presence of clouds, DE VRIES [1955] has proposed the following form for H_{lo}^{net}:

$$H_{lo}^{net} = \varepsilon\sigma[\Theta_{ea}^4 - \Theta_{ai}^4 g(p_w, m)], \tag{3.36}$$

with $\qquad\qquad g(p_w, m) = (a + bp_w^{\frac{1}{2}})(1 - vm) + vm. \tag{3.37}$

The form of g has been chosen in such a manner that (3.35) and (3.36) are identical for $\Theta_{ea} = \Theta_{ai}$. Further experimental work, especially in dry climates, will be needed to decide on the most suitable form of $g(p_w, m)$.

3.17. The radiation balance of the earth

A schematic representation of the energy balance of the earth's surface, the atmosphere and the earth as a whole is shown in Fig. 3.13. It serves to illustrate the relative importance of the different terms in the balance. As

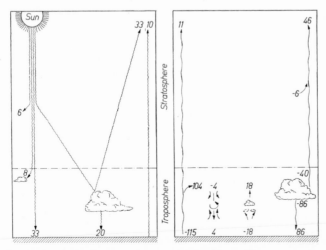

Fig. 3.13. Average radiation balance of the earth. The data are for an average year and the whole surface of the earth. (After WILLET [1944].)

the figures are rough averages only, they cannot be applied to actual situations.

In this figure the incoming solar radiation flux density at the top of the atmosphere H_{sh}^{top} has arbitrarily been given the value of 100 per cent. On the average, 33% reaches the surface directly and another 20% indirectly as diffuse short-wave radiation from the atmosphere. The surface reflects an amount of 10% and thus absorbs an amount of 43% of short-wave radiation.

A fraction of 6% of short-wave radiation is absorbed in the stratosphere and 8% in the troposphere. Clouds reflect, on the average, 33% back into outer space. Hence, the albedo of the entire earth is 43%.

The 43% absorbed by the surface plus the 14% absorbed by the atmosphere are re-emitted into space in the form of long wave radiation. The emittance of the surface is 115%, of which 104% is absorbed by the atmosphere (mainly the troposphere) and 11% is lost into space. The surface loses another 18% as latent heat used in the evaporation of water. It receives 86% as long wave radiation from the atmosphere (mainly the troposphere).

A small fraction of energy is transferred to the surface as sensible heat by turbulent transfer and conduction. A value of 4% is assumed here, but this value is very uncertain.

The 18% latent heat is gained by the troposphere as heat of condensation. The troposphere loses an amount of 40% as long wave radiation into space. For the stratosphere this value is 6%.

The solar radiation which is used in photosynthesis has been left out of consideration. Neither has the continuous heat flow from deeper layers of the earth to the surface been taken into account. Both quantities are smaller than the probable error in the estimates of the other components of the average energy balance.

It will be seen that the various items balance for the surface, the troposphere, the stratosphere and thus for the entire earth. If this were not so, the average temperature of the earth or the atmosphere would change gradually. Such a change is not observed during periods of the order of 10 to 100 years. Whether or not the climate of certain parts of the earth or the earth as a whole is changing slowly, is a matter of controversy. If such changes should be real, they are so small that they would not influence the general figures given in this section.

3.18. Instruments for radiation measurements

The simplest instrument for measuring solar radiation is the *Campbell-*

Stokes sunshine recorder. It actually measures the *duration of bright sunshine.* The instrument consists of a glass sphere of approximately 9.5 cm diameter. An image of the sky is formed on a strip of heavy paper, which shows a burning mark caused by the sun's image when the intensity of the direct solar beam surpasses a certain limiting value. The duration of bright sunshine is measured from the length of the burned trace. Special instructions must be followed in measuring the trace length.

The *total global radiation* can be measured accurately by means of a *solarimeter,* which contains a thermopile with a blackened horizontal surface. The sensitive surface is protected against atmospheric influences and the cooling effect of wind by a hemispherical glass cover.

In the most common instruments "warm" junctions of the thermopile are situated at the center line, while the "cold" junctions are at the edge. The latter are connected by small copper bars to a block of metal which is at air temperature. The temperature difference between the cold junctions and the warm ones is to a good degree of approximation proportional to the irradiancy of the pile. The thermoelectric voltage or current can be recorded by conventional means, e.g. by a recording potentiometer or galvanometer. A solarimeter of this type is discussed in great detail by BENER [1951].

Less common for agrometeorological measurements is the *bolometer.* It records the increase of the electrical resistance of a thin blackened platinum or nickel strip, placed in an evacuated glass vessel, due to the heating by radiant energy. The change in resistance is usually measured by means of a Wheatstone bridge. An absolute measurement of the absorbed radiant flux is possible by comparing the heating by the radiation with that caused by a constant electrical current which is sent through the bolometer.

The same principle is applied in the Ångström *pyrheliometer,* which is often used as a standard instrument for the calibration of a solarimeter. The instrument has two blackened manganin strips, one of which is exposed to the direct solar beam, while the other is heated by an electrical current which is regulated such that both strips have the same temperature.

Light sensitive semiconductors (*photodiodes*) convert solar radiation into electrical energy with a ten times higher efficiency than the thermopile. This means that a galvanometer of low sensitivity can be used to measure the photoelectric current. However, the sensitivity depends on the wave length and this fact makes the photodiode unsuitable for absolute measurements of total global radiation. The relative efficiency of the conversion of radiation into electric energy for a certain photodiode (solar battery) is shown in Fig. 3.14.

The thermopile can also be used for measuring atmospheric and terrestrial radiation. Since glass strongly absorbs long wave radiation a different

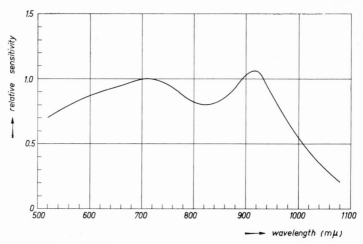

Fig. 3.14. Relative sensitivity of a solar battery cell as a function of wave length. The sensitivity at 700 mμ has been set equal to 1.0. The average efficiency for the conversion of radiant flux into electric power is of the order of 16% for the total solar spectrum.

cover must be used. Thin sheets of polyethylene are suitable for this purpose; a layer of 20 μ transmits approximately 90 per cent of atmospheric radiation. Alternatively one may leave the pile uncovered. It is then necessary to apply forced ventilation to eliminate the influence of wind. Obviously the instrument cannot be used during rain and the black surface must be cleaned frequently from atmospheric dust and other contamination.

The *total net radiation* can be measured by means of a horizontal plane thermopile with half of its junctions facing the sky and the other half facing the ground. Both sides of the pile are blackened; the upper side receives the total global and the atmospheric radiation, the lower side the reflected short-wave radiation and the terrestrial radiation. Thus the temperature difference between the upper and the lower plane is a measure of the net radiation. The instrument can be applied with covers of polyethylene, or with no protective covers and forced ventilation. A recording made with a net radiometer is shown in Fig. 3.12. A more detailed discussion of net radiation, the measurement and the importance for agriculture has been given by SCHOLTE UBING [1959].

The dependence of the reflection coefficient on the inclination of the solar rays introduces an error in measurements using a radiometer covered by plane-protecting films. SCHULZE [1953] used hemispherical covers to avoid this error.

CHAPTER 4

PERIODIC TEMPERATURE VARIATIONS IN A HOMOGENEOUS SOIL

W. R. VAN WIJK and D. A. DE VRIES

Laboratory of Physics and Meteorology of the Agricultural University Wageningen, The Netherlands

4.1. The variation of surface temperature

The principal cause of the variation of the temperature at the soil surface is the changing intensity of short-wave radiation. Absorption of both short-wave and long wave radiation practically takes place in a soil layer of a fraction of a millimeter thickness. Thus a flat surface of a bare soil can be considered as a plane heat source during a period of a positive net radiation flux, and as a heat sink when the latter is negative.

The temperature in the upper soil layers fluctuates in the course of time corresponding to alternating intervals of heat storage and release of heat. Though the soil temperature is not a true periodic function of time, owing to the variability of the weather, it has many features in common with a periodic function. Recordings of soil temperature at a shallow depth evince two main periods, viz. a diurnal and an annual variation.

If the soil is covered with a dense vegetation, the upper leaves form a surface where a considerable fraction of the incoming radiation is absorbed. The remaining part is absorbed in the lower regions of the vegetation and at the soil surface. The transfer of the heat absorbed at the surface into the soil occurs in the same manner as with a bare surface. Under equal meteorological conditions the daily maximum temperature of the covered surface will be lower than that of the bare surface, owing to the shading effect of the vegetation.

With a more open vegetative cover a considerable fraction of the incident radiation may reach the soil surface. So, for instance, TANNER and PETERSON [1960] found 0.26, 0.31 and 0.44 for the fractions of light transmitted through corn planting treatments with north-south direction of the rows and 16000 full grown plants per acre for distances between the rows of respectively 40, 60 and 80 inches, whereas under a dense potato crop in July at Wageningen about 1 to 3% of the visible light reached the ground.

In connection with the study of heat transfer into the soil the soil surface can also be considered as the location of a heat source or sink for a vegetated soil. The treatment of the heat transfer into the air is greatly complicated by the presence of a vegetation. A distributed heat source of finite thickness must then be introduced in the layer occupied by the plants.

Another case in which gradual absorption of radiation in a layer of finite vertical thickness must be taken into account is a body of water, e.g. a lake, a river, or a canal. The problem of heat transfer in a water body is of particular interest in connection with the study of water losses due to evaporation, as, for instance, in planning irrigation schemes.

4.2. The phenomenon of heat conduction, thermal conductivity

Heat is transported in soils mainly by conduction, i.e. the transfer of thermal energy on a molecular scale. To facilitate the mathematical treatment it will be assumed throughout this chapter that the soil is homogeneous with respect to heat transfer by conduction. This means that the thermal properties of the soil in bulk are independent of the space coordinates.

Further simplifying assumptions are:
1. The heat flow is unidimensional in a vertical direction.
2. The medium is at rest, which means that no motion of matter on a macroscopic scale occurs.*
3. No heat is generated in the medium or converted into other forms of energy, as for instance latent heat of vaporization or solidification.

The mathematical theory of unidirectional heat conduction in a homogeneous medium is based on the proportionality of the heat flux density with the temperature gradient. This can be exemplified by considering a cube in the medium with one side parallel to the axis of z. When the two faces perpendicular to that side are kept at constant temperatures ϑ_1 and ϑ_2, heat flows at a constant rate from the higher temperature (ϑ_2) to the lower temperature (ϑ_1). The following empirical relation holds between the heat flux density, H, and the temperature difference

$$H = \frac{\lambda(\vartheta_2 - \vartheta_1)}{l};$$

(4.1)

H is the quantity of heat flowing per unit of time across a unit of surface

---

* The molecules are not at rest, of course. On the contrary, the irregular thermal motion of the molecules is the cause of the conduction of heat. A violent thermal motion corresponds to a high temperature. This motion is passed on by molecular collisions to places where the temperature is lower.

perpendicular to the z-axis; l is the length of a side of the cube; λ is a factor of proportionality depending on the material of the cube, termed the *thermal conductivity*. If l is measured in cm, ϑ in °C and H in cal cm^{-2} sec^{-1}, λ is expressed as cal cm^{-1} sec^{-1} °C^{-1} (Fig. 4.1).

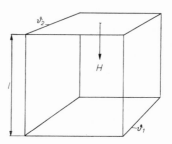

Fig. 4.1. Unidirectional stationary heat conduction in a homogeneous medium. Heat flux density H times the length l of the cube divided by the temperature difference $(\vartheta_2 - \vartheta_1)$ is the thermal conductivity λ (in cal cm^{-1} sec^{-1} °C^{-1}) of the medium under consideration.

For the limiting case of l becoming infinitesimal (4.1) becomes

$$H = -\lambda \partial\vartheta/\partial z. \qquad (4.2)$$

The negative sign indicates that the direction of the heat flow is opposite to the direction in which the temperature increases.

The differential quotient $\partial\vartheta/\partial z$ is called the *temperature gradient*. In the general case that ϑ depends on the coordinates x, y and z the temperature gradient is the differential quotient of the temperature as a function of the distance in the direction of steepest increase of ϑ.*

Strictly speaking, (4.2) cannot be applied to soils as a soil is not a homogeneous but a composite medium. However, for must purposes (4.2) holds when an appropriate average value of λ is introduced. This average λ can be defined on the basis of (4.1), where l must be large in comparison with the linear dimensions of the soil granules.

The average thermal conductivity of a soil depends on its mineral composition, its texture and its structure, and on its content of air, water and organic matter. Since the thermal conductivity of air is much smaller than that of

---

* The heat flux density considered as a vector quantity is then given by:
$$H = -\lambda \nabla\vartheta,$$
which is the general form of (4.2). The vector $\nabla\vartheta$ has the components $\partial\vartheta/\partial x$, $\partial\vartheta/\partial y$, $\partial\vartheta/\partial z$ in the directions of x, y and z respectively. The equation holds for heat conduction in an isotropic medium.

TABLE 4.1

Thermal properties of soil constituents at 20 °C and 1 atm

Material	Density ϱ (g cm^{-3})	Specific heat c (cal g^{-1} °C^{-1})	Vol. heat capacity C (cal cm^{-3} °C^{-1})	Thermal conductivity λ (10^{-3} cal cm^{-1} sec^{-1} °C^{-1})	Thermal diffusivity a (10^{-3} cm^2 sec^{-1})
Quartz	2.65	0.175	0.46	20	43
Many soil minerals*	2.65	0.175	0.46	7	15
Soil organic matter*	1.3	0.46	0.60	0.6	1.0
Water	1.00	1.00	1.00	1.42	1.42
Air	0.0012	0.24	0.00029	0.062	0.21

* Approximate average values.

water or of the solid constituents (see Table 4.1), a high air content corresponds to a low thermal conductivity. The composition of a soil and its air and water content vary generally with depth, thus λ will be a function of z. This variation will be taken into account in a later chapter.

The thermal conductivity varies also with temperature, but under normal conditions this variation can be ignored in applications to soils. The thermal properties of soils will be discussed in greater detail in a separate chapter.

When the temperature distribution does not vary with time, the heat flux is also independent of t. This is called a stationary state, which must be distinguished from the state of thermal equilibrium where the temperature is constant throughout the medium. Equation (4.1) is based on a stationary state.

When the temperature is a function of space coordinates *and* time one has a nonstationary state. This is the normal situation in agricultural problems. Equation (4.2) applies to stationary and nonstationary states; because ϑ can depend on z and t a partial derivative notation is used for $\partial\vartheta/\partial z$.

4.3. The differential equation of heat conduction in one dimension

In (4.2) both H and ϑ are generally unknown functions of z and t. A differential equation for ϑ will now be derived by the application of the principle of heat conservation. It was already stated in the previous section that the conversion of heat into other forms of energy, or *vice versa*, will be left out of consideration.

A horizontal slab of material of thickness dz at depth z will be considered. A schematic representation of the heat fluxes entering and leaving the slab is given in Fig. 4.2.

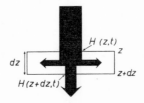

Fig. 4.2. Schematic representation of heat storage $H(z,t) - H(z + dz,t)$ in a slab of soil per unit of time and cross section, thus in a volume $1 \times dz$ cm³.

Let $H(z,t)$ denote the heat flux density at the depth z and the instant t and let similarly $H(z + dz,t)$ denote the heat flux density at the slightly different depth $z + dz$ and the same instant t. The difference $H(z,t) - H(z + dz,t) = -(\partial H/\partial z)dz$ is stored in the slab per unit of time and cross section, thus in a volume dz.

This amount of heat will cause a temperature change per unit of time that can be written as $C(\partial\vartheta/\partial t)dz$. Here C is the volumetric heat capacity, i.e. the amount of heat required to raise the temperature of a unit volume of soil by one degree*, $\partial\vartheta/\partial t$ represents the temperature change per unit of time.

Equating the heat storage found from the difference in heat flux density to the heat storage as expressed by the temperature change, one obtains

$$- \partial H/\partial z = C\partial\vartheta/\partial t, \tag{4.3}$$

and by using (4.2)

$$\frac{\partial}{\partial z}\left(\lambda \frac{\partial\vartheta}{\partial z}\right) = C\frac{\partial\vartheta}{\partial t}. \tag{4.4}$$

For a homogeneous medium λ and C do not depend on z, so that division by C leads to

$$\frac{\partial\vartheta}{\partial t} = a\frac{\partial^2\vartheta}{\partial z^2}, \tag{4.5}$$

where $a = \lambda/C = \lambda/\varrho c$ is called the *thermal diffusivity*; a has the dimension of $cm^2\ sec^{-1}$, which is the same as that of a diffusion coefficient.

Equations (4.4) and (4.5) are differential equations for $\vartheta(z,t)$ which must be obeyed by any possible temperature variation caused by unidirectional heat conduction in a homogeneous medium. It can be proven mathematically that the temperature at any instant $t > 0$ and any depth in a slab of material bounded by the horizontal planes z_1 and z_2 is completely determined when proper initial and boundary conditions are given.**

The initial condition means that the temperature distribution at time $t = 0$, viz. $\vartheta(z,0)$, must be known in the layer $z_1 \leqslant z \leqslant z_2$. This is obvious for physical reasons. When the situation is stationary ϑ does not depend on t and in that case no initial condition is necessary.

---

* The relation between C(cal $cm^{-3}\ {}^\circ C^{-1}$) and the specific heat c(cal $g^{-1}\ {}^\circ C^{-1}$), which is the heat capacity per unit of mass, is $C = \varrho c$, where ϱ(g cm^{-3}) is the density of the medium. In a composite medium the average value of C can be written as $C = \Sigma_i\varrho_i c_i x_i$, where the summation extends over all constituents and x_i is the volume fraction of the ith constituent (cf. Table 4.1).

** Completely determined means that there exists only one function $\vartheta(z,t)$ that satisfies the differential equation and the conditions. The mathematical analysis shows that certain restrictions must be imposed on the temperature fields, but these requirements are always fulfilled in the problems discussed in this book.

The boundary conditions express what happens at the boundaries of the slab of homogeneous material, i.e. at $z = z_1$ and $z = z_2$. Various types of boundary conditions are possible. In the present chapter it will be assumed that either the temperature or the heat flux at the boundaries are prescribed functions of time. The bounding surfaces considered in this chapter are the soil surface ($z = 0$) and infinite depth ($z = \infty$). The positive direction of the z-axis is taken in a downward direction.

4.4. Harmonic variation of temperature with time

In this section it will be assumed that at all depths the temperature varies as a pure harmonic function of time around an average value. This assumption leads to a rather crude approximative description of the actual fluctuations caused by the succession of day and night, or winter and summer. It has to be modified for a quantitative interpretation of actual soil temperatures. Nevertheless, the simplified treatment contains many essential features of the more complete description, so that it is quite useful for an introductory discussion of temperature variations in a soil.

To fix ideas the diurnal variation will be considered first. In that case the period of the temperature variation is 24 hr or 86400 sec.

Let ϑ_a be the average temperature in the soil during a period; ϑ_a is assumed to be the same at all depths. The zero point of the time scale will be chosen such that at $t = 0$ the surface is at the average temperature. In that case the surface temperature $\vartheta(0, t)$ can be written as

$$\vartheta(0, t) = \vartheta_a + {}^A\vartheta_0 \sin \omega t, \tag{4.6}$$

in which ${}^A\vartheta_0$ is the amplitude at the surface and ω the radial frequency. ω equals 2π times the frequency of the temperature variation, thus for the diurnal variation $\omega = 2\pi/86400 = 7.27 \times 10^{-5} \text{ sec}^{-1}$. The argument of the sine function is expressed in radians in the present text.*

Equation (4.6) is the boundary condition for $z = 0$. It will further be assumed that at infinite depth ($z = \infty$) the temperature is constant and equal to ϑ_a. Because of the assumption that the surface temperature is a periodic function of time *for all times* (hence for $t > -\infty$) no separate initial condition is needed.

---

* When (4.6) is applied to the annual variation the value of ω is $2\pi/365 \times 86400 = 1.99 \times 10^{-7} \text{ sec}^{-1}$.

It can be shown that under these conditions the temperature at an arbitrary depth is also a sine function of time of the form

$$\vartheta(z,t) = \vartheta_a + {}^A\vartheta_z \sin[\omega t + \varphi(z)], \tag{4.7}$$

in which ${}^A\vartheta_z$ and $\varphi(z)$ are functions of z but not of t. They can be determined by substituting the solution (4.7) in the differential equation (4.5) and equating the coefficients of $\sin \omega t$ and $\cos \omega t$ on both sides (see section 4.4.1). This leads to the solution

$$\vartheta(z,t) = \vartheta_a + {}^A\vartheta_0 \exp(-z/D) \sin(\omega t - z/D). \tag{4.8}$$

The constant D is called the *damping depth*. It is related to the thermal properties of the soil and the frequency of the variations as follows:

$$D = (2\lambda/C\omega)^{\frac{1}{2}} = (2a/\omega)^{\frac{1}{2}}. \tag{4.9}$$

It can be easily seen that $\vartheta(z,t)$ satisfies the boundary conditions for $z = 0$ and $z = \infty$. The same solution would be obtained if, instead of the condition of periodicity, the following initial condition would be obeyed

$$\vartheta(z,0) = \vartheta_a + {}^A\vartheta_0 \exp(-z/D) \sin(-z/D). \tag{4.10}$$

Comparison of (4.6) and (4.8) shows that at the depth z the amplitude ${}^A\vartheta_z$ is smaller than ${}^A\vartheta_0$ by a factor $\exp(-z/D)$, and that there is a shift in phase $-z/D$. The decrease of the amplitude with depth and the increasing phase lag are typical for the propagation of a periodic temperature variation in a soil. They also occur if λ and C vary with depth, though, of course, the amplitude and phase shift are then different functions of z than in the simple case solved here.

The physical explanation of the damping and retardation of the temperature variation with depth lies in the fact that a certain amount of heat is stored or released in a layer when the temperature in that layer increases, respectively decreases.

The damping depth depends on the period of the temperature variation. It is $\sqrt{365} \approx 19$ times larger for the annual variation than for the diurnal variation in a given soil (see equation (4.9)).

Calculating by way of example the damping depth for a soil for which $\lambda = 2.3 \times 10^{-3}$ cal cm^{-1} sec^{-1} °C^{-1}, and $C = 0.44$ cal cm^{-3} °C^{-1} one obtains $D = 12$ cm for the diurnal variation and $D = 229$ cm for the annual variation.

At a depth $z = D$ the amplitude is $1/e = 0.37$ times the amplitude at the surface; it is only about $0.05 {}^A\vartheta_0$ at $z = 3D$, or 36 cm for the diurnal varia-

TABLE 4.2

Average thermal properties of soils and snow

Soil type	Porosity x_t	Volumetric water content x_w	Thermal conductivity λ (10^{-3} cal cm^{-1} sec^{-1} °C^{-1})	Vol. heat capacity C (cal cm^{-3} °C^{-1})	Damping depth D_d (cm)
Sand	0.4	0.0	0.7	0.3	8.0
	0.4	0.2	4.2	0.5	15.2
	0.4	0.4	5.2	0.7	14.3
Clay	0.4	0.0	0.6	0.3	7.4
	0.4	0.2	2.8	0.5	12.4
	0.4	0.4	3.8	0.7	12.2
Peat	0.8	0.0	0.14	0.35	3.3
	0.8	0.4	0.7	0.75	5.1
	0.8	0.8	1.2	1.15	5.4
Snow	0.95	—	0.15	0.05	9.1
	0.8	—	0.32	0.2	6.6
	0.5	—	1.7	0.5	9.7

x_t is the volume of pore space per unit volume of soil, x_w that of water per unit volume of soil. D_d is the damping depth for the diurnal variation; the damping depth for the annual variation is 19 times greater.

tion in the foregoing example. In the common types of soil the diurnal variation does not penetrate below 50 cm and the annual variation not below 10 m. This important general conclusion follows from (4.9) in connection with the data on the thermal properties of soils given in Table 4.2. The figures in that table are average values; the influence of composition of the solid phase and of the water content on the thermal properties is clearly demonstrated.

4.4.1. MATHEMATICAL TREATMENT OF HARMONIC TEMPERATURE VARIATIONS, COMPLEX NUMBERS*

It will first be verified that the temperature given by (4.8) satisfies the differential equation (4.5), when D is given by (4.9).

One has

$$\partial\vartheta/\partial t = {}^A\vartheta_0\omega \exp(-z/D) \cos(\omega t - z/D),$$

$$\partial\vartheta/\partial z = {}^A\vartheta_0 \exp(-z/D)[-(1/D)\sin(\omega t - z/D) - (1/D)\cos(\omega t - z/D)],$$

$$\partial^2\vartheta/\partial z^2 = {}^A\vartheta_0\exp(-z/D)[(1/D^2)\sin(\omega t - z/D) + (1/D)^2 \cos(\omega t - z/D)$$
$$+ (1/D^2)\cos(\omega t - z/D) - (1/D^2)\sin(\omega t - z/D)]$$
$$= 2{}^A\vartheta_0 (1/D^2) \exp(-z/D)\cos(\omega t - z/D).$$

Substitution of these expressions in (4.5) leads to

$$2a/D^2 = \omega, \quad \text{or} \quad D = \pm(2a/\omega)^{\frac{1}{2}}.$$

The negative root must be excluded, because it would lead to an infinite value of the amplitude at $z = \infty$, which is physically impossible. Mathematically this means that the boundary condition at $z = \infty$ is not obeyed by the solution with the negative root. In a layer of finite depth the solution is generally a linear combination of two elementary solutions, one with positive, the other with negative D.

The solution for the present case will now be derived more directly by the method of complex variables. This method is particularly advantageous in problems of periodic temperature variations in inhomogeneous media, such as those treated in Chapter 6.

A *complex number* can be written as $a + bi$, in which a and b are real numbers and $i = (-1)^{\frac{1}{2}}$. The number a is the *real part* and bi the *imaginary part* of the complex number. For the imaginary part bi one writes sometimes $i\text{Im }\alpha$, in which $b = \text{Im}\alpha$ and $\alpha = a + bi$. Two complex numbers are equal when both their real and imaginary parts are the same.

Now a complex $\vartheta(z, t)$ is introduced with a real and an imaginary part

---

* The reader who is not interested in mathematical developments may omit the study of this section.

that are functions of z and t. If ϑ satisfies (4.5) each part must be a solution, because a, z and t are real. The same is obviously true for any linear differential equation with real independent variables and real coefficients.

Instead of writing $a + bi$ for a complex number one may use the expression $\varrho(\cos\varphi + i\sin\varphi)$, with $\varrho = (a^2 + b^2)^{\frac{1}{2}}$ and $\varphi = \text{arct}(b/a)$. According to de Moivre's theorem one has $\cos\varphi + i\sin\varphi = \exp i\varphi$. Thus $\varrho \exp(i\varphi)$ with real ϱ and φ is also a notation for a complex number.

A solution that is a harmonic function of time can be written as $\vartheta(z,t) = \zeta(z)\exp i\omega t$, where ζ is a complex function of z only, hence $\zeta(z) = \varrho(z)\exp(i\varphi(z))$. Substitution in (4.5) gives

$$a \, d^2\zeta/dz^2 - i\omega\zeta = 0. \qquad (4.11)$$

This is an ordinary linear differential equation with constant coefficients. A solution is $\exp(\gamma z)$, if γ satisfies the equation

$$a\gamma^2 - i\omega = 0. \qquad (4.12)$$

Thus $\gamma = \pm (i\omega/a)^{\frac{1}{2}}$, or, since the square roots of i are $\pm (1 + i)/\sqrt{2}$, one has

$$\gamma = \pm (1 + i)/D,$$

where D is given by (4.9). The general solution of (4.5) with harmonic temperature variation is then a linear combination of the two solutions given by

$$\exp(\pm z/D)[\cos(\omega t \pm z/D) + i\sin(\omega t \pm z/D)], \qquad (4.13)$$

where one solution has the positive, the other the negative sign for z/D.

The boundary condition that ϑ should remain finite for $z = \infty$ implies that only the negative sign should be retained in the present case. The boundary condition for $z = 0$, equation (4.6), is satisfied by $-i$ times the imaginary part of the complex solution.

4.5. Combined diurnal and annual variation

The theory of the preceding section may be used for a rough prediction of soil temperature fluctuations and for calculating an approximate value of the damping depth from soil temperature recordings.

The special choice of the zero point of the time scale in (4.6) as the instant at which the surface temperature is at its average value and increasing, is often inconvenient in the applications. When an arbitrary zero point t_0 is introduced (4.6) becomes

$$\vartheta(0,t) = \vartheta_{a0} + {}^A\vartheta_0 \sin \omega (t - t_0) = \vartheta_{a0} + {}^A\vartheta_0 \sin(\omega t + \varphi_0), \qquad (4.14)$$

and (4.8)

$$\vartheta(z,t) = \vartheta_{az} + {}^A\vartheta_0 \exp(-z/D) \sin(\omega t + \varphi_0 - z/D). \qquad (4.15)$$

The suffixes 0 and z have been added to the average temperature to indicate that the latter generally varies with depth in soils. Thus ϑ_{az} can be a function of z and t that satisfies (4.5) and does not change perceptibly in the course of one period.

The constant $\varphi_0 = -\omega t_0$ is called the *phase constant*. It can be found from the instant at which ϑ reaches a certain characteristic value. For instance, when the maximum value at depth z is reached at t_1, one has $\omega t_1 + \varphi_0 - z/D = \pi/2$.

The annual variation is one of the reasons that ϑ_a for the diurnal variation varies with depth. The combined effect of the annual and the diurnal variation can be expressed by writing

$$\vartheta(z,t) = \vartheta_{ay} + {}^A\vartheta_{0y} \exp(-z/D_y) \sin(\omega_y t + \varphi_{0y} - z/D_y)$$

$$+ {}^A\vartheta_{0d} \exp(-z/D_d) \sin(\omega_d t + \varphi_{0d} - z/D_d), \quad (4.16)$$

where the indices y and d refer to the annual and the diurnal temperature waves respectively. Hence, ϑ_{ay} is the yearly average temperature; it can still be a function of z which must satisfy (4.5). Thus $d^2\vartheta_{ay}/dz^2 = 0$, or $\vartheta_{ay} = \vartheta_{ay0} + \alpha z$.

The formulas in this and the preceding section can be applied to calculate D from measured soil temperature variations. Of course, this can only be done when the temperature variation is harmonic or nearly so, as may be the case during a succession of bright days or for averages calculated from long series of observations. If one plots the time at which the maximum temperature (or any other constant value of the phase) occurs as a function of depth, a straight line is obtained when (4.15) is satisfied. D can then be calculated from the slope. The same can be done by plotting the natural logarithm of the amplitude as a function of z. When the two values of D obtained in this manner are equal (or nearly so) one may infer that the solution (4.15) is applicable. Usually different D-values are found from the variation of the amplitude and the phase with depth. This is an indication that the thermal properties of the soil are not constant. Obviously recordings of temperature in at least two different depths are required to apply this procedure.

Equation (4.15) can also be used for estimating the temperature at the surface, which is often difficult to measure, from measurements at two or more depths. The values of $^A\vartheta_0$ and φ_0 can be obtained by means of calculation or graphical extrapolation. However, caution is needed in this case, as fluctuations of a short duration, which may be caused by variations in wind velocity or in irradiance, are damped out rapidly since their radial frequency is large (cf. equation (4.9)). They can be important at the surface although they are imperceptible at a shallow depth. Moreover, the variation of the thermal properties of the soil with depth is often most pronounced in the uppermost layers.

4.6. Harmonic variation of the heat flux density, the energy balance

The heat flux density, H, (cal cm^{-2} sec^{-1}) for a sinusoidal variation of temperature can be obtained from (4.2) together with (4.15). One has

$$H(z,t) = -\lambda\partial\vartheta_{az}/\partial z +$$
$$^A\vartheta_0(\lambda C\omega)^{\frac{1}{2}}\exp(-z/D)\sin(\omega t + \varphi_0 - z/D + \tfrac{1}{4}\pi). \quad (4.17)$$

The term $-\lambda\partial\vartheta_{az}/\partial z$ is often small in comparison with the amplitude of the second term on the right-hand side. It will be ignored in the following discussion. Since in the present notation the z-coordinate increases with depth, H is counted positive when heat flows downwards.

It follows from (4.17) that H is also a harmonic function of time with a phase that is $\tfrac{1}{4}\pi$ advanced as compared with the temperature variation at the same depth. The same result would have been obtained if a harmonic variation of H had been assumed to occur at the surface instead of a harmonic variation of ϑ.

The phase shift of $\tfrac{1}{4}\pi$ between the variation of H and that of ϑ corresponds to a time shift of 3 hr for the diurnal variation and $1\tfrac{1}{2}$ month for the annual variation.

On clear days in Western Europe the maximum temperature at a surface covered by short grass occurs at approximately 13 hr. Thus maximum heat flux density in a homogeneous soil does not occur at the time of maximum insolation, but earlier. This is due to the interaction of the various components in the energy balance of the surface. As the terms in the energy balance are influenced by the shape, the condition, and the vegetative cover (if any) of the surface, it is not surprising that the time at which the temperature reaches its maximum may vary considerably at one location and shows wide differences for different locations. For instance, in desert regions 15 or 16 hr has been observed.

The influence of the various terms in the energy balance on the time shift between maximum surface temperature and maximum insolation will be illustrated by a simplified mathematical treatment. The energy balance can be written as:

$$(1 - \varrho) H_{sh} - H_{lo}^{net} = H_{ai} + H_{ev} + H_{so}. \tag{4.18}$$

For the present purpose it will be assumed that all terms in (4.18) show a sinusoidal variation about an average value. Hence, the energy balance must be satisfied both for the averages and for the sinusoidal variations with time.

The zero point of the time scale will be chosen such that the surface temperature is represented by (4.6), so that $\varphi_0 = 0$. It will further be assumed that the net long wave radiant flux density varies in phase with the surface temperature:

$$H_{lo}^{net} = \bar{H}_{lo}^{net} + {}^A H_{lo}^{net} \sin \omega t. \tag{4.19}$$

The bar in this equation and the following denotes the average value.

The short-wave radiation intensity will be in phase with solar altitude on a clear day. The corresponding flux density is written as

$$H_{sh} = \bar{H}_{sh} + {}^A H_{sh} \sin(\omega t + \varphi_{sh}). \tag{4.20}$$

Evaporation and heat transfer to the air are both dependent on the transfer properties of the lower atmospheric layers. The same phase is therefore assumed for both. Further it will be assumed that the average value of H_{ai} is zero. One has

$$H_{ai} = {}^A H_{ai} \sin(\omega t + \varphi_{ai}), \tag{4.21}$$

$$H_{ev} = \bar{H}_{ev} + {}^A H_{ev} \sin(\omega t + \varphi_{ai}). \tag{4.22}$$

Finally the heat flux density in the soil can be written as

$$H_{so} = {}^A H_{so} \sin(\omega t + \tfrac{1}{4}\pi) = {}^A \vartheta_0 (\lambda C \omega)^{\frac{1}{2}} \sin(\omega t + \tfrac{1}{4}\pi) \tag{4.23}$$

according to (4.17).

Substitution of these expressions in (4.18) leads to

$$(1 - \varrho) \bar{H}_{sh} - \bar{H}_{lo}^{net} = \bar{H}_{ev} \tag{4.24}$$

and

$$(1 - \varrho) {}^A H_{sh} \sin(\omega t + \varphi_{sh}) - {}^A H_{lo}^{net} \sin \omega t = ({}^A H_{ai} + {}^A H_{ev}) \sin(\omega t + \varphi_{ai})$$
$$+ {}^A H_{so} \sin(\omega t + \tfrac{1}{4}\pi). \tag{4.25}$$

Since the last equation must hold for all values of t two relations between the amplitudes and phases can be derived from it by developing $\sin(\omega t + \varphi)$ into $\sin\omega t \cos\varphi + \cos\omega t \sin\varphi$ and equating the coefficients of $\sin\omega t$ and $\cos\omega t$ on both sides.

This leads to

$$(1 - \varrho)\,{}^A H_{sh} \cos\varphi_{sh} - {}^A H_{lo}^{net} = ({}^A H_{ai} + {}^A H_{ev}) \cos\varphi_{ai} + \tfrac{1}{2}{}^A H_{so}|/2, \qquad (4.26)$$

$$(1 - \varrho)\,{}^A H_{sh} \sin\varphi_{sh} = ({}^A H_{ai} + {}^A H_{ev}) \sin\varphi_{ai} + \tfrac{1}{2}{}^A H_{so}|/2. \qquad (4.27)$$

Solving for φ_{sh} one obtains

$$\text{tg } \varphi_{sh} = \frac{({}^A H_{ai} + {}^A H_{ev}) \sin\varphi_{ai} + \tfrac{1}{2}{}^A H_{so}|/2}{{}^A H_{lo}^{net} + ({}^A H_{ai} + {}^A H_{ev}) \cos\varphi_{ai} + \tfrac{1}{2}{}^A H_{so}|/2}. \qquad (4.28)$$

Since the amplitudes are positive and φ_{ai} generally is smaller than $\tfrac{1}{4}\pi$ it follows from (4.28) that φ_{sh} is also smaller than $\tfrac{1}{4}\pi$. The larger the values of ${}^A H_{ai}$, ${}^A H_{ev}$ and ${}^A H_{lo}^{net}$ are, the smaller is the time lapse between the occurrence of the maximum of insolation and the maximum of surface temperature. This conclusion is supported by experimental evidence if the weather and soil conditions are such that the simplifying assumptions underlying the derivation of (4.28) are approximately fulfilled.

If one wants to predict φ_{sh} on the basis of (4.28) further relations between the various amplitudes and phases must be found. A theory of the transfer of heat and water vapor in air will be discussed in Chapter 8. Here some results of that theory will be given without further proof.

In principle the theory of the propagation of temperature waves in air can be developed along the same lines as those used in the previous sections for soils. However, heat is transferred in air by forced and free convection and not by conduction as in soils. When forced convection, i.e. air movement under the influence of pressure differences predominates, the transfer of heat in the lower atmospheric layers can be described mathematically as conduction with an apparent thermal conductivity that increases linearly with height, thus $\lambda = b(z + z_0)$. Here b depends on the wind speed and z_0 on the roughness of the surface.

Assuming that the expression for λ holds for all z and that the volumetric heat capacity C_{ai} is a constant, one has for the temperature in air

$$\vartheta(z,t) = \vartheta_a + {}^A\vartheta_0 \frac{\ln\tfrac{1}{2}\gamma r}{\ln\tfrac{1}{2}\gamma r_0} \sin\left[\omega t - \text{arct}\left(\frac{4}{\pi}\ln\tfrac{1}{2}\gamma r\right) + \text{arct}\left(\frac{4}{\pi}\ln\tfrac{1}{2}\gamma r_0\right)\right]. \qquad (4.29)$$

Here $r = 2(\lambda_a C_{ai}\omega)^{\frac{1}{2}}/b$, thus r is a function of z (z is now assumed to increase with height); r_0 is the value of r for $z = 0$; ln denotes the natural logarithm; $\gamma = 1.781$ is Euler's constant.*

From (4.2) and (4.29) one finds for the heat flux density at the surface

$$H_{ai} = -\frac{^A\vartheta_0 b}{2\ln\frac{1}{2}\gamma r_0} \sin\left[\omega t + \tfrac{1}{2}\pi + \text{arct}\left(\frac{4}{\pi}\ln\tfrac{1}{2}\gamma r_0\right)\right]. \qquad (4.30)$$

Equations (4.29) and (4.30) are approximative expressions for $r \ll 1$, so that $\ln\frac{1}{2}\gamma r_0$ is negative and $^A H_{ai} = -{}^A\vartheta_0 b/2\ln\frac{1}{2}\gamma r_0$ is positive. The phase constant $\varphi_{ai} = \frac{1}{2}\pi + \text{arct}(4/\pi\ln\frac{1}{2}\gamma r_0)$ is also positive. It generally has a value between 0.1 and 0.2 when (4.29) applies.

The variation of H_{lo}^{net} depends on that of surface radiation and atmospheric radiation. When $^A\vartheta_0$ is small compared with the absolute average surface temperature Θ_{ea} the variation of the surface emittance can be written as $4\varepsilon\sigma(\Theta_{ea})^3 {}^A\vartheta_0 \sin\omega t$ (cf. equation (3.36)). The calculation of the variation of atmospheric radiation is much more difficult, because the variation of air temperature and vapor pressure at different heights must be taken into account. When atmospheric radiation is considered to be constant one has

$$^A H_{lo}^{net} = 4\,\varepsilon\sigma(\Theta_{ea})^3 {}^A\vartheta_0, \qquad (4.31)$$

when (3.35) is applied with $\Theta_{ea} = \Theta_{ai}$ (cf. section 3.16) one finds

$$^A H_{lo}^{net} = 4\,\varepsilon\sigma(\Theta_{ea})^3 {}^A\vartheta_0[1 - f(p_w)](1 - rm). \qquad (4.32)$$

The "best" value for $^A H_{lo}^{net}$ will lie between the two values given by (4.31) and (4.32). It must be stressed, however, that the representation of the variation of H_{lo}^{net} as a sine function of ωt is a crude procedure.

The variation of H_{ev} depends not only on atmospheric conditions, but also on moisture movement towards the surface in the upper layers of the soil. When these layers are sufficiently wet, soil water movement does not limit evaporation and H_{ev} is determined by the moisture distribution and the transport properties of the atmosphere. The other extreme is represented by the case of a dry soil, when $H_{ev} = 0$.

It follows from the discussion in this section that a calculation of φ_{sh} is very involved. Some numerical examples for the case of no evaporation will be given in section 4.9.

---

* In some textbooks ln 1.781 = 0.5772 is called Euler's constant.

4.7. Periodic storage and release of heat

The periodic variation of temperature is accompanied by a periodic storage of heat in the soil and release of heat from it. This effect has a mitigating influence on the climate near the soil surface. To find its magnitude one has to integrate the heat flux density at the surface with respect to the time. Hence, the amount of heat stored into the soil between the instants t_0 and t is given by the expression $\int_{t_0}^{t} H(0,s)\mathrm{d}s$, where $H(0,t)$ again represents the heat flux density at the soil surface counted positive when heat flows downwards.

Substituting the expression (4.17) for H, one has with $z = 0$ and $\partial\vartheta_{az}/\partial z = 0$

$$\int_{t_0}^{t} H(0,s)\,\mathrm{d}s = {}^{A}\vartheta_0(\lambda C/\omega)^{\frac{1}{2}}[\sin(\omega t + \varphi_0 - \tfrac{1}{4}\pi) - \sin(\omega t_0 + \varphi_0 - \tfrac{1}{4}\pi)]. \quad (4.33)$$

The amount of heat stored into the soil per unit of surface area is also a sine function of the time in this case. Its amplitude is ${}^{A}\vartheta_0(\lambda C/\omega)^{\frac{1}{2}}$ and its full range of variation is twice this amount.

Storage of heat takes place so long as $H(0,t)$ is positive. This is from 4 till 16 hr, assuming that the maximum of $\vartheta(0,t)$ occurs at 13 hr. During the remaining twelve hours heat moves in the soil towards the surface. Especially during night time, when the terms H_{ai} and H_{ev} in (4.18) are often small, the release of heat from the soil is an important factor in the prevention of excessively low minimum temperatures.

Similarly the amount of heat stored below the depth z per unit of area is found to be

$$\int_{t_0}^{t} H(z,s)\,\mathrm{d}s = {}^{A}\vartheta_0(\lambda C/\omega)^{\frac{1}{2}}\exp(-z/D)\{\sin(\omega t + \varphi_0 - z/D - \tfrac{1}{4}\pi)$$
$$- \sin[\omega t_0 + \varphi_0 - z/D - \tfrac{1}{4}\pi]\}. \quad (4.34)$$

The full range of heat amount that is periodically stored and released below the depth z is $2\,{}^{A}\vartheta_0(\lambda C/\omega)^{\frac{1}{2}}\exp(-z/D)$.

Equation (4.34) can also be derived from (4.15). When the second term on the right-hand side in the latter is multiplied by C one obtains the heat content above the average per unit volume of soil at depth z. Integration with respect to z between the limits z and infinity leads to (4.34) with the second term in square brackets equal to zero. This is caused by a special choice of t_0 implied in the present procedure.

4.8. Comparison of the theory with observations

Though a very extensive literature on soil temperature exists (see, for instance, the bibliography given in the Met. Abstracts, 2 [1951]), very few papers can be used for a quantitative comparison with theory. This is because in most cases the thermal properties of the soil are unknown. Often recorded temperatures are used to calculate the damping depth and the thermal diffusivity from (4.15) by the procedure mentioned in section 4.5.

Some records of soil temperatures are given in Figs. 4.3, 4.4, and 4.5. The first of these refers to a clay soil, the second to a peat soil both covered by short grass, the third to a bare tropical lateritic soil. The damping depths have been calculated from the amplitudes and from the phase shifts of the temperature extremes.

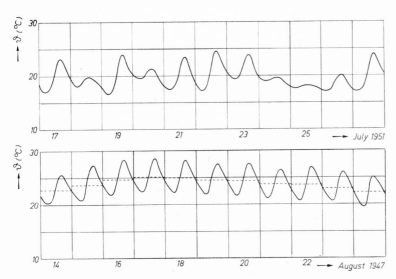

Fig. 4.3. Soil temperature variations at 10 cm depth in a clay soil under a short grass cover at Wageningen, the Netherlands. The upper curve shows large deviations from a periodic function owing to variable weather conditions, while the lower curve corresponding to a sequence of bright days has a periodic character. The average daily temperatures are indicated by the dotted lines which have been drawn such that they divide the surfaces bounded by the temperature curves for each day equally.

A damping depth of approximately 15 cm is found from the amplitudes in Fig. 4.6a. The phase shifts corresponding to the maximum and minimum temperatures scatter widely but lead in the average to a D-value of the same order. Note that ϑ_a varies somewhat with depth.

Though D probably varies with depth no improvement is obtained by applying (4.15) first to the layer between 10 and 20 cm and secondly to the layer between 20 and 30 cm, because (4.15) is only valid for a homogeneous soil of infinite depth. A different solution must be applied to a layer of

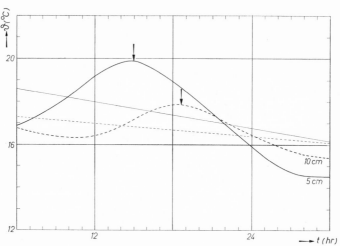

Fig. 4.4. Temperature variations at two different depths in a peat soil (After W. KREUTZ [1943].) From the positions of the maxima, indicated by arrows, $D = 5.4$ cm is calculated. From the amplitudes one finds $D = 6.7$ cm. From the basic waves in the Fourier analysis these figures are 6.4 cm and 6.0 cm respectively. It has been assumed that the daily temperature variation is superposed on a linear variation indicated by the sloping lines.

finite depth, as will be shown in Chapter 6. Similarly, if the graphical procedure described in section 4.5 is used, one straight line should be drawn that gives a best fit to all points.

An interesting illustration of the theory is given in Fig. 4.6b. A rapid variation of total global radiation occurred in the afternoon owing to variable cloudiness. This caused the surface temperature to fluctuate with a period of about 1 hr. This fluctuation is superposed on the diurnal wave. Each variation is propagated in the soil independent of the other.

The damping depth of a sinusoidal wave with a period of 24 hr is approximately 15 cm for this soil. Thus, according to (4.9) a damping depth of $15/\sqrt{24} \approx 3$ cm corresponds to a period of 1 hr. Temperature variations with this period are consequently practically damped out at 10 cm depth. They are indeed imperceptible in the temperature record for 10 cm. The record of the air temperature at 2 m shows the short-period fluctuations quite clearly.

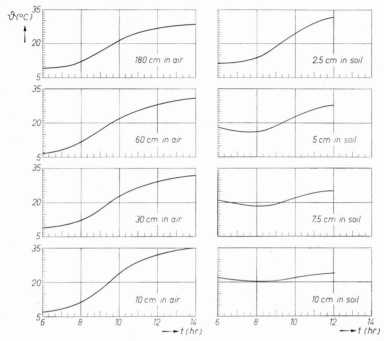

Fig. 4.5. Soil and air temperature variation on a clear day with little wind at Poona, India. Measurements in and above a bare tropical lateritic soil. (After L. A. RAMDAS [1951].)

4.9. The influence of soil thermal properties on the temperature regime

In this section the problem will be discussed how the temperature variations near the surface are influenced by the thermal properties of the soil. To obtain a basis of comparison it will be assumed that the soils are bare, homogeneous and of infinite depth, and that atmospheric conditions are the same for the different soils.

As an introduction the simpler case where the variation of the heat flux density at the surface is the same for the different soils, will be considered first. It then follows from (4.23) that the surface amplitudes are inversely proportional to $(\lambda C)^{\frac{1}{2}}$.

By way of example temperatures for a sandy soil and a peat soil were calculated on this basis. The thermal properties have been chosen as follows: for the sand $\lambda = 0.0042$ cal cm^{-1} sec^{-1} °C^{-1}, $C = 0.5$ cal cm^{-3} °C^{-1}, and for the peat $\lambda = 0.0007$ cal cm^{-1} sec^{-1} °C^{-1}, $C = 0.75$ cal cm^{-3} °C^{-1}. For the diurnal variation the values of D are then 15.2 and 5.1 cm for the sand and the peat (cf. Table 4.2), those of $(\lambda C)^{\frac{1}{2}}$ are 0.0458 and 0.0229 cal cm^{-2} sec$^{-\frac{1}{2}}$ °C^{-1}. Hence, the surface amplitude for the peat is twice that for the sand

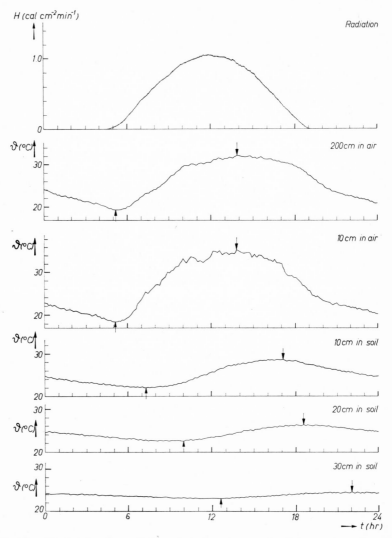

Fig. 4.6. a. Short-wave solar radiation, air temperatures and soil temperatures for a clay soil with grass cover at Wageningen, the Netherlands, on a bright day, August 17, 1947. The extreme values of the temperatures are indicated by arrows.

on the basis of the present assumptions. With the smaller D the decrease of the amplitude is more rapid and the increase of the phase shift with depth in the soil is greater.

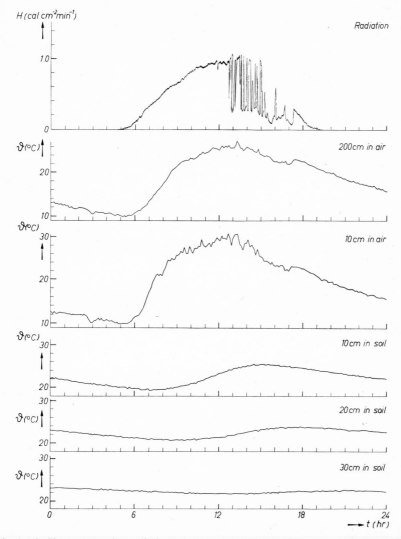

Fig. 4.6. b. Short-wave solar radiation, air temperatures and soil temperatures for a clay soil with grass cover at Wageningen, the Netherlands, on a day with broken sky in the afternoon, August 24, 1947. Note the absence of the short period temperature fluctuations in the soil.

When atmospheric conditions are the same for both soils the amplitudes and phases of the heat flux density at the surface will differ, because they depend on the thermal properties of the soil as well. A discussion of this case must be based on the application of the energy balance at the surface. The theoretical treatment of the problem given below is highly simplified. Nevertheless, it indicates the order of the differences in temperature near the surface that can be expected for soils with different thermal properties.

It will be assumed that the equations given in section 4.6 can be applied to the present problem. As a further simplifying assumption the variation of the evaporative heat flux will be neglected, hence $^AH_{ev} = 0$.

The ratio of the amplitudes of the heat fluxes into the air and the soil follows at once from (4.17) and (4.30). One has

$$^AH_{so}/^AH_{ai} = -2\,b^{-1}(\lambda_{so}\,C_{so}\omega)^{\frac{1}{2}}\ln(\tfrac{1}{2}\gamma r_0), \qquad (4.35)$$

with $r_0 = 2\,(b^{-1}z_0\,C_{ai}\omega)^{\frac{1}{2}}$.

It follows from (4.35) that the ratio $^AH_{so}/^AH_{ai}$ is dependent upon the frequency of the variation. The heat which is generated at the earth's surface is distributed over soil and air in a ratio that not only depends on the thermal properties of the two media, but also on ω. The greater fraction entering the soil, the more rapidly the temperature fluctuates, other conditions remaining the same. This is a consequence of the rapid increase of the conductivity in air with height.

By way of example the ratio $^AH_{so}/^AH_{ai}$ will be calculated for the sand and the peat mentioned above. The values for air chosen are $z_0 = 0.1$ cm, $b = 1.5 \times 10^{-3}$ cal cm^{-2} sec^{-1} °C^{-1}, and $C_{ai} = 2.9 \times 10^{-4}$ cal cm^{-3} °C^{-1}. The adopted value of z_0 pertains to a fairly smooth surface (irregularities less than about 1 cm in height), that of b to light winds. With these values one has for the diurnal variation $r_0 = 2.37 \times 10^{-3}$, $\ln\tfrac{1}{2}\gamma r_0 = -6.17$, and for the annual variation $r_0 = 1.24 \times 10^{-4}$, $\ln\tfrac{1}{2}\gamma r_0 = -9.12$.

With these data one finds for the sand $^AH_{so}/^AH_{ai} = 3.2$ for the diurnal variation and 0.25 for the annual variation. For the peat these figures become 1.6 and 0.125.

A rapid, but very approximate, estimate of the influence of soil thermal properties on the heat flux densities in soil and air can be obtained by ignoring the differences in phase between H_{so} and H_{ai} and by assuming that the total amount of heat available for distribution between soil and air does not depend on the soil type. One then has $^AH_{so} + {}^AH_{ai} = $ constant. Comparing the sand and the peat soil this gives for the diurnal variation

$$^AH_{so}^{sa}(1 + 1/3.2) = {}^AH_{so}^{pe}(1 + 1/1.6),$$

or $^A H_{so}^{pe}/^A H_{so}^{sa} = 0.81$. The ratio of the temperature amplitudes for the two soils is then 1.62, instead 2.0 as was the case for equal $^A H_{so}$. Thus, if $^A\vartheta_{so}^{sa} = 8\,^\circ C$ one now concludes to $^A\vartheta_{so}^{pe} = 13\,^\circ C$ instead of $16\,^\circ C$. The diurnal temperature variations in the sand and the peat soil and the different heat flux densities at the soil surfaces are represented in Figs. 4.7 and 4.8.

This difference in surface temperature amplitude is of practical importance. In the spring and in the fall the danger of night frost is materially enhanced on a soil whose minimum temperature is several degrees lower. The more frequent occurrence of night frosts on peat soils as compared with sand or clay is well known in practice.

A similar calculation for the annual variation gives $^A H_{so}^{pe}/^A H_{so}^{sa} = 0.56$ and $^A\vartheta_0^{pe}/^A\vartheta_0^{sa} = 1.11$. The influence of the soil properties on the surface amplitude is now much less pronounced.

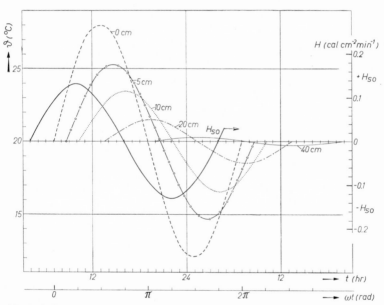

Fig. 4.7. Variation of temperature with depth for a sand soil. The full curve is the sensible heat flux density into the soil H_{so} at the soil surface (right hand vertical scale). The dotted curves represent the temperatures at various depths (left hand vertical scale). A value of $\lambda = 0.0042$ cal cm^{-1} sec$^{-1}\,^\circ$C^{-1} and $C = 0.5$ cal cm$^{-3}\,^\circ$C^{-1} has been assumed resulting in a damping depth $D = 15.2$ cm.

A more complete calculation can be based on the expressions for the various terms in the energy balance given in section 4.6. In the present example the value of $\varphi_{ai} = \frac{1}{2}\pi + \mathrm{arct}[(4/\pi) \ln \frac{1}{2}\gamma r_0]$ is 0.127 rad for the diurnal variation, that of $^{A}H_{ai} = -\;^{A}\vartheta_0 b/2 \ln \frac{1}{2}\gamma r_0$ is $1.21 \times 10^{-4}\;^{A}\vartheta_0$ cal cm^{-2} sec^{-1}.

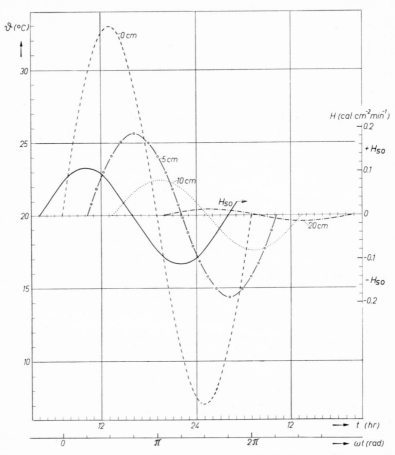

Fig. 4.8. Variation of temperature with depth for a peat soil. The full curve is the sensible heat flux density into the soil at the soil surface (right-hand vertical scale). The dotted curves represent the temperatures at various depths (left-hand vertical scale). A value of $\lambda = 0.0007$ cal cm^{-1} sec^{-1} °C^{-1} and $C = 0.75$ cal cm^{-3} °C^{-1} has been assumed resulting in a damping depth $D = 5.1$ cm.

For the variation of H_{10}^{net} equation (4.32) will be used with $f(p_{w}) = 0.66$, $m = 0$, and $\Theta_{ea} = 281$ °K. One obtains $^{A}H_{10}^{\mathrm{net}} = 4.08 \times 10^{-5}\;^{A}\vartheta_0$ cal cm^{-2} sec$^{-1} = 0.337\;^{A}H_{ai}$.

Substitution of these values in (4.28) with $^A H_{ev} = 0$ leads to

$$\text{tg } \varphi_{sh} = \frac{0.126 + 0.707 \, ^A H_{so}/^A H_{ai}}{0.337 + 0.992 + 0.707 \, ^A H_{so}/^A H_{ai}}.$$

One then finds with the above values of $^A H_{so}/^A H_{ai}$ for the sandy soil $\varphi_{sh}^{sa} = 0.59$ rad and for the peat soil $\varphi_{sh}^{pe} = 0.47$ rad. Finally one obtains from (4.27), assuming that ϱ and $^A H_{sh}$ are the same for both soils, $^A H_{so}^{pe}/^A H_{so}^{sa} = 0.78$ and $^A \vartheta_0^{pe}/^A \vartheta_0^{sa} = 1.56$. The equality of ϱ means that both soils have the same reflectivity for short-wave radiation.

It is worth noting that the maximum surface temperature is reached earlier on the peat soil (13 hr, 48 min) than on the sand (14 hr, 15 min). If $^A H_{ev}$ is not zero the maximum will be reached earlier on both soils. The same holds true, if (4.31) is used instead of (4.32) to calculate $^A H_{lo}^{net}$.

4.10. The influence of surface roughness and of wind velocity on the temperature regime

In the example of the preceding section the temperature variations near the surface were compared for a sandy soil and a peat soil for a given value of the parameters z_0 and b. As will be discussed in Chapter 8, z_0 depends on the irregularity of the surface and b is related to the wind velocity at a given height.

To illustrate the influence of these parameters on the temperature variations near the surface for different soils, calculations similar to those of the preceding section have been made for a clay soil and a peat soil with two values of z_0 and two wind velocities. The results are represented in Table 4.3.

In the calculations the relation $u = bk^{-2} C_{ai}^{-1} \ln (z/z_0 + 1)$ is used (see Chapter 8), in which u is wind velocity in m sec^{-1} at a height $z = 200$ cm above the surface, $k = 0.40$ and $C_{ai} = 2.9 \times 10^{-4}$ cal cm^{-3} °C^{-1}.

The values adopted for z_0 are 0.1 and 10 cm. The lower value applies to a fairly smooth surface, the higher value applies to a soil covered by a fairly tall vegetation. The present approach is then no longer applicable, but the value has been added to illustrate the influence of z_0 in the entire range of possible values. It follows from the table that the influence of z_0 on the ratio $^A \vartheta_{so}^{pe}/^A \vartheta_{so}^{cl}$ is small for the diurnal variation and very small for the annual variation.

The two values adopted for u correspond to light and moderate winds. The influence of wind on the ratio of the surface amplitudes is considerable in all cases, especially with the diurnal variation.

TABLE 4.3

Effect of roughness of the surface and of wind velocity on the daily (d) and yearly (y) heat wave in clay and peat

$z_0 = 0.1$ cm

u (m sec^{-1})	b (cal cm^{-2} sec^{-1} °C^{-1})	$\mathrm{d}(r_0)$	$\mathrm{y}(r_0)$	$\ln \mathrm{d}(\gamma r_0/2)$	$\ln \mathrm{y}(\gamma r_0/2)$
5	3.05×10^{-3}	1.664×10^{-3}	0.742×10^{-4}	-6.711	-9.62
1	0.61×10^{-3}	3.716×10^{-3}	1.944×10^{-4}	-5.709	-8.68

u		$\sqrt{(\lambda_{so} C_{so})}$	$\mathrm{d}(^A H_{so}/^A H_{ai})$	$\mathrm{y}(^A H_{so}/^A H_{ai})$	$\mathrm{d}(\varphi_{ai})$	$\mathrm{y}(\varphi_{ai})$	$\mathrm{d}(\varphi_{sh})$	$\mathrm{y}(\varphi_{sh})$	$\mathrm{d}(A\vartheta_{so}^{pe}/A\vartheta_{so}^{cl})$	$\mathrm{y}(A\vartheta_{so}^{pe}/A\vartheta_{so}^{cl})$
5	clay	0.03195	1.20	0.0899	0.120	0.081	0.417	0.103	1.39	1.03
5	peat	0.0196	0.73	0.055	0.120	0.081	0.333	0.087		
1	clay	0.03195	5.10	0.400	0.140	0.092	0.649	0.230	1.48	1.07
1	peat	0.0196	3.13	0.248	0.140	0.092	0.588	0.177		

TABLE 4.3 (continued)

Effect of roughness of the surface and of wind velocity on the daily (d) and yearly (y) heat wave in clay and peat

$z_0 = 10$ cm

u (m sec^{-1})	b (cal cm^{-2} sec^{-1} °C^{-1})	$d(r_0)$	$y(r_0)$	$\ln d(\gamma r_0/2)$	$\ln y(\gamma r_0/2)$
5	7.62×10^{-3}	1.052×10^{-2}	0.550×10^{-3}	-4.669	-7.619
1	1.52×10^{-3}	2.358×10^{-2}	1.232×10^{-3}	-3.862	-6.813

	$\sqrt{(\lambda_{so} C_{so})}$	$d({}^{A}H_{so}/{}^{A}H_{ai})$	$y({}^{A}H_{so}/{}^{A}H_{ai})$	$d(\varphi_{ai})$	$y(\varphi_{ai})$	$d(\varphi_{sh})$	$y(\varphi_{sh})$	$d({}^{A}\vartheta_{so}^{pe}/{}^{A}\vartheta_{so}^{cl})$	$y({}^{A}\vartheta_{so}^{pe}/{}^{A}\vartheta_{so}^{cl})$
5 clay	0.03195	0.33	0.0285	0.167	0.102	0.253	0.091	1.12	1.01
5 peat	0.0196	0.20	0.0175	0.167	0.102	0.209	0.085		
1 clay	0.03195	1.38	0.1280	0.198	0.114	0.474	0.201	1.29	1.04
1 peat	0.0196	0.85	0.0785	0.198	0.114	0.395	0.182		

In this table: $r_0 = 2(b^{-1} z_0 C_{ai} \omega)^{\frac{1}{4}}$; $\gamma = 1.781$ is Euler's constant;

$${}^{A}H_{so}/{}^{A}H_{ai} = -2b^{-1}(\lambda_{so} C_{so} \omega)^{\frac{1}{2}} \ln (\gamma r_0/2); \quad \varphi_{ai} = \pi/2 + \text{arct}\,[4/\pi \ln (\gamma r_0/2)];$$

$$\varphi_{sh} = \frac{\sin \varphi_{ai} + 0.707\,{}^{A}H_{so}/{}^{A}H_{ai}}{0.337 + \cos \varphi_{ai} + 0.707\,{}^{A}H_{so}/{}^{A}H_{ai}};$$

$$\frac{{}^{A}\vartheta_{so}^{pe}}{{}^{A}\vartheta_{so}^{cl}} = \frac{{}^{A}H_{so}^{pe}}{{}^{A}H_{so}^{cl}} \sqrt{\frac{\lambda_{cl} C_{cl}}{\lambda_{pe} C_{pe}}}.$$

${}^{A}H_{so}^{pe}/{}^{A}H_{so}^{cl}$ can be obtained from the ratio ${}^{A}H_{so}/{}^{A}H_{ai}$ and assuming ${}^{A}H_{so} + {}^{A}H_{ai} =$ constant.

The striking difference between the ratios $^A H_{so}/^A H_{ai}$ for the diurnal and for the annual wave following from the calculations is also observed in practice. Since the heat conductivity in air cannot increase indefinitely with height these ratios, as shown in the table, will be somewhat too low. If, for instance, λ would become constant from a certain height up onwards the ratios would increase. The smaller this height is, and the lower the frequency of the variations the more pronounced becomes the influence of such a boundary for the increase of λ with height. The phase relations are also influenced by a changing dependence of λ from z.

The applicability of the expressions for λ assumed here will be discussed in detail in Chapter 8.

4.11. The annual temperature variation

Most of the considerations given for the diurnal variation can also be applied to the annual variation, as has already been shown in a number of cases in the preceding sections. However, the applicability of the simplified approach, based on the assumptions of homogeneity of the soil and constancy of thermal properties of soil and air, is even more limited in the case of the annual variation than in that of the diurnal variation. This is due to the facts that the annual variations penetrate much deeper than the diurnal

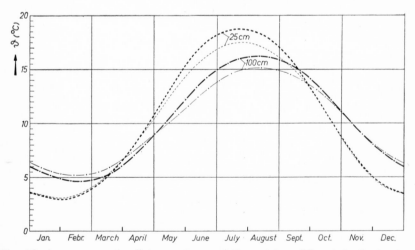

Fig. 4.9. Average annual soil temperature variations at two different depths for two stations, Wageningen and de Bilt, in the Netherlands.

ones and that changes in atmospheric and soil conditions are generally much more pronounced in the course of a year than of a day.

When averages over many years are taken the variation of soil temperature closely approximates a simple sine function. This is illustrated by the data for two stations in the Netherlands shown in Fig. 4.9.

As an example of the heat flow in the soil in different climates values for some selected stations are given in Table 4.4. They are based upon measurements in a single year. This explains why the net amount of incoming heat differs from zero. The values of H_{so} in Table 4.4 were computed by ALBRECHT [1940] from soil temperature and heat capacity per unit volume (cf. section 4.7). The temperatures were based on actual measurements at several depths. When necessary, they were extrapolated to greater depths assuming a constant thermal diffusivity. The volumetric heat capacities were measured in some cases, estimated in others. The values of H_{so} are, therefore, affected with a considerable degree of uncertainty. Nevertheless they clearly illustrate the influence of latitude and continentality.

The influence of the annual variation on the average temperature of the diurnal variation has already been mentioned in section 4.5 (see equation (4.16)). Since the diurnal variation is practically limited to a layer of three times the diurnal damping depth (D_d) the variation of ϑ_{ad} will be of importance in a layer extending between $z = 0$ and $z = 3D_d$. One has, with $3D_d/D_y = 0.157$ and $\exp(0.157) = 0.855$

$$\vartheta_y(3D_d) = \vartheta_{ay} + 0.855 \,^A\vartheta_{0y}\sin(\omega_y t + \varphi_{0y} - 0.157). \qquad (4.36)$$

At a depth of $3D_d$ the amplitude of the annual wave is reduced by about 15% in comparison with the variation at the surface and the phase is retarded by 0.157 rad which corresponds to 9 days. The difference of ϑ_y at $z = 0$ and $z = 3D_d$ is (omitting the index y)

$$\vartheta(0,t) - \vartheta(3D_d,t) = \,^A\vartheta_0\sin(\omega t + \varphi_0) - 0.855 \,^A\vartheta_0\sin(\omega t + \varphi_0 - 0.157)$$
$$= 0.20 \,^A\vartheta_0\sin(\omega t + \varphi_0 + 0.71). \qquad (4.37)$$

The maximum difference occurs approximately 41 days before the surface maximum of the annual temperature wave. Inserting $^A\vartheta_{0y} = 10\,°C$ as an average for Western Europe extreme differences of $\pm\,2\,°C$ can be expected in the beginning of June and of December.

The systematic variation of ϑ_{ad} with depth, due to the annual variation can be estimated by this method for any depth and taken into account when necessary. However, in many applications deviations from the simplifying assumptions, such as inhomogeneity of the soil, are of greater consequence.

TABLE 4.4

Annual heat wave in the soil for different climates. Values of the heat flux density at the soil surface, H_{so}(cal cm^{-2} month^{-1}), and of the surface temperature, ϑ_0(°C), for four stations

	Sodankyla (67 °N 27 °E) Nov. 1915–Oct. 1916		Potsdam (52 °N 13 °E) Year 1903		Ikengueng (42 °N 108 °E) May 1931–Apr. 1932		Djakarta (6 °S 107 °E) Year 1922	
	H_{so}	ϑ_0	H_{so}	ϑ_0	H_{so}	ϑ_0	H_{so}	ϑ_0
Jan.	− 119	−12.9	− 248	− 1.2	− 224	− 9.8	10	29.4
Febr.	− 132	−11.6	− 96	+ 1.6	− 119	− 6.9	+ 38	28.8
March	− 210	−12.8	+ 88	6.5	− 20		− 5	29.8
April	+ 664	− 5.2	321	6.6	+ 310		+ 4	29.7
May	1716	+ 1.5	536	15.8	595	+15.2	+ 4	28.9
June	1209	14.8	568	18.5	606	23.5	− 35	28.1
July	1018	20.8	384	20.0	494	21.1	− 20	28.1
Aug.	+ 80	11.5	+ 112	16.9	+ 130	23.6	+ 43	28.5
Sept.	− 338	+ 4.8	− 120	15.0	− 190	15.7	33	30.0
Oct.	− 808	− 5.1	− 332	9.0	− 464	+10.7	10	29.8
Nov.	− 742	−14.0	− 504	+ 3.9	− 639	− 3.1	+ 10	30.0
Dec.	− 649	−25.3	− 528	− 1.4	− 628	−13.0	− 17	29.2
	+1689		+ 181		− 249		+ 75	

4.12. General periodic temperature variation, Fourier analysis

In case of a surface temperature which is periodic in the time but not a simple sine function, the theory of the preceding sections has to be modified. It will again be assumed that the thermal diffusivity is constant, i.e. that is does not depend on time or depth.

It is proved in textbooks of mathematics that an arbitrary periodic function with the radial frequency ω can be represented by a series of sine and cosine functions with radial frequencies that are integral multiples of ω, thus

$$\vartheta(0,t) = \vartheta_a + \sum_{k=1}^{\infty}(a_k \cos k\omega t + b_k \sin k\omega t). \tag{4.38}$$

The right-hand side of this equation is called a Fourier series.*

Leaving the determination of the coefficients a_k and b_k to the next paragraph, equation (4.38) is rewritten in a somewhat different form

$$\vartheta(0,t) = \vartheta_a + \sum_{k=1}^{\infty}{}^A\vartheta_{0k} \sin(k\omega t + \varphi_k). \tag{4.39}$$

The relation between the constants in (4.38) and (4.39) are

or:
$$a_k = {}^A\vartheta_{0k} \sin\varphi_k, \qquad b_k = {}^A\vartheta_{0k} \cos\varphi_k;$$
$$\tag{4.40}$$
$${}^A\vartheta_{0k}^2 = a_k^2 + b_k^2, \qquad \varphi_k = \text{arct}(a_k/b_k).$$

Thus a general periodic variation can be expressed as a superposition of sinusoidal variations. This leads to a periodic solution of (4.5) that is a superposition of solutions of the form of (4.8)

$$\vartheta(z,t) = \vartheta_a + \sum_{k=1}^{\infty}{}^A\vartheta_{0k}\exp(-zk^{\frac{1}{2}}/D) \sin(k\omega t + \varphi_k - zk^{\frac{1}{2}}/D), \tag{4.41}$$

with $D = (2a/\omega)^{\frac{1}{2}}$. It can easily be verified that ϑ given by (4.41) satisfies (4.5) with the boundary conditions given by (4.39) and $\vartheta(\infty,t) = \vartheta_a$.

The sine functions in the right-hand side of (4.39) and (4.41) are called the *fundamental* or *first harmonic* if $k = 1$, the *second harmonic* if $k = 2$, etc.

In special cases a function can be represented by a finite number of harmonics; then ${}^A\vartheta_{0k} = 0$ for k exceeding a certain number n. In other cases the series is infinite. It will be seen that in analyzing soil and air temperatures only a limited number of harmonics need be considered.

---

* A periodic function must satisfy certain restrictive conditions to be developable in a Fourier series. These conditions are always fulfilled by the functions that represent a periodical variation of soil or air temperature. The theory of Fourier series is given in the textbooks on mathematical physics mentioned in the bibliography.

It follows from (4.41) that the amplitude of a harmonic decreases more rapidly with depth the higher its order is. The relative importance of the first harmonic increases therefore with depth. Since it often predominates already at the surface, a general understanding of the propagation of temperature waves in the soil can be obtained from a study of simple harmonic variations.

4.13. Calculation of the coefficients in a Fourier expansion

The coefficients in the Fourier series for $\vartheta(0, t)$ in (4.38) are obtained by multiplication of both sides with $\cos n\omega t$ or $\sin n\omega t$, where n is a positive integer, and integrating with respect to t over a full period. This gives

$$\int_0^{2\pi/\omega} \vartheta(0, t) \cos n\omega t \, dt = \int_0^{2\pi/\omega} \vartheta_a \cos n\omega t \, dt$$

$$+ \sum_{k=1}^{\infty} \left(\int_0^{2\pi/\omega} a_k \cos k\omega t \cos n\omega t \, dt + \int_0^{2\pi/\omega} b_k \sin k\omega t \cos n\omega t \, dt \right),$$

and a similar equation with $\sin n\omega t$ substituted for $\cos n\omega t$. Now

$$\int_0^{2\pi/\omega} \cos k\omega t \cos n\omega t \, dt = 0, \qquad \int_0^{2\pi/\omega} \sin k\omega t \cos n\omega t \, dt = 0, \tag{4.42}$$

and

$$\int_0^{2\pi/\omega} \cos k\omega t \sin n\omega t \, dt = 0, \qquad \int_0^{2\pi/\omega} \sin k\omega t \sin n\omega t \, dt = 0, \tag{4.43}$$

for any combination of integer n and k with $n \neq k$.
For $k = n$ one has

$$\int_0^{2\pi/\omega} \cos^2 n\omega t \, dt = \pi/\omega, \qquad \int_0^{2\pi/\omega} \sin n\omega t \cos n\omega t \, dt = 0$$

$$\int_0^{2\pi/\omega} \sin^2 n\omega t \, dt = \pi/\omega. \tag{4.44}$$

Further

$$\int_0^{2\pi/\omega} \cos n\omega t \, dt = 0, \qquad \int_0^{2\pi/\omega} \sin n\omega t \, dt = 0, \quad \text{for} \quad n > 0, \tag{4.45}$$

and for $n = 0$

$$\int_0^{2\pi/\omega} \sin n\omega t \, \mathrm{d}t = 0, \qquad \int_0^{2\pi/\omega} \cos n\omega t \, \mathrm{d}t = \int_0^{2\pi/\omega} \mathrm{d}t = 2\pi/\omega. \qquad (4.46)$$

From these relationships one concludes

$$\int_0^{2\pi/\omega} \vartheta(0,t) \cos n\omega t \, \mathrm{d}t = a_n \, \pi/\omega, \qquad \int_0^{2\pi/\omega} \vartheta(0,t) \sin n\omega t \, \mathrm{d}t = b_n \, \pi/\omega, \qquad (4.47)$$

with (4.38)

$$\vartheta(0,t) = \tfrac{1}{2} a_0 + \sum_{n=1}^{\infty} (a_n \cos n\omega t + b_n \sin n\omega t).$$

Inserting $n = 0$ in (4.47) leads to $a_0 = 2\vartheta_\mathrm{a}$, $b_0 = 0$.

Many methods exist for computing the coefficients a_n and b_n. Among them are numerical, graphical, mechanical, electrical and optical methods. A special procedure can save much time, if a great number of curves must be analyzed. When a Fourier analysis occurs only occasionally and only a few harmonics need be considered, the simple numerical integration described below has proved to be quite satisfactory.

The uncertainty in the measured temperatures sets a limit to the order n of the harmonics that have a physical meaning. When a_n and b_n are of the same order of magnitude as the uncertainty in the temperatures, the relative errors in these coefficients become high and the corresponding terms may be considerably in error. In the applications the Fourier expansion should therefore be terminated, when the coefficients are no longer well above the level of uncertainty. It is tacitly assumed that the magnitude of the coefficients decreases with increasing n. In the analysis of soil or air temperatures this is usually so.

To calculate a_n and b_n for a given function $\vartheta(0,t)$ the period $2\pi/\omega$ is divided into N equal time intervals and the integrals in (4.47) are approximated by summations as follows

$$a_n = \frac{\omega}{\pi} \int_0^{2\pi/\omega} \vartheta(0,t) \cos n\omega t \, \mathrm{d}t \approx \frac{2}{N} \sum_{j=1}^{N} \vartheta(0,t_j) \cos n\omega t_j. \qquad (4.48)$$

Here t_j is the value of t at the end of the interval with number j, hence $t_j = 2\pi j/N\omega$. A similar expression is obtained for b_n except that $\sin n\omega t_j$ appears instead of $\cos n\omega t_j$.

In applying the procedure to the diurnal variation $N = 24$ will be chosen here*. The 24 hourly values of $\vartheta(0, t_j)$ may, for instance, be obtained from a continuous temperature record or from hourly observations. The same procedure can, of course, be applied to an analysis of temperatures at depth z; $\vartheta(z, t)$ then appears in the formulas instead of $\vartheta(0, t)$.

The numerical work can be somewhat facilitated by using the fact that equal absolute values of $\cos n\omega t_j$ and $\sin n\omega t_j$ occur in one period. In the analysis of the first harmonic, for instance, the same absolute values of $\cos \omega t_j$ and $\sin \omega t_j$ occur for 4 different values of j when $N = 24$. Instead of multiplying $\vartheta(0, t)$ by each of these and adding the products afterwards, the order of operations can be reversed. This is done by arranging the values of $\vartheta(0, t_j)$ in 4 rows, such that in the first and the third row the figures are plotted from left to right, in the second and fourth row from right to left, as is shown in Table 4.5. The four figures corresponding to the same absolute values of $\cos \omega t_j$ or $\sin \omega t_j$ appear in the same column and can be

TABLE 4.5

Scheme for calculation of first order Fourier coefficients a_1 and b_1

	0	$\pi/12$	$\pi/6$	$\pi/4$	$\pi/3$	$5\pi/12$	$\pi/2$	
	1.000	0.966	0.866	0.707	0.500	0.259	0	cos
+		ϑ_1	ϑ_2	ϑ_3	ϑ_4	ϑ_5	ϑ_6	+
+	ϑ_{12}	ϑ_{11}	ϑ_{10}	ϑ_9	ϑ_8	ϑ_7		−
−		ϑ_{13}	ϑ_{14}	ϑ_{15}	ϑ_{16}	ϑ_{17}	ϑ_{18}	−
−	ϑ_{24}	ϑ_{23}	ϑ_{22}	ϑ_{21}	ϑ_{20}	ϑ_{19}		+
sin	0	0.259	0.500	0.707	0.866	0.966	1.000	

added, after multiplication with the proper plus or minus sign. The sum is then multiplied by the value of the sine or the cosine shown in the same column.

Similar schemes can be worked out for the calculation of Fourier coefficients of a higher order. PEERLKAMP [1944] has published such schemes for an analysis of the annual waves for $n = 1, 2, 4$ and 8 and with $N = 52$.

By way of example an analysis is carried out of the temperature curve at 10 cm depth shown in Fig. 4.3. The arrangement of the 24 values $\vartheta(10, t_j)$ is given in Table 4.6. From this Table and (4.47) one obtains

---

* The number of intervals to be used depends on the order of the harmonic that is considered. The integral in (4.48) is poorly approximated by the summation, if N is not about an order of magnitude greater than n. As a rule of thumb one should take N at least 8 times as large as n.

$\frac{1}{12}(-0.8 - 2.4 \times 0.966 - 1.9 \times 0.866 - 1.4 \times 0.707 - 1.2 \times 0.500 - 0.700 \times 0.259)$
$-0.55,$

$\frac{1}{12}(-3.8 \times 0.259 - 6.5 \times 0.500 - 8.6 \times 0.707 - 10.4 \times 0.866 - 11.3 \times 0.966 - 6.0)$
$-3.00.$

TABLE 4.6

Scheme for calculation of first order Fourier coefficients of soil temperature at 10 cm depth at Wageningen on August 17, 1947

	0	$\pi/12$	$\pi/6$	$\pi/4$	$\pi/3$	$5\pi/12$	$\pi/2$	
	1.000	0.966	0.866	0.707	0.500	0.259	0	cos
+		23.7	23.2	22.9	22.6	22.4	22.2	+
+	25.5	24.3	23.2	22.5	22.1	22.1		−
−		26.8	27.4	27.9	28.4	28.4	28.2	−
−	24.7	25.0	25.5	26.1	26.7	27.4		+
sin	0	0.259	0.500	0.707	0.866	0.966	1.000	

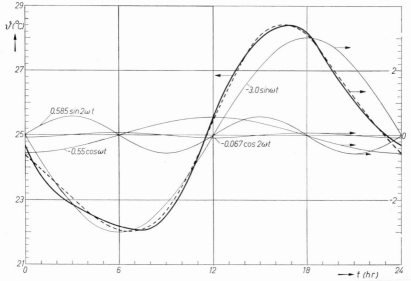

Fig. 4.10. Diurnal temperature variation in a clay soil at 10 cm depth at Wageningen on August 17, 1949, together with the first four terms in its Fourier expansion (thin lines) and the sum of these terms (dotted line). The temperature variation (heavy line) has been smoothed in this figure.

Thus the first harmonic is represented by

$$-0.55 \cos \omega t - 3.00 \sin \omega t = 3.05 \sin(\omega t - 2.96).$$

A calculation of the coefficients of the second harmonic leads to $a_2 = -0.067$, $b_2 = 0.585$. The value of ϑ_a is the arithmetic average of the 24 values of $\vartheta(10, t_j)$; one has $\vartheta_a = 25.0 \,°C$. Neglecting harmonics of the third and higher orders one finds

$$\vartheta(10, t) = 25.0 - 0.55 \cos \omega t - 3.00 \sin \omega t - 0.067 \cos 2\omega t + 0.585 \sin 2\omega t$$
$$= 25.0 + 3.05 \sin(\omega t - 2.96) + 0.59 \sin(2\omega t - 0.114).$$

The different terms in the right-hand side of this expression and their sum are shown in Fig. 4.10 together with $\vartheta(10, t)$. The differences between the observed temperature and its representation by the calculated harmonics are small. They are of the same order as the experimental error ($\pm 0.3 \,°C$) for the entire period.

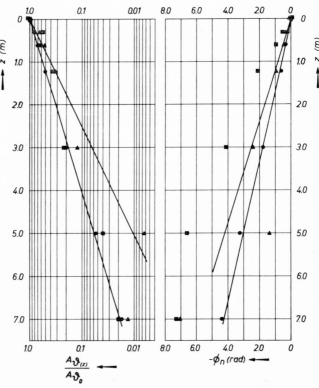

Fig. 4.11. Values of $^A\vartheta(z)/^A\vartheta_0$ and $-\varphi$ as functions of depth. This figure is derived from the data given in Table 4.7.

4.14. Example of the penetration of the harmonics into a soil

Nakamura measured the annual temperature wave for Tokyo during the years 1889 until 1892 (TAMURA [1905]). The average annual variation at seven different depths was subjected to a Fourier analysis. The results are represented in Table 4.7. The error of observation is some tenths of a degree centigrade. The amplitude of the 3rd harmonic is only slightly above this level even at a shallow depth. The analysis was therefore not extended to higher harmonics.

The values of $-\log(^A\vartheta(z)/^A\vartheta_0)$ and of $-\varphi$ are represented in Fig. 4.11 as functions of the depth. The damping depth for the harmonic, $D_n = (2a/n\omega)^{\frac{1}{2}} = D/n^{\frac{1}{2}}$ is found from the slope of the lines, according to the formulas $\ln(^A\vartheta_n(z)/^A\vartheta_{0n}) = \varphi_n(z) = -z/D_n$. The damping depth of the first harmonic

TABLE 4.7

Average temperature $\vartheta_{ay}(^\circ C)$, amplitudes $^A\vartheta_n(^\circ C)$ and phase shifts φ_n(rad) of Fourier components of the annual temperature variation at Tokyo

Depth z(m)	ϑ_{ay}	$^A\vartheta_1$	$^A\vartheta_2$	$^A\vartheta_3$	φ_1	φ_2	φ_3
0	15.8	12.64	1.54	0.50	0.	0	0
0.3	16.3	10.31	1.04	0.29	0.175	0.335	0.531
0.6	16.0	9.02	0.82	0.31	0.334	0.489	0.990
1.2	16.4	6.53	0.51	0.19	0.689	0.969	2.14
3.0	15.7	2.64	0.19	0.11	1.753	2.45	4.16
5.0	15.5	0.70	0.01	0.02	3.22	1.38	6.59
7.0	15.3	0.22	0.02	0.01	4.37	7.00	7.23

is $D = 170$ cm and that of the second harmonic is $D_2 = 0.7\,D$ in accordance with the theory for a homogeneous soil.

The lines representing the relationships of $\ln(^A\vartheta(z)/^A\vartheta_0)$ and of φ with z have a somewhat different slope in case of the second harmonic. This is largely due to the points at the greater depths. However, the accuracy of these points is questionable, as $^A\vartheta_2$ is of the order of the experimental error below 1.2 m. The amplitude of the third harmonic is near or below the observational error at any depth. The corresponding points scatter widely and it is impossible to derive a value of D_3 from them.

4.15. The correction of Lamont

Lamont's correction applies to the case where the temperature shows a small systematic nonperiodic variation superposed on a much larger periodic variation. The temperature then does not return to its original value after the completion of a period. The Fourier coefficients, calculated in the manner described in the preceding section, must then be corrected for the non-periodic variation.

Lamont derived the correction for the first harmonic in case the non-periodic variation is a linear function of the time. The variation of the surface temperature can then be written as

$$\vartheta(0,t) = \vartheta^{\mathrm{per}}(t) + (\omega \Delta\vartheta/2\pi)t, \quad \text{for} \quad 0 \leqslant t \leqslant 2\pi/\omega, \tag{4.49}$$

in which $\Delta\vartheta$ is the change in temperature at the end of the period considered.

It is now assumed that the temperature can be represented by (4.49) during all periods. In other words, a periodic function is considered which shows a discontinuity of magnitude $-\Delta\vartheta$ at the end of each period. This new periodic function can be expanded in a Fourier series, the various coefficients a_n and b_n are the sum of those for the true periodic part, $\vartheta^{\mathrm{per}}(t)$, and those for the part represented by the second term on the right hand side of (4.49). The latter can also be found from (4.48). Denoting them by primes one has

$$a'_0 = \Delta\vartheta, \quad a'_1 = 0, \quad b'_1 = -\Delta\vartheta/\pi.$$

The first terms in the expansion of $\vartheta(0,t)$ are then

$$\vartheta(0,t) = \vartheta_{\mathrm{a}}^{\mathrm{per}} + \tfrac{1}{2}\Delta\vartheta + \cos\omega t + (b_1^{\mathrm{per}} - \Delta\vartheta/\pi)\sin\omega t + \ldots \tag{4.50}$$

The value of b_1 has thus to be increased by $\Delta\vartheta/\pi$ to obtain the corresponding coefficient for the true periodic part. This correction is called Lamont's correction.

As an example the correction will be calculated for the temperature curve at 5 cm depth in Fig. 4.3. In this case $\Delta\vartheta = 2.4\,°C$. The value calculated for b_1 is $1.09\,°C$, so that one has $b_1^{\mathrm{per}} = 1.09 + 2.4/\pi = 1.85\,°C$.

In reality no discontinuity occurs at the end of a period, so that still another correction must be applied due to the deviation from true periodicity. Corrections of this type will be discussed in the next chapter.

4.16. Variation of the thermal diffusivity with time

Throughout the present chapter it has been assumed that the thermal properties of the soil are constant. Actually, λ, C and a can vary with time, in space and with the temperature. The dependence on the temperature is only slight in the case of soils and can be ignored for most practical purposes. Variation of the thermal properties with depth is rather the rule than the exception; the influence of such a variation will be discussed in Chapters 6 and 8. In this paragraph a simplified treatment will be given of the case where the thermal diffusivity varies with time.

A periodic variation of a with time can, for instance, be caused by a periodic change of the soil moisture content during a day or a year. The diffusivity of the upper layers of a grass covered peat soil may, for example, decrease by a factor of three during a growing season due to the depletion of soil moisture.

To facilitate the mathematical treatment it will be assumed that the thermal diffusivity is the same function of the time at all depths. This is again a simplification, as the upper soil layers usually dry out more and sooner than the deeper ones. Yet in some applications it is sufficient to consider an average value of the diffusivity and to ignore its variation with depth.

Writing for the time-dependent diffusivity

$$a(t) = a_0 f(t), \tag{4.51}$$

where a_0 is a constant and $f(t)$ some function of the time, equation (4.5) can be rewritten as follows

$$a_0 \frac{\partial^2 \vartheta}{\partial z^2} = \frac{1}{f(t)} \frac{\partial \vartheta}{\partial t} = \frac{\partial \vartheta}{\partial \tau}. \tag{4.52}$$

Here the new variable $\tau = \int_0^t f(t) dt$ is introduced instead of the time. Thus in the new time scale, determined by τ, equation (4.52) is identical with (4.5) in t. The solution of the latter satisfy (4.52) if τ is substituted for t and a_0 for a.

In this manner the results of the preceding sections can be generalized to include a time-dependent diffusivity. It is then necessary, of course, that the boundary conditions have the same form in τ as those for the constant diffusivity have in t.

As an example the case will be discussed where the diffusivity varies sinusoidally in the course of a year in such a manner that its maximum value is three times its minimum value. In this case one has

$$a(t) = a_0 f(t) = a_0 [1 + 0.5 \sin(\omega t - \delta)], \tag{4.53}$$

in which a_0 is the average diffusivity and δ a phase constant, which must be chosen such that the minimum of a occurs when the soil moisture content is lowest. Integrating the term in brackets in (4.53) between the limits 0 and t one obtains

$$\tau = t - \frac{0.5}{\omega} [\cos(\omega t - \delta) - \cos \delta]. \tag{4.54}$$

It will further be assumed that the surface temperature is a sinusoidal function of τ

$$\vartheta(0, \tau) = \vartheta_{ay} + {}^A\vartheta_0 \sin \omega \tau. \tag{4.55}$$

Let the surface temperature reach its average value on April 1. This instant must then be taken as the origin of the t and τ scales. Let further $a(t)$ have its minimum on September 1, which is approximately the time of maximum depletion of soil moisture for the middle latitudes in the northern hemi-

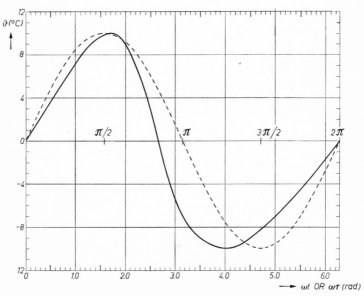

Fig. 4.12. Numerical values of ϑ as a function of τ (dotted line) and as a function of t (full drawn line). The temperature at a given depth as a function of t is a distorted sine curve.

sphere. The maximum of $a(t)$ will then occur six months earlier, i.e. on March 1. This corresponds to the beginning of the growing season, when soil moisture is at its maximum. From these assumptions it follows that $\sin(\omega t - \delta) = -1$ on September 1, thus for $t = 5\pi/6$, so that $\delta = 4\pi/3$.

At the depth z the temperature is given by an equation analogous to (4.8), viz.

$$\vartheta(z,\tau) = \vartheta_{\mathrm{ay}} + {}^A\vartheta_0 \exp(-z/D_y) \sin(\omega\tau - z/D_y), \qquad (4.56)$$

with $D_y = (2a_0/\omega_y)^{\frac{1}{2}}$. Thus D_y is the damping depth for the average value of the diffusivity.

Some numerical values of ϑ, both as a function of τ and of t, are shown in Fig. (4.12). It is seen that the temperature at a given depth as a function of the time t is a distorted sine curve. The shape of these curves changes with depth due to the fact that t is not a linear function of τ.

GENERAL TEMPERATURE VARIATIONS IN A
HOMOGENEOUS SOIL

W. R. VAN WIJK

*Laboratory of Physics and Meteorology of the Agricultural University Wageningen,
The Netherlands*

5.1. Small deviations from periodicity

The theory in Chapter 4 is based upon the assumption that the temperature is a periodic function of the time. This is of course never exactly the case. If on successive days the differences in soil temperature at the same depth and at the same time of the day are small compared with the maximum temperature variation, deviations of periodicity are small. It is to such days that the theory in Chapter 4 is applicable. A Fourier analysis can then be used to improve the assumption of a simple sinusoidal temperature wave. A further step is to correct for the small deviations from periodicity. Lamont's correction is an example. A general correction procedure will be discussed in this chapter.

When strong deviations of periodicity occur as, for instance, when cloudiness varies, soil temperature cannot be understood by the theory given in Chapter 4. A Fourier analysis gives no improvement and essentially non-periodic solutions of the equation of heat conduction are needed to understand the propagation of heat in the soil.

First small deviations from periodicity will be treated. A correction term, the "transient term", must now be considered in addition to the periodic terms.

Later, arbitrary temperature variations will be discussed.

5.2. The transient term

A periodic solution of the equation of heat conduction is entirely determined by the given boundary conditions. The initial temperature distribution in the soil cannot arbitrarily be given. It must be identical with the temperature distribution which occurs one period or an integral number of periods later.

The situation is different if the surface temperature is a periodic function of the time from $t = 0$ on but was some other function for negative t. In that case the initial temperature distribution must be taken into account. The temperature at an arbitrary depth z will generally deviate at $t = 0$ from the value of the periodic solution which satisfies the periodic surface temperature. At a later instant the deviation will be smaller and it will approach zero after a long lapse of time.

Let for $t > 0$

$$\vartheta(0,t) = \vartheta_a + \sum_{k=1}^{k=\infty} {}^A\vartheta_k \sin(k\omega t + \varphi_k) \tag{5.1}$$

be the surface temperature. If this equation had been valid for all negative values of the time as well, the temperature at depth z would have been given by (4.41), but now a correction term $\vartheta_{co}(z,t)$ must be added.

$$\vartheta(z,t) = \vartheta_a + \vartheta_{co}(z,t) + \sum_{k=1}^{k-\infty} {}^A\vartheta_k \exp[-z(\sqrt{k})/D] \times \sin[k\omega t + \varphi_k - z(\sqrt{k})/D]. \tag{5.2}$$

The function $\vartheta_{co}(z,t)$ is the correction term for nonperiodicity; it is called *the transient term*. It can be shown that $\vartheta_{co}(z,t)$ is determined for all positive t and z by its initial values $\vartheta_{co}(z,0)$. This statement will not be proved here. Thus for the computation of $\vartheta_{co}(z,t)$, the function $\vartheta_{co}(z,0)$ must be known for all z values. The function $\vartheta_{co}(z,0)$ will be denoted by $\chi(z)$ in the following formulas. The theory gives the expression

$$\vartheta_{co}(z,t) = \frac{1}{\sqrt{\pi}} \int_{\frac{-z}{2(at)^{\frac{1}{2}}}}^{\infty} \chi[2\xi(at)^{\frac{1}{2}} + z]e^{-\xi^2}d\xi - \frac{1}{\sqrt{\pi}} \int_{\frac{z}{2(at)^{\frac{1}{2}}}}^{\infty} \chi[2\xi(at)^{\frac{1}{2}} - z]e^{-\xi^2}d\xi. \tag{5.3}$$

From a study of this formula one will observe that $\vartheta_{co}(z,t)$ is the temperature in a soil whose surface is kept at zero temperature and in which the initial temperature distribution was $\vartheta_{co}(z,0) = \chi(z)$.

Indeed $\vartheta_{co}(0,t) = 0$ for any positive t, since the integrals in (5.3) become equal if $z = 0$ except for their opposite sign and thus cancel. For $t = 0$ the second integral vanishes and the first integral transforms into

$$\frac{1}{\sqrt{\pi}} \int_{-\infty}^{+\infty} \chi(z)e^{-\xi^2}d\xi = \chi(z). \tag{5.4}$$

Thus $\chi(z) = \vartheta_{co}(z,0)$ for a soil in which the temperature is given by (5.3). A zero value for $\vartheta_{co}(z,t)$ is approached for infinite t.

Returning now to (5.2) one sees that $\vartheta_{co}(z,0)$ is the deviation from the periodic solution at $t = 0$ in the actual soil. After the periodic solution has been calculated, $\vartheta_{co}(z,0) = \chi(z)$ can be determined by subtracting the latter from the observed temperature. However, only a few points are generally recorded, so for instance at $z = 10$, 20 and 30 cm in Fig. 4.6. Though one may further assume that χ approaches zero for infinite z the fact remains that only a few points of the initial temperature distribution curve are known. This leads to an uncertainty in $\chi(z)$ and consequently also in $\vartheta_{co}(z,t)$, which depends upon the number of depths at which the soil temperature has been recorded*. An accurate graphical or numerical evaluation of the integrals in (5.3) is, therefore, often not worth the effort and an approximative method may be used instead.

5.3. Quick method for estimating the transient term

It is convenient to have a method at our disposal which gives an estimate of the order of magnitude of the error introduced in the analysis of soil temperature by ignoring the deviations from periodicity. Or more precisely, in calculating soil temperatures using the assumption that the variation is a periodic function from $t = 0$ on, one is interested to know when the contribution to the temperature at some instant t due to the initial distribution reaches a certain limit, for instance, 0.2 °C at a given level z.

TABLE 5.1

Values of the error function $\operatorname{erf} x = \dfrac{2}{\sqrt{\pi}} \displaystyle\int_0^x e^{-\xi^2}\, d\xi$

x	$\operatorname{erf} x$	x	$\operatorname{erf} x$	x	$\operatorname{erf} x$
0.00	0.0000	0.60	0.6039	1.6	0.9763
0.05	0.0564	0.70	0.6778	1.7	0.9838
0.10	0.1125	0.80	0.7421	1.8	0.9891
0.15	0.1680	0.90	0.7969	1.9	0.9928
0.20	0.2227	1.00	0.8427	2.0	0.9953
0.25	0.2763	1.10	0.8802	2.1	0.9970
0.30	0.3286	1.20	0.9103	2.2	0.9981
0.35	0.3794	1.30	0.9340	2.3	0.9988
0.40	0.4284	1.40	0.9523	2.4	0.9993
0.45	0.4755	1.50	0.9661	2.5	0.9995
0.50	0.5205				

---

* The uncertainty in the transient term provides a further criterion as to the physical significance of a harmonic in the Fourier development of soil temperature. A harmonic whose amplitude is of the same order of magnitude as $\vartheta_{co}(z,t)$ will be greatly affected by the degree of uncertainty in $\chi(z)$.

Such an estimate is obtained if a constant average value χ_0 of χ in the range $0 < z < z_m$ is inserted in (5.3) and $\chi = 0$ for greater depths. The appropriate value of z_m depends on the initial temperature distribution and must be chosen suitably for each individual case.

The function $\vartheta_{co}^{av}(z, t)$ indicates the average value of $\vartheta_{co}(z, t)$. It can be expressed in terms of the *error function*:

$$\text{erf}\, x = \frac{2}{\sqrt{\pi}} \int_0^x e^{-\xi^2}\, d\xi.$$

This function is discussed in the textbooks of mathematical physics (e.g. FRANK and V. MISES [1943]; or MORSE and FESHBACH [1953]) and is tabulated in Jahnke-Emde. Some values are given in Table 5.1. One has

$$\vartheta_{co}^{av}(z, t) = \chi_0\, \text{erf}\, \frac{z}{2(at)^{\frac{1}{2}}} + \tfrac{1}{2}\chi_0 \left\{ \text{erf}\left(\frac{z_m - z}{2(at)^{\frac{1}{2}}}\right) - \text{erf}\left(\frac{z_m + z}{2(at)^{\frac{1}{2}}}\right) \right\}. \qquad (5.5)$$

5.4. Example of the influence of the transient term

The influence of the transient term on the diurnal temperature variation in an Iowa silt loam will now be estimated. The temperature was measured at the three depths, 0.6, 5.0 and 10.0 cm. Taking the difference between maximum and minimum value as twice the amplitude and ignoring the transient term, a preliminary value of the thermal diffusivity was found as $a = 4.10 \times 10^{-3}$ cm² sec⁻¹, which will be used in (5.3) and (5.4). The corresponding damping depth is 10.6 cm. The initial values of the transient term were calculated as the difference between the initial soil temperature and that 24 hr later. In doing this it is assumed that the latter is the temperature as it is caused by the periodic surface temperature alone. Thus the transient term is still ignored after 24 hr. The function χ is given in Table 5.2. The temperature was assumed to be practically constant from $3D = 31.8$ cm on, thus $\chi = 0$ for greater depths.

TABLE 5.2

Initial temperature as a
function of depth in
Iowa Silt Loam

z(cm)	$\chi(°C)$
0.64	-4.5
5.0	-3.6
10	-2.9

Plotting these data as a function of depth revealed that χ closely approximated a straight line.

The variable ξ in the first integrand in (5.3) varies in the range $-z/[2\sqrt{(at)}]$ to ∞. In the second integrand its range is $+z/[2\sqrt{(at)}]$ to ∞. After 6 hr at the depth 10 cm, the lower limits of the integrals are -0.53 and $+0.53$ respectively. To obtain the value of the transient term at $z = 10$ cm after 6 hr, the integrands are calculated for different values of ξ and plotted as a function of ξ. The integrals are then evaluated as the area enclosed by the curves so obtained and the coordinate axes. The procedure is then repeated for other depths and times. The results are collected in Table 5.3.

One observes that the correction for nonperiodicity is still approximately

TABLE 5.3

Calculation of transient term for Iowa Silt Loam

z (cm)	$\chi(z)$ ($°C$)	after 6 hr		after 12 hr		after 24 hr	
		$\vartheta_{co}(z,t)$	$\vartheta_{co}^{av}(z,t)$	$\vartheta_{co}(z,t)$	$\vartheta_{co}^{av}(z,t)$	$\vartheta_{co}(z,t)$	$\vartheta_{co}^{av}(z,t)$
0	(-4.65)						
0.64	-4.5	-0.09	-0.08	0	-0.04	0	-0.02
5.0	-3.6	-0.60	-0.58	-0.22	-0.33	-0.09	-0.16
10	-2.9	-0.93	-1.09	-0.43	-0.62	-0.28	-0.30
33	(0.0)						

The values of $\chi(z)$ between parentheses are extrapolated values. Two columns are given for $\vartheta_{co}(z,t)$, at each time. The first column contains the results of the calculation according to (5.3), the second column those from (5.5). A thermal diffusivity $a = 4.10 \times 10^{-3}$ cm² sec⁻¹ has been used in the calculations.

$-1\,°C$ after 6 hr at $z = 10$ cm. This must be compared with the amplitude at $z = 10$ cm which is $4.5\,°C$. After 12 hr the contribution of the correction term is $-0.4\,°C$ etc. Algebraic subtraction of the correction term from the total temperature provides the periodic part of the temperature to which the method of Fourier analysis and the theory set forth in the former chapter is applicable.

In the simplified method (equation (5.5)) the average value χ_0 was determined such that the area between the χ curve and the axes was set equal to $3D\chi_0$. This yielded $\chi_0 = -2.18\,°C$. The value $z_m = 31.8$ cm must be inserted in the arguments of the error functions. One now obtains after six hours
$$\vartheta_{co}^{av}(10.6) = -2.18\,\mathrm{erf}\,(0.533) - 1.09\,[\mathrm{erf}\,(1.159) - \mathrm{erf}\,(2.223)] = -1.09\,°C$$
which is in satisfactory agreement with the value of 0.93 obtained in the former method.

5.5. Sudden release of heat

The propagation of temperature due to a sudden release of heat at the surface of the soil is a typical nonperiodic phenomenon. An abrupt change in irradiation owing to drifting clouds, or a steep change in surface temperature at the beginning of a period of freezing weather are examples.

The temperature change is caused by an abrupt variation in heat supply at the surface. Such a variation in heat supply would occur if an instantaneous heat source or, in case of a decrease of heat supply, an instantaneous heat sink were superposed on the continuous heat supply to the surface. Solutions of the equation of heat conduction corresponding to instantaneous heat sources will now be discussed. The solution of a heat sink is obtained by substitution of a negative sign for the rate of heat supply in the equations derived for a heat source.

Consider the equation of heat conduction (4.5). A new variable $y = z/(\sqrt{t})$ will now be introduced. Since

$$\frac{\partial \vartheta}{\partial z} = \frac{d\vartheta/dy}{\sqrt{t}},$$

$$\frac{\partial^2 \vartheta}{\partial z^2} = \frac{d^2 \vartheta/dy^2}{t}$$

and

$$\frac{\partial \vartheta}{\partial t} = \frac{-\frac{1}{2}z(d\vartheta/dy)}{t\sqrt{t}}$$

the partial differential equation is transformed into an ordinary differential equation

$$\frac{a d^2 \vartheta}{dy^2} = -\frac{1}{2}y\frac{d\vartheta}{dy}. \tag{5.6}$$

Thus $\ln(d\vartheta/dy) = -\frac{1}{4}y^2/a + \text{constant}$ or $d\vartheta/dy = C_0 \exp(-\frac{1}{4}y^2/a)$ from which one concludes

$$\frac{\partial \vartheta}{\partial z} = \frac{C_0}{\sqrt{t}}\exp(-\frac{1}{4}z^2/at) \tag{5.7}$$

and

$$\frac{\partial \vartheta}{\partial t} = -\frac{zC_0}{2t\sqrt{t}}\exp(-\frac{1}{4}z^2/at). \tag{5.8}$$

The substitution $y = z/\sqrt{t}$ is often made to obtain solutions of (4.5). The differential coefficients $\partial \vartheta/\partial z$ and $\partial \vartheta/\partial t$ are also solutions of (4.5).

The physical meaning of solutions of the type of (5.7) and (5.8) will now be investigated. It will be shown that the slightly more general function

$$\vartheta(z,t) = \frac{Q}{C[4\pi a(t-\eta)]^{\frac{1}{2}}} \exp\left(\frac{-(z-\zeta)^2}{4a(t-\eta)}\right) \quad t > \eta$$
$$\vartheta(z,t) = 0 \qquad\qquad\qquad\qquad\qquad\qquad t \leqslant \eta \tag{5.9}$$

represents the increase of the temperature in a medium extending to infinity for positive and for negative z due to a sudden release of heat in the plane $z = \zeta$ and at the instant $t = \eta$. The quantity of heat released is Q cal cm^{-2}. If $\zeta = 0$ and $\eta = 0$ the function $\vartheta(z,t)$ is the temperature in a soil which was at zero temperature at all depths before $t = 0$ and at whose surface Q cal cm^{-2} are released at $t = 0$. Of these Q cal cm^{-2} one half, thus $\frac{1}{2}Q$ cal cm^{-2}, flows towards the soil i.e. in the direction of positive z values. The other half flows in the direction of negative z values. The symbols C, a, z, t in (5.9) have the normal meaning; Q, η and ζ are constants and t must be greater than η. By definition $\vartheta(z,t) = 0$ for negative values of $t - \eta$.*

An amount of heat from this source equal to $C\vartheta(z,t)\mathrm{d}z$ is present in a slice of the medium of one cm^2 horizontal area and of thickness $\mathrm{d}z$ at the instant t. As changes of phase or chemical reactions are excluded, the total quantity of heat in a bar of one cm^2 horizontal cross section and extending to infinity in both vertical directions must always be equal to Q after $t = \eta$.

Introducing the new variable $x = (z - \zeta)[4a(t - \eta)]^{-\frac{1}{2}}$, thus $\mathrm{d}x = \mathrm{d}z[4a(t - \eta)]^{-\frac{1}{2}}$ in (5.9) and integrating gives the result

$$\int_{-\infty}^{+\infty} C\vartheta(z,t)\mathrm{d}z = \frac{Q}{\sqrt{\pi}} \int_{-\infty}^{+\infty} \mathrm{e}^{-x^2} \mathrm{d}x = Q. \tag{5.10}$$

The integral is equal to Q for positive values of $t - \eta$, whereas it is zero for negative $t - \eta$.

As the heat spreads from the layer $z = \zeta$ the amount of heat, present in the portion of the bar between any two given planes z_1 and z_2, varies with time.

Let us in particular consider a slice of one cm^2 horizontal area bounded by the planes $z = \zeta - \frac{1}{2}d$ and $z = \zeta + \frac{1}{2}d$. The plane $z = \zeta$ is situated midway between. One now obtains for the amount of heat in the slice at time t

$$\int_{z=\zeta-\frac{1}{2}d}^{z=\zeta+\frac{1}{2}d} C\vartheta(z,t)\mathrm{d}z = Q\,\mathrm{erf}\left(\frac{d}{2[4a(t-\eta)]^{\frac{1}{2}}}\right). \tag{5.11}$$

---

* The reader is advised to verify that (5.9) is a solution of (4.5) by carrying out the differentiations in respect to z and to t and substituting the results in (4.5). The solution is discussed in the textbooks of mathematical physics and in Carslaw – Jaeger's book. An elucidating discussion was also given by RAYLEIGH [1911].

The same substitutions have been used as in (5.10). If t approaches η the erf function approaches 1 whatever the positive value of d. This means that all heat was concentrated in the immediate neighborhood of the plane $z = \zeta$ at t very close to η. Hereafter the heat spreads over the entire soil and thus after a long lapse of time the heat content of the finite bar must become small. It approaches 0 for infinite t. This conclusion follows also from (5.11).

Thus the function in (5.9) has the characteristic properties of a propagation of an impulse of heat from an instantaneous source. It can rigorously be shown that it is actually the desired solution*. In the homogeneous medium half of the heat flows into the medium above the plane and half flows into the medium below it. Thus if, in a soil bounded by a surface $z = 0$, Q cal cm^{-2} penetrate into the soil, $2Q$ must be inserted in (5.9) and $\zeta = 0$. One then obtains equation 5.11a.

$$\vartheta(z,t) = \frac{2Q}{C[4\pi a(t-\eta)]^{\frac{1}{2}}} \exp\left(\frac{-z^2}{4a(t-\eta)}\right) \quad \begin{matrix} t > \eta \\ z \geqslant 0 \end{matrix}$$

$$\vartheta(z,t) = 0 \quad \begin{matrix} t \leqslant \eta \\ z \geqslant 0. \end{matrix} \tag{5.11a}$$

In all cases where the plane $z = \zeta$ acts as a heat sink a negative value must be inserted for Q.

5.6. Gradual release of heat

A gradual release of heat can be treated mathematically as a continuous succession of individual infinitesimal impulses. The total rise in temperature is a superposition of the individual infinitesimal temperature rises caused by the individual infinitesimal impulses. Let $H(\eta)d\eta$ be the infinitesimal amount of heat generated per unit area in the plane $z = \zeta$ in the interval of time η to $\eta + d\eta$ then the resulting infinitesimal temperature rise is given by equation (5.9) if $Q = H(\eta)d\eta$ is substituted. The total temperature rise is obtained by integration

$$\vartheta(z,t) = \frac{1}{C\sqrt{\pi}} \int_{t_0}^{t} H(\eta)[4a(t-\eta)]^{-\frac{1}{2}} \exp\left(\frac{-(z-\zeta)^2}{4a(t-\eta)}\right) d\eta. \quad t > t_0 \tag{5.12}$$

It is assumed that $H(\eta) = 0$ for $\eta < t_0$, i.e. heat generation starts at the

---

* Note that the initial temperature distribution together with the boundary condition do not determine the solution of the equation of heat conduction if heat is generated or absorbed.

time t_0. If it ends at t_1 a zero value must be inserted for $H(\eta)$ from t_1 on.

By way of example $\vartheta(z,t)$ will be calculated assuming constant $H(\eta) = H_0$. The same substitutions as before, $x = (z - \zeta)[4a(t - \eta)]^{-\frac{1}{2}}$ and $dx = 2a(z - \zeta)[4a(t - \eta)]^{-\frac{3}{2}}d\eta$, lead to

$$\vartheta(z,t) = \frac{H_0}{C\sqrt{\pi}} \int_{(z-\xi)/[4a(t-t_0)]^{\frac{1}{2}}}^{\infty} \frac{z - \zeta}{2ax^2} e^{-x^2} dx, \tag{5.13}$$

which after some reduction and recalling $x^{-2}dx = -dx^{-1}$ and $aC = \lambda$ becomes

$$\vartheta(z,t) = \frac{H_0}{2\lambda} \left\{ \frac{[4a(t - t_0)]^{\frac{1}{2}}}{\pi^{\frac{1}{2}}} \exp\left[\frac{-(z-\zeta)^2}{4a(t - t_0)}\right] - (z - \zeta) \operatorname{erfc}\left[\frac{z - \zeta}{[4a(t - t_0)]^{\frac{1}{2}}}\right] \right\}. \tag{5.14}$$

The notation $\operatorname{erfc} x$ is used to denote $(1 - \operatorname{erf} x)$.

In its application to a soil equation (5.14) is used for a semi-infinite medium. The heat flux density in a downward direction is then $\frac{1}{2}H_0$ since in equation (5.14) H_0 is the heat generated per unit of area and per unit of time in the plane $z = \zeta$ of the medium which extends to infinity in both directions. Therefore, if equation (5.14) is used to calculate the temperature in a soil at whose surface the heat flux density $H_{so} = H_0$ one must multiply the right hand side with a factor 2. When this is done and $\zeta = 0$ is substituted one obtains for a soil

$$\vartheta(z,t) = 0; \quad H_{so} = 0 \quad \text{at} \quad z = 0 \quad \text{for} \quad t \leqslant t_0.$$

$$\vartheta(z,t) = \frac{H_0}{\lambda} \left\{ \frac{[4a(t - t_0)]^{\frac{1}{2}}}{\pi^{\frac{1}{2}}} \exp\left[\frac{-z^2}{4a(t - t_0)}\right] - z \operatorname{erfc}\left[\frac{z}{[4a(t - t_0)]^{\frac{1}{2}}}\right] \right\}. \tag{5.14a}$$

and $H_{so} = H_0$ at $z = 0$ for $t > t_0$.

This equation is an approximate expression of the temperature variation due to the penetration of heat into the soil during a short period of sunshine on a cloudy day if the heat flux density at the soil surface can be considered as constant during that period. Since H_0 does not increase instantly at the beginning of the sunny period, (5.14) is an approximation. The effect of the gradual increase becomes less important the greater the distance in time since the change in H_0 took place. Equation (5.14) and other equations will be discussed in respect to an actual weather situation in section 5.9.

Inserting $z = 0$ in (5.14a) leads to

$$\vartheta(0,t) = \frac{H_0 [4a(t - t_0)]^{\frac{1}{2}}}{\lambda \pi^{\frac{1}{2}}} \qquad t > t_0 \tag{5.15}$$

for the temperature at the soil surface.

A period of sunshine which is abruptly ended at the instant t_1 can be approximated by a heat impulse of finite duration. In (5.12) one has then $H(\eta) = 0$ except in the interval of time t_0 to t_1 when it is constant and equal to $2H_0$. The limit of integration in (5.12) now becomes t_1 for $t > t_1$ but it stays t for $t < t_1$. Performing the same substitutions as before one is led to (5.14a) if $t < t_1$.

From

$$H(\eta) = 0 \quad ; \quad \zeta = 0 \text{ in equation (5.12) for } t \leqslant t_0$$
$$H(\eta) = 2H_0; \quad \zeta = 0 \text{ in equation (5.12) for } t_0 < t < t_1$$
$$H(\eta) = 0 \quad ; \quad \zeta = 0 \text{ in equation (5.12) for } t \geqslant t_1$$

one obtains in this way

$$\vartheta(z,t) = 0 \qquad t \leqslant t_0$$

$$\vartheta(z,t) = \text{ equation (5.14a)} \qquad t_0 < t < t_1$$

$$\vartheta(z,t) = \frac{H_0}{\lambda} \left\{ \frac{[4a(t-t_0)]^{\frac{1}{2}}}{\pi^{\frac{1}{2}}} \exp\left[\frac{-z^2}{4a(t-t_0)} \right] - z \operatorname{erfc}\left[\frac{z}{[4a(t-t_0)]^{\frac{1}{2}}} \right] \right\}$$
$$- \frac{H_0}{\lambda} \left\{ \frac{[4a(t-t_1)]^{\frac{1}{2}}}{\pi^{\frac{1}{2}}} \exp\left[\frac{-z^2}{4a(t-t_1)} \right] - z \operatorname{erfc}\left[\frac{z}{[4a(t-t_1)]^{\frac{1}{2}}} \right] \right\} \qquad t \geqslant t_1$$
$$(5.14b)$$

when at $z = 0$ $H_{so} = 0$ for $t < t_0$ and $t \geqslant t_1$ and
$$H_{so} = H_0 \text{ for } t_0 < t < t_1.$$

Equation (5.15) was used (BRUNT [1932]) to calculate the drop in temperature after sunset on a clear still night. A negative value of H_0 must then be used corresponding to a constant heat "sink" at the surface i.e. a constant rate of heat removal. The problem is of importance for the prediction of night frosts. A more elaborate calculation of surface temperature in connection with night frost prediction has been given by GROEN [1947].

A better fit of the theoretical curves can be obtained by taking the time dependence of $H(\eta)$ into account. If $H(\eta)$ is a linear or an exponential function of the time, equation (5.13) can still be integrated analytically. If $H(\eta)$ is only known as a curve from the record of solar radiation a numerical or graphical integration must be carried out. This will, however, not be discussed here as a much simpler method exists to calculate heat flux density and thermal diffusivity from temperature records of heat impulses. This method which uses the so-called Laplace transformation is set forth in section 5.9.

In the decomposition of organic matter heat is generated over an entire range of depths. In the mathematical treatment H must now be considered as a function of both variables η and ζ. The quantity of heat generated per unit of horizontal area in the interval of time η to $\eta + d\eta$ and between the layers ζ and $\zeta + d\zeta$ must be inserted instead of $H(\eta)d\eta$ in (5.13) and the right hand side of that equation integrated in respect to $d\zeta$ from $\zeta = 0$ to $\zeta = \infty$.

5.7. Initial and boundary conditions given

The equation of heat conduction is linear in ϑ. Such an equation has the pecularity that any linear combination of solutions is itself also a solution. This fact will now be used to construct a solution which satisfies given boundary and initial conditions as the sum of two solutions each of a less general nature. Writing $\vartheta = {}^{b}\vartheta + {}^{i}\vartheta$ one determines ${}^{b}\vartheta$ such that it satisfies the given boundary condition and is equal to zero for $t = 0$ at all depths. The function ${}^{i}\vartheta$ takes the prescribed initial values and is zero at the upper boundary. For infinite depth ${}^{b}\vartheta = 0$ and ${}^{i}\vartheta = \vartheta_{a}$ at all times.

Let ${}^{b}\vartheta(d,t)$ be the temperature at the upper boundary $z = d$. It can be shown that

$$
{}^{b}\vartheta(z,t) = \int_{0}^{t} {}^{b}\vartheta(d,\eta)\Big(\frac{\partial}{\partial t}\,{}^{b1}\vartheta(z-d, t-\eta)\Big)\, d\eta, \tag{5.16}
$$

in which ${}^{b1}\vartheta(z,t)$ is the temperature in the soil for zero initial temperature if the plane $z = 0$ is kept at unit temperature from $t = 0$ on (DUHAMEL [1833]; vide CARSLAW-JAEGER [1950]). The theorem holds for $z \geqslant d$.*

Recalling that $\mathrm{erf}\,[z/2\sqrt{(at)}]$ is a solution of the equation of heat conduction

---

* The physical meaning of (5.16) can be clarified by considering a stepwise variation of the temperature at $z = d$ as follows: in the short interval of time η to $\eta + d\eta$ the temperature ${}^{b}\vartheta(d,\eta)$ may be considered as constant.

It changes into ${}^{b}\vartheta(d, \eta + d\eta)$ at the end of the interval. This change is equivalent to the superposition of three temperature impulses: first a sudden rise from zero to ${}^{b}\vartheta(d,\eta)$ at $t = \eta$ and a constant temperature at $z = d$ from then on, secondly a temperature drop $- {}^{b}\vartheta(d,\eta)$ at $t = \eta + d\eta$ which annihilates the rise at $t = \eta$ for all times $t > \eta + d\eta$, and thirdly the rise from zero to ${}^{b}\vartheta(d, \eta + d\eta)$.

The contribution of the first two impulses to the soil temperature at an arbitrary instant of time t later than $\eta + d\eta$ is

$$
{}^{b}\vartheta(d,\eta)\,{}^{b-1}\vartheta(z, t-\eta) - {}^{b}\vartheta(d,\eta)\,{}^{b1}\vartheta(z, t-\eta-d\eta) = {}^{b}\vartheta(d,\eta)\Big(\frac{\partial}{\partial t}\,{}^{b1}\vartheta(z, t-\eta)\Big)\, d\eta.
$$

The third impulse occurs at the end of the interval. It is the boundary temperature for the next interval of time. Summation of the contribution over all intervals of time during the period $0 < \eta < t$ leads to (5.13).

and that $\text{erf}(0) = 0$ and $\text{erf}(\infty) = 1$ it is easy to see that

$$^{b1}\vartheta(z,t) = 1 - \text{erf}\left(\frac{z}{2\sqrt{(at)}}\right), \tag{5.17}$$

from which follows

$$\frac{\partial}{\partial t}\, ^{b1}\vartheta(z,t) = \frac{z}{2\sqrt{(\pi at^3)}}\exp\left(-\frac{z^2}{4at}\right). \tag{5.18}$$

The function $^{i}\vartheta$ is derived from (5.9) in which $\eta = 0$; $Q(\zeta)\mathrm{d}\zeta$ is substituted for Q and the righthand side is integrated from d to ∞ in respect to ζ. The physical interpretation of this procedure is that an increase in temperature is calculated which is caused by heat sources $Q(\zeta)\mathrm{d}\zeta$ spread over the entire soil.

Consider now the function

$$f(z,t) = \frac{1}{C\sqrt{(4\pi at)}}\int_d^\infty Q(\zeta)\exp\left(-\frac{(z-\zeta)^2}{4at}\right)\mathrm{d}\zeta. \tag{5.19}$$

The exponential function is close to zero if t is small and z differs from ζ. Although the factor $1/\sqrt{(4at)}$ becomes infinite for t approaching zero the product of this factor and the exponential still approaches zero as is shown in textbooks on analysis.

Thus for very small t the function $f(z,t)$ vanishes at all depths except in the immediate neighborhood of the layer where $z = \zeta$. Instead of integrating between the limits d to ∞ the integration interval can be extended from $-\infty$ to $+\infty$ as the contribution of the integration from $-\infty$ to d vanishes for t approaching zero. Further $Q(z)$ may be written for $Q(\zeta)$ and

$$\lim_{t=0} f(z,t) = \frac{Q(z)}{C\sqrt{(4\pi at)}}\int_{-\infty}^{+\infty}\exp\left(-\frac{(z-\zeta)^2}{4at}\right)\mathrm{d}\zeta$$

$$= \frac{Q(z)}{C\sqrt{(4\pi at)}}\int_{-\infty}^{+\infty}\exp\left\{-\xi^2\right\}\mathrm{d}\xi = \frac{Q(z)}{C}. \tag{5.20}$$

The function $f(z,t)$ apparently satisfies the initial conditions if $Q(z) = C^{i}\vartheta(z,0)$ but it does not satisfy the condition imposed on $^{i}\vartheta(z,t)$ that $^{i}\vartheta(d,t) = 0$ for all positive values of t. It is, therefore, necessary to subtract a solution of the equation of heat conduction which is equal to $f(d,t)$ for $z = d$ and which does not contribute to the initial temperature. Doing this one obtains

$$^{i}\vartheta(z,t) = \frac{1}{C\sqrt{(4\pi at)}}\left[\int_d^\infty Q(\zeta)\left\{\exp\left[-\frac{(z-\zeta)^2}{4at}\right] - \exp\left[-\frac{(z+\zeta-2d)^2}{4at}\right]\right\}\mathrm{d}\zeta\right]. \tag{5.21}$$

The correction for nonperiodicity in section 5.2 is a special application of (5.18).

5.8. Use of Laplace transforms

In the preceeding sections soil temperature has been expressed as a function of depth and of time. Often, however, the variation of time of ϑ is not of direct interest for the problem under consideration and all that is needed to solve a number of important problems is the knowledge of an average value of ϑ during a certain interval of time.

The thermal properties of a soil, a, λ, C, for instance, can in principle be determined from any function of ϑ in which they occur as a parameter. In such cases it is not necessary to perform the laborious calculations in section 5.7 by which ϑ is obtained as a function of z and of t.

It will be shown that the Laplace transform of ϑ is a very convenient aid in the study of soils and as will be discussed in chapter 8 also in the study of the air near the ground. To avoid misunderstanding it may be pointed out that an unconventional use of the Laplace transform is made here. Instead of using it as an intermediate step in obtaining the solution $\vartheta(z,t)$ of the equation of heat conduction as is usually done, the Laplace transform will now be used *instead* of $\vartheta(z,t)$ and of $H(z,t)$.

The Laplace transform $\mathscr{L}\{f(z,t)\}$ of a function $f(z,t)$ is defined by the relationship

$$\mathscr{L}\{f(z,t)\} = \int_0^\infty f(z,t)\, \mathrm{e}^{-pt} \mathrm{d}t. \tag{5.22}$$

$\mathscr{L}\{f(z,t)\}$ is a function of the variables z and p. The Laplace transformation is treated in Carslaw-Jaeger's book and in many textbooks on theoretical physics or in special monographs (e.g. DOETSCH [1943]). For the present application three fundamental theorems are important. They are*

(i) $$\mathscr{L}\left\{\frac{\partial^n}{\partial z^n} f(z,t)\right\} = \frac{\partial^n}{\partial z^n} \mathscr{L}\{f(z,t)\} \tag{5.23}$$

---

* Equation (5.23) and (5.24) follow directly from (5.22) provided that $f(z,t)\mathrm{e}^{-pt}$ approaches zero sufficiently rapidly for large values of t. When 5.24 is applied to the soil temperature $\vartheta(z,t)$, $f(z,0)$ is the initial temperature at depth z. The third theorem, equation (5.25), is also a consequence of (5.22). If $^b\vartheta(d,t)$ is substituted for $f_1(z,\eta)$ and $\partial\,[^{b1}\vartheta(z-d,t)]/\partial t$ for $f_2(x,t)$ one obtains the integral appearing on the righthand side of (5.16). Thus Duhamel's theorem (5.16) expressed in Laplace transforms becomes

$$\mathscr{L}\{^b\vartheta(z-d,t)\} = \mathscr{L}\{^b\vartheta(d,t)\}\ \mathscr{L}\left\{\frac{\partial}{\partial t}\ ^{b1}\vartheta(z-d,t)\right\}. \tag{5.26}$$

(ii) $$\mathscr{L}\left\{\frac{\partial}{\partial t}f(z,t)\right\} = p\mathscr{L}\left\{f(z,t)\right\} - f(z,0) \qquad (5.24)$$

(iii) $\mathscr{L}\left\{f_1(z,t)\right\}\mathscr{L}\left\{f_2(x,t)\right\} = \mathscr{L}\left\{\int_0^t f_1(z,\eta)f_2(x,t-\eta)\,\mathrm{d}\eta\right\}$

$$= \mathscr{L}\left\{\int_0^t f_1(z,t-\eta)f(z,\eta)\,\mathrm{d}\eta\right\}. \qquad (5.25)$$

The Laplace transform of the equation of heat conduction

$$\mathscr{L}\left\{a\frac{\partial^2\vartheta}{\partial z^2} - \frac{\partial\vartheta}{\partial t}\right\} = \mathscr{L}\left\{a\frac{\partial^2\vartheta}{\partial z^2}\right\} - \mathscr{L}\left\{\frac{\partial\vartheta}{\partial t}\right\} = 0$$

can be transformed into a differential equation for the Laplace transform of the temperature using (5.23) and (5.24).

$$a\frac{\mathrm{d}^2}{\mathrm{d}z^2}\mathscr{L}\left\{\vartheta(z,t)\right\} - p\mathscr{L}\left\{\vartheta(z,t)\right\} + \vartheta(z,0) = 0. \qquad (5.27)$$

This is an ordinary differential equation as the differentiation in respect to the time has been replaced by a multiplication by p. A constant initial value of the temperature will be assumed. Then $\vartheta(z,0) = 0$ if $\vartheta(z,t)$ from now on denotes the difference of the temperature at the time t and the initial temperature at the time t and the initial temperature.
Equation (5.27) is solved by

$$\mathscr{L}\left\{\vartheta(z,t)\right\} = \text{const. } \exp\left[-z\sqrt{(p/a)}\right]. \qquad (5.28)$$

Only the negative sign of the root $\pm\sqrt{(p/a)}$ must be retained since $\mathscr{L}\left\{\vartheta(z,t)\right\}$ as well as $\vartheta(z,t)$ must approach zero for infinite z at all times (equation (5.22)).*

The thermal diffusivity of a soil can directly be determined from (5.28) if temperature records at two different depths z_1 and z_2 are available. The Laplace transforms of the temperature records ${}^b\vartheta(z_1,t)$ and ${}^b\vartheta(z_2,t)$ are obtained for a suitably chosen value of p by multiplication of the temperature

---

* The constant in (5.28) is a function of p. Consider for instance, the Laplace transform of the temperature which is unity at a given level $z = d$. This function will be denoted as ${}^{b1}\vartheta(z-d,t)$. Inserting ${}^{b1}\vartheta(0,t) = 1$ for $f(0,t)$ in (5.22) one obtains $\mathscr{L}\{1\} = 1/p$. Thus $\mathscr{L}\{{}^1\vartheta(z-d,t)\}$ reduces to $1/p$ for $z = d$ and in this case

$$\mathscr{L}\left\{{}^{b1}\vartheta((z-d),t)\right\} = \frac{\exp[-(z-d)\sqrt{(p/a)}]}{p}. \qquad (5.29)$$

According to (5.24) one has

$$\mathscr{L}\left\{\frac{\partial}{\partial t}{}^{b1}\vartheta((z-d),t)\right\} = \exp\left[-(z-d)\sqrt{(p/a)}\right] \qquad (5.30)$$

for the Laplace transform of the second factor in the integrand in Duhamel's theorem (5.16).

by exp $(-pt)$ and performing a numerical or graphical integration. The ratio of the two integrals equals $\exp[-(z_1 - z_2)\sqrt{(p/a)}]$ from which a can be calculated. The relation between the recorded temperature and its Laplace transform is shown in Fig. 5.1.

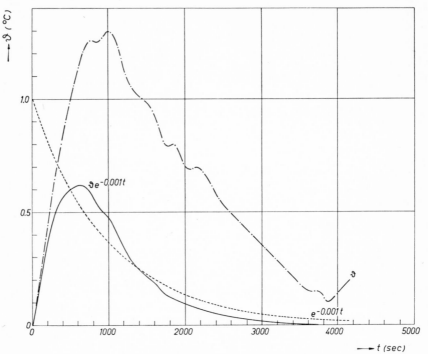

Fig. 5.1. Recorded temperature and its Laplace transform.
—·—·— Recorded temperature impulse at 1 cm depth (ϑ)
----- Exponential function for $p = 0.001$
———— Product of these two curves.
The area under the last curve gives the Laplace transform for $p = 0.0001$.

Any positive (nonzero) value of p may in principle be chosen. If p is large $\vartheta(z,t)\exp(-pt)$ approaches zero rapidly and a part of the temperature record, i.e. when pt is large, does not contribute to the Laplace integral. A small value of p results in an integral to which also remote values of the temperature have contributed. Thus the choice of a certain value of p implies the introduction of a "weight factor" to the recorded temperature data. This weight factor depends on the lapse of time since the beginning of the phenomenon studied.

The method of using Laplace transforms for the determination of a property of the medium in which the temperature or some other quantity is propagated is not restricted to the ordinary equation of heat conduction. It can be applied to linear partial differential equations in general and will be used in the present text later for the determination of the apparent heat conductivity of air.

5.9. Application to soils

The theory given in sections 5.6, 5.7 and 5.8 will now be applied to actual soils. Records of soil temperature on a cloudy day with short periods of bright sunshine are shown in Fig. 5.2. The soil was a light sandy clay

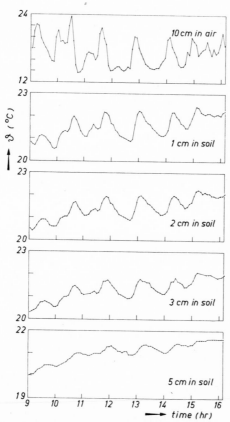

Fig. 5.2. Soil temperature on a cloudy day with periods of bright sunshine
(22 July 1958, Wageningen).

covered by short grass. The alternation of clouds and sunshine caused temperature variations which were practically limited to the upper 10 cm of the soil. This infers that the thermal diffusivity of a shallow layer determines the penetration of these temperature variations although the formulas are valid for an infinite soil. The theory may also be applied to an inhomogeneous soil if only the upper layer to which the temperature variations are practically limited is fairly homogeneous.

First the method of Laplace transforms will be considered. Equation (5.28) expresses the Laplace transform of the temperature as a function of depth if the soil was at a homogeneous initial temperature. Even if this condition is not fulfilled, (5.28) may be applied to the temperature variations caused by the short period fluctuations of the heat flux density. Indeed, since the equation of heat conduction is a linear equation, temperature variations resulting from different causes are simply superposed. The course which the temperature would have taken if the short period variations had not occurred may, therefore, be considered as the zero level from which $\vartheta(z, t)$ is measured. The interpolated course of the "background" temperature at each depth must be substracted from the recorded temperature. Equation (5.28) can then be applied to the temperature differences.

Let us consider the temperature rise commencing at 12 hr 45. In this case

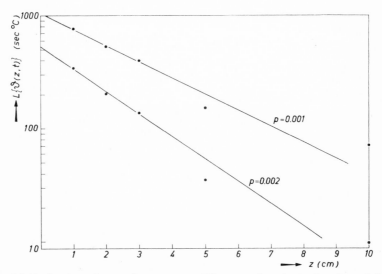

Fig. 5.3. Laplace transforms of temperature differences plotted as a function of depth (12 hr 45 m, 22 July 1958, Wageningen). According to eq. (5.28) ln $[\mathscr{L}\{\vartheta(z,t)\}]$ is a linear function of z. The slope of the straight is equal to $\sqrt{(p/a)}$.

the interpolation of the background temperature presented little difficulty. The thermal diffusivity was determined from the slope of the straight line which was obtained by plotting $\log \mathscr{L}\{\vartheta(z,t)\}$ as a function of z. A value $a = 0.0092 \text{ cm}^2 \text{ sec}^{-1}$ was found for a value of $p = 0.001 \text{ sec}^{-1}$ and $a = 0.0095$ for $p = 0.002$ (Fig. 5.3).

The temperature as a function of the time at any arbitrary depth can be calculated from the recorded temperature at a shallower depth by (5.16). This calculation was performed for $z = 2$ cm and $z = 3$ cm. The rise in temperature at $z = d = 1$ cm was taken as $^{b}\vartheta(d,\eta)$ in (5.16). Selecting a value of t and one of the depths 2 or 3 cm, the function $\partial[^{b1}\vartheta(z - d, t - \eta)]/\partial t$ in (5.18) was calculated for a series of values of η. The variable η is in the range 0 to t sec. The individual values of the function in (5.19) are then multiplied by $^{b}\vartheta(d,\eta)$ corresponding to the same value of η. Numerical integration of the resulting product gives $^{b}\vartheta(z,t)$. This procedure was carried out for a number of t values and both depths 2 and 3 cm. The results are shown in Fig. 5.4.

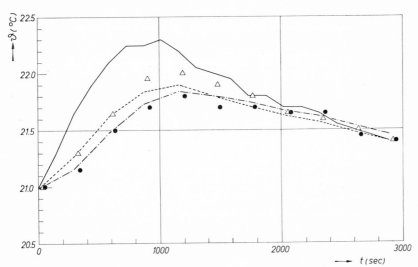

Fig. 5.4. Comparison of measured and calculated soil temperatures (equation (5.16)) for the impulse of July 22, 1958 at Wageningen. The zero point of the time scale corresponds to 12 hr 45 m.

———————— recorded temperature at 1 cm depth.

△   recorded temperature at 2 cm depth.

●   recorded temperature at 3 cm depth.

------------ calculated temperature at 2 cm depth with $a = 9.4 \times 10^{-3} \text{ cm}^2 \text{ sec}^{-1}$.

—·—·—— calculated temperature at 3 cm depth with $a = 9.4 \times 10^{-3} \text{ cm}^2 \text{ sec}^{-1}$.

This method has also been used to determine the thermal diffusivity. Different a-values must then be successively inserted in (5.18) and the numerical integrations are performed for each of these a-values. The curve which gives the best fit to the recorded temperature corresponds to the correct value of a. The procedure is laborious. It possesses the same advantage as the method of Laplace transforms as only the validity of the equation of heat conduction (4.5) is assumed. No assumptions are made concerning the boundary condition $^b\vartheta(d,\eta)$ in (5.18).

5.10 Determination of λ and C

As an example of the use of the study of heat impulses and the use of Laplace transforms we shall now discuss the determination of λ and C in the upper soil layer.

The problem is of a high practical value. The thermal constants of the upper few cm of a soil are in general considerably different from those of the deeper soil layers owing to a different structure, composition (organic matter) and water content. In studies of the heat balance of the distribution of heat between air and soil, of evaporation from a soil etc., a knowledge of the properties of the soil very near the surface is essential.

The volumetric heat capacity of a given soil is a direct measure of the water content (cf. chapter 7) and, therefore, the method which will now be described is also important in the study of water movement in unsaturated soils. The method is not limited to shallow soil layers, but can also be applied to deeper layers and to soil samples studied in the laboratory.

Let us consider (5.12) in which we now substitute $\zeta = 0$ and $H(\eta) = 2H_{so}(\eta)$, with H_{so} the heat flux density towards the soil (positive z direction).

According to (5.25) the Laplace transform of the temperature at a depth z can be written as

$$\mathscr{L}\left\{\vartheta(z,t)\right\} = \mathscr{L}\left\{H_{so}(t)\right\} \cdot \frac{1}{\lambda}\sqrt{\frac{a}{p}} \cdot \exp\left(-z\sqrt{\frac{p}{a}}\right).$$

The factor by which $\mathscr{L}\left\{H_{so}(t)\right\}$ is multiplied is the Laplace transform of the factor by which $\frac{1}{2}H(\eta)$ is multiplied in (5.12) (cf. DOETSCH [1943]). As has been done in the preceding example $\vartheta(z,t)$ will be used to denote the temperature *differences* caused by, in this case, an intentional change of H_{so} from $t = 0$ to $t = t_1$. Equation (5.12), which was derived for a zero initial temperature of the medium is then applicable to these temperature differences. The course of the temperature at the depth z in the absence of the intentional change of the heat flux density is now the zero point of the temperature variation at z.

Thermocouples were rigidly mounted together on a plastic frame and by the aid of a mould were pressed into sand to the depths of 0.50, 0.70, 1.00, 1.70 and 2.5 cm. The horizontal circular annulus of the frame (Fig. 5.5) rested on the sand surface. A heat flux plate was placed on that annulus and irradiated homogeneously by a 250 watt incandescant lamp. The heat flux plate was of the commercial type. It consisted of a thin disc of a plastic material with thermowelds on both faces. The records of the resulting temperature at the four depths and the heat flux are shown in Fig. 5.5 in which also a sketch of the frame with the thermocouples is given.

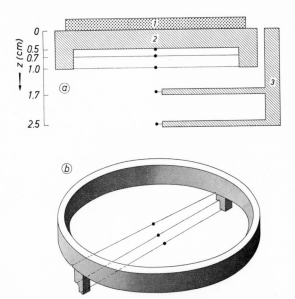

Fig. 5.5. Device for measuring λ and C of the upper soil layer (true size).

a. Relative positions of heat flux plate (1), frame for upper thermocouples (2) and frame for somewhat lower placed thermocouples (3).

b. Frame (2 of a) with thermowelds at 0.5, 0.7 and 1.0 cms depths.

It follows from the records that the temperature variation did not penetrate farther than approximately 2.5 cm. Therefore, an average λ and a of the layer situated above 2.5 cm is found from the evaluation of the records.

The depth to which the temperature variation penetrates can be varied by varying the duration of the irradiation. This provides a means of determining also λ and a of deeper layers.

The Laplace transforms of $\vartheta(z,t)$ and $H_{so}(t)$ were calculated numerically using different values of p.

The resulting $\mathscr{L}\{\vartheta(z,t)\}$ was plotted as a function of z on semilogarithmic paper. Since

$$\ln \mathscr{L}\{\vartheta(z,t)\} = \ln\left[\mathscr{L}\{H_{so}(t)\} \cdot \frac{1}{\lambda}\sqrt{\left(\frac{a}{p}\right)}\right] - z\sqrt{\left(\frac{p}{a}\right)}$$

a straight line should be obtained from whose slope $-\sqrt{(p/a)}$ the thermal diffusivity a can be calculated. The intersection of the line with vertical axis $z = 0$ occurs at the value

$$\ln\left[\mathscr{L}\{H_{so}(t)\} \cdot \frac{1}{\lambda}\sqrt{\left(\frac{a}{p}\right)}\right].$$

Thus λ can be calculated as well and $C = \lambda/a$ is now also known. The graphs of the Laplace transforms are shown in Fig. 5.6.

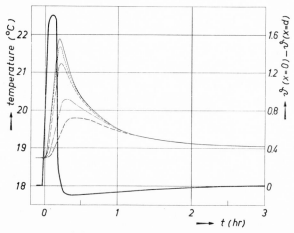

Fig. 5.6. Temperature records in sand and record of $\vartheta_{(x=0)} - \vartheta_{(x=d)}$ of the heat flux plate. The heavy full drawn line gives $\vartheta_{(x=0)} - \vartheta_{(x=d)}$ (right-hand scale). The other curves represent the temperature at depths 0.5, 0.7, 1.0, 1.7 and 2.5 cm in this order. The upper curve corresponds to 0.5 cm.

From the two curves an average value of $a = 0.00324$ cm^2 sec^{-1} and a $\lambda = 0.000745$ cal cm^{-1} sec^{-1} °C^{-1} is obtained resulting in $C = 0.233$ for the dry sand. Once λ is known, one can calculate the heat flux density under natural conditions $H_{so} = -\lambda(\partial\vartheta/\partial z)$ by determining $\partial\vartheta(z,t)/\partial z$ from the temperature curves in the absence of the heat flux plate.

The use of the heat flux plate needs some special consideration. The meters are calibrated directly in heat flux units, but this calibration refers to stationary flow and cannot be used in these experiments. The most convenient method to calculate $\mathscr{L}\{H_{so}(t)\}$ is again by the use of Laplace transforms.

Let d be the thickness of the heat flux plate. The solution of (5.27) applicable to the heat flux plate is

$$\mathscr{L}\{\vartheta(x,t)\} = A \exp[- x\sqrt{(p/a)}] + B\exp[+ x\sqrt{(p/a)}].$$

Now both signs of the root $\pm\sqrt{(p/a)}$ must be retained, as the medium of the plate does not extend to infinity. The symbol x has been used for the depth in the plate to avoid confusion with the soil, $x = 0$ at the upper face of the plate and $x = d$ at the lower face in contact with the sand. In this case $d = 0.325$ cm, $\lambda = 0.000555$ cal cm^{-1} sec^{-1} $°$C^{-1}, $C = 0.560$ cal cm^{-3} $°$C^{-1} thus $\gamma = \sqrt{(p/a)}$ $= \sqrt{(pC/\lambda)} = 1.00399$ for $p = 0.001$ and $\gamma = 1.41986$ for $p = 0.002$.

The heat flux plate is used in such a way that the temperature difference of the two faces $x = 0$ and $x = d$ is recorded. Hence the Laplace transform of the recorded curve is

$$\mathscr{L}\{\vartheta(x = 0,t)\} - \mathscr{L}\{\vartheta(x = d,t)\} = A(1 - e^{-\gamma d}) + B(1 - e^{\gamma d})$$

which is known by numerical integration.

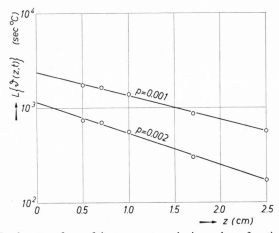

Fig. 5.7. Laplace transform of the temperature rise in sand as a function of depth

The Laplace integral of the temperature at $x = d$ is equal to $\mathscr{L}\{\vartheta(z = 0,t)\}$ which is found as the intersection of the straight lines in figure 5.7 with the vertical axis. Therefore, one also knows

$$\mathscr{L}\{\vartheta(x = d,t)\} = \mathscr{L}\{\vartheta(z = 0,t)\} = A e^{-\gamma d} + B e^{\gamma d}.$$

The constants A and B can now be calculated. In this case $A = 2874.40$, $B = 231.54$ with $p = 0.001$ and $A = 1614.75$, $B = 83.31$ with $p = 0.002$. The Laplace transform of the heat flux density at $x = d$, H_{so}, is now easily calculated

$$\mathscr{L}\{H_{so}(t)\} = -\lambda \mathscr{L}\{\partial \vartheta(x,t)/\partial x\}_{x=d}$$
$$= -\lambda \gamma [-A e^{-\gamma d} + B e^{\gamma d}]$$

in which λ refers to the heat flux plate.

A detailed discussion of the use of Laplace transforms in the study of heat propagation in the air and in the soil near the earth's surface has been given by VAN WIJK and BRUIJN [1963].

5.11. Penetration of frost, thawing

Penetration of frost and the opposite process, thawing of a soil, are complicated cases of heat transmission. At the boundary solid-liquid, latent heat of fusion is released or absorbed respectively and, further, this boundary is shifted in course of time. An additional complication may arise from the increase in volume of water when it turns into ice causing phenomena of frost heaving.

Empirical formulas are used to calculate the depth to which the soil freezes as a function of time. So, for instance, The Corps of Engineers [1949] gives

$$x = \left[\frac{24 KF}{L + C(V_0 - 32 + F/2T)}\right]^{\frac{1}{2}}, \tag{5.31}$$

in which

x = depth of frost penetration in feet,
K = thermal conductivity in B.T.U. ft^{-1} °F^{-1} hr^{-1},
F = freezing index (days × frost in °F),
L = average latent heat in B.T.U. ft^{-3},
V_0 = mean annual air temperature in °F,
T = duration of freezing period in days,
C = average volumetric heat capacity in B.T.U. ft^{-3} °F^{-1}.

This formula can also be applied to a layered soil with layers 1, 2, 3, ... n of thickness d_1, d_2, d_3, ... d_n; latent heats L_1, L_2, L_3, ... L_n and volumetric heats C_1, C_2, C_3, ... C_n, with

$$L = \frac{L_1 d_1 + L_2 d_2 + L_3 d_3 + \ldots + L_n d_n}{d_1 + d_2 + d_3 + \ldots d_n},$$

$$C = \frac{C_1 d_1 + C_2 d_2 + C_3 d_3 + \ldots C_n d_n}{d_1 + d_2 + d_3 + \ldots d_n},$$

in which $d_1 + d_2 + d_3 + \ldots + d_n$ equals the depth of freezing. This is of importance in the case of a snow cover; one then takes the snow layer as one of the layers in the above formula.

In this and similar formulas the freezing depth increases approximately as the square root of the length of the period of freezing weather. The $\sqrt{t}$ law was already obtained by F. Neumann as the solution for an idealized case. As it is very instructive to follow Neumann's reasoning, his solution will now be discussed.

Equation (5.5) gives the temperature in a soil which was at x_0 for $t = 0$ and for z in the range 0 to z_m and zero below z_m at $t = 0$, whereas the temperature is zero for infinite z at any time. The corresponding equation for heat penetration in a soil whose surface temperature ϑ_0 is kept constant and which was at an initial temperature x_0 throughout the entire body of soil, is

$$\vartheta(z,t) = (x_0 - \vartheta_0)\operatorname{erf}[z/\sqrt{(4at)}] + \vartheta_0. \tag{5.32}$$

The difference of the actual temperature and the initial temperature, $\vartheta(z,t) - \vartheta_0$, has been substituted for $\vartheta_{co}^{av}(z,t)$ in (5.5), as the datum level of the temperature will not be taken at zero but at ϑ_0 in the present case. It is assumed that the constant initial temperature x_0 prevailed through the entire soil; this infers $z_m = \infty$ in (5.5) and the two terms between the braces in the right-hand side of (5.5) cancel.

One concludes from (5.32) that a given temperature is found at a depth which increases proportional to $\sqrt{t}$, as $\operatorname{erf}[z/\sqrt{(4at)}]$ remains constant for this relationship. This fact may also be expressed by saying that a given value of the temperature is propagated in the soil at a rate proportional to the square root of the time.

Equation (5.32) is now applied to the penetration of frost. The surface temperature is then negative (°C). The constant temperature x_0 prevails in the entire soil before freezing starts at $t = 0$ at the surface. From that time on two layers must be considered. The upper layer of frozen soil extends from $z = 0$ to $z = z_b$. The thermal constants are denoted by λ_f, C_f and a_f in the frozen soil. Below $z = z_b$ the thermal constants of the unfrozen soil are λ_u, C_u, a_u. The boundary where the temperature is 0°C, moves downwards with the time. If the boundary is displaced over the depth dz_b the latent heat of fusion must be carried off. This amounts to $rx_w dz_b$ cal cm^{-2} for one cm^2 of horizontal area in which x_w is the volumetric water content of the soil, which is approximately equal to the mass of water (g) per unit of volume, and r is the latent heat of fusion per gram of water. Thus three equations must be satisfied at the boundary

$$\vartheta_f(z_b, t) = 0, \tag{5.33}$$

$$\vartheta_u(z_b, t) = 0 \tag{5.34}$$

and

$$\lambda_f \frac{\partial \vartheta_f}{\partial z} - \lambda_u \frac{\partial \vartheta_u}{\partial z} = r x_w \frac{dz_b}{dt}. \tag{5.35}$$

The temperatures in the frozen and unfrozen soil are denoted by ϑ_f and ϑ_u, respectively.

Assuming that both ϑ_f and ϑ_u are given by an expression of the type of (5.32), one must have $z_b = \alpha \sqrt{t}$ with α a constant. This constant depends necessarily on the surface temperature ϑ_0 and the initial temperature χ_0, as the rate of penetration of the temperature $0°$C which prevails at the boundary z_b will obviously depend on both temperatures. The larger α is the more rapidly does the frost penetrate into deeper layers. According to the above mentioned assumption one has

$$\vartheta_f(z, t) = (\vartheta_1 - \vartheta_0) \mathrm{erf}\,[z/\sqrt{(4a_f t)}] + \vartheta_0, \tag{5.36}$$

$$\vartheta_u(z, t) = (\chi_0 - \vartheta_2) \mathrm{erf}\,[z/\sqrt{(4a_u t)}] + \vartheta_2. \tag{5.37}$$

Here ϑ_1 and ϑ_2 are also constants. They have to be chosen such that (5.33) to (5.35) are satisfied for $z = z_b$. Obviously $\vartheta_f(0, t) = \vartheta_0$ and $\vartheta_u(z, 0) = \chi_0$ since $\mathrm{erf}(0) = 0$ and $\mathrm{erf}(\infty) = 1$.

Inserting $z = z_b = \alpha \sqrt{t}$ and remembering

$$\frac{\partial \mathrm{erf}\,[z/\sqrt{(4at)}]}{\partial z} = \frac{\exp\,[-z^2/(4at)]}{\sqrt{(\pi at)}},$$

one obtains at the boundary

$$(\vartheta_1 - \vartheta_0)\,\mathrm{erf}\,[\alpha/\sqrt{(4a_f)}] + \vartheta_0 = 0, \tag{5.38}$$

$$(\chi_0 - \vartheta_2)\,\mathrm{erf}\,[\alpha/\sqrt{(4a_u)}] + \vartheta_2 = 0, \tag{5.39}$$

$$\frac{\lambda_f(\vartheta_1 - \vartheta_0)}{\sqrt{(\pi a_f)}} \exp\left[-\frac{\alpha^2}{4a_f}\right] + \frac{\lambda_u(\chi_0 - \vartheta_2)}{\sqrt{(\pi a_u)}} \exp\left[-\frac{\alpha^2}{4a_u}\right] = \tfrac{1}{2}\,r\,x_w\,\alpha. \tag{5.40}$$

These are three equations from which the constants α, ϑ_1, and ϑ_2 can be solved, which proves that the solutions (5.36) and (5.37) apply and the boundary penetrates proportional to $\sqrt{t}$. Though the conditions for which this result is obtained are only exceptionally encountered in practice, the method provides to some extent a justification of the empirical relationships in which the penetration of frost is proportional to $\sqrt{t}$.

5.12. Some empirical data on soil temperature

A large amount of data concerning soil temperatures under various vegetative covers or for bare soil and different meteorological conditions has been published. A review of the literature up to 1951 is given in Meteorological Abstracts [1951].

The value of these literature data is, however, often seriously limited by the fact that neither the thermal constants of the soils nor the meteorological conditions at the time of the experiments have been stated. It is then obviously impossible to use the reported temperatures for a calculation of soil temperature at some other period, for instance, during a part of the growing season.

In this paragraph some miscellaneous data on thermal constants of soil temperatures are given as an illustration of the actual behavior of soils.

In Table 5.4 thermal diffusivity and damping depths are given for three typical soils as a function of water content. The temperature was 18 °C and samples of the soils were studied in the laboratory.

TABLE 5.4

Thermal diffusivity a (cm^2 sec^{-1}) and damping depth D (cm) for three soils as a function of the volume fraction of water x_w. The sandy soil was pure quartz sand, the clay soil contained 37 per cent by weight of particles smaller than 16μ, the peat soil consisted of 96 per cent organic matter by weight. The volume fraction of solid material was 0.57 for the sand and the clay soil, it was 0.10 for the peat soil

	Sand		Clay			Peat	
x_w	$a \times 10^2$	D	$a \times 10^2$	D	x_w	$a \times 10^2$	D
0.43	0.87	15.5	0.65	13.4	0.90	0.131	6.0
0.30	1.03	16.8	0.71	14.0	0.80	0.135	6.1
0.20	1.15	17.8	0.77	14.5	0.70	0.132	6.0
0.15	1.21	18.3	0.79	14.7	0.50	0.118	5.7
0.10	1.25	18.5	0.68	13.7	0.30	0.086	4.9
0.05	1.06	17.1	0.42	10.7	0.10	0.062	4.1
0.00	0.23	8.0	0.23	8.0	0.00	1.000	5.2

The thermal diffusivity of a sandy soil near Potsdam (Germany) as measured by Süring [1929], is given in Table 5.5. Note that the thermal diffusivity is fairly constant to a depth of 12 m, but as follows from Table 5.2, this does not necessarily mean that the water content of the soil was approximately constant too. Throughout most of the region which is important for agriculture the thermal conductivity varies only little with varying water content.

This fact also explains the well-known difficulty of determining changes in soil moisture content from a change in damping depth or in thermal conductivity of a soil in situ.

TABLE 5.5

Thermal diffusivity for a sandy soil near Potsdam

depths (m)	$a \times 10^2$ (cm^2 sec^{-1})
0.2 – 1	1.04
1 – 2	0.98
2 – 4	1.06
4 – 6	1.15
6 – 12	1.13

To illustrate the influence of the type of a vegetative cover some data pertaining to a field and a forest are given in Table 5.6 (SCHUBERT [1930]).

TABLE 5.6

Average diurnal temperature (°C) and differences between maximum and minimum temperatures (°C) in a sandy soil at Eberwald, Germany, June 1879 (SCHUBERT [1930])

depth (cm)	daily average (°C)		full range of variation $(2 \, ^{\Delta}\vartheta)(°C)$	
	field	forest	field	forest
1	20.06	17.29	11.5	6.7
15	19.97	16.19	5.8	2.5
30	17.33	15.19	1.6	0.9
60	15.85	13.19	0.2	0.1

SINUSOIDAL TEMPERATURE VARIATION IN A LAYERED SOIL

W. R. VAN WIJK AND W. J. DERKSEN

Laboratory of Physics and Meteorology of the Agricultural University Wageningen,
The Netherlands

6.1. Examples of layered soils

Natural soils are generally not homogeneous even if their mineral composition and structure do not vary with depth. In a period of dry weather the upper layers will be drier than the subsoil and the converse situation occurs in a rainy period. The assumption of a homogeneous soil may still be a good approximation in dealing with phenomena in which the soil is involved to a depth which is large compared with the depths of the layers where the thermal constants are markedly different from the average value. In a more detailed investigation, however, deviations from the average behavior will be found.

To illustrate, the variable part of the heat stored can often be calculated with a fair degree of accuracy using average thermal constants for the upper 30 cm of soil, but the temperature at 1 cm below the surface cannot.

The next step to improve the theory is to consider two layers with different thermal properties. A direct application of the theory of heat conduction in a layered soil to a problem of some practical importance is the explanation of the influence of soil tillage on the temperature regime in the upper layers.

Tillage changes the thermal properties of the upper layer. This layer acquires a looser structure, thus its air content is increased. The temperatures in the soil near the surface will differ from those in a homogeneous soil under equal conditions of irradiation. Though it is found that the differences are often small, they may become important when the temperature is a critical factor. So, for instance, with a crop that is susceptible to night frost, a difference of one degree centigrade may then be fatal.

A second example is the application of a surface mulch. This is a practice used by farmers in arid and warm climates to reduce evaporation or to keep the soil cooler.*

A mulch is sometimes used in temperate and cold climates to keep the

---

* A mulch is a layer of foreign material put on the surface. A sand mulch, a straw mulch, a mulch of plant debris and a paper mulch are the most common types.

soil warmer during the winter months since the mulch acts as an insulating cover. This is particularly practiced in horticulture.

A layer of leaves on the ground in a forest is a natural mulch. The increased frequency of night frost on a cover of leaves litter is well known.

A vegetative cover may also be considered as a natural mulch. The stagnant air between the plants forms a layer through which the heat, which is absorbed by the upper leaves of the plants is transported to the ground.

These examples may suffice to show that penetration of heat in a medium consisting of two or occasionally of more layers deserves attention in a study of plant environment. First the theory will be developed for a soil consisting of two layers. The thermal properties in each layer are assumed constant. The theory of heat conduction in a homogeneous soil can then be applied to each layer separately with the additional condition that the temperature and the heat flux density remain continuous at the boundary of the layers.

6.2. Sinusoidal temperature variation in soil consisting of two layers

Let the upper layer extend to a depth d; the lower layer extends from d towards infinity. The thermal conductivities are λ_1 and λ_2 and the volumetric heat capacities C_1 and C_2 respectively. Quantities pertaining to the upper layer will be denoted by the subscript 1, those referring to the lower layer by the subscript 2. The temperature wave in a soil consisting of two layers has been treated by PEERLKAMP [1944].

Since the lower layer extends to infinity the theory of the previous chapters is immediately applicable to it, but two boundaries must be considered in the upper layer. One is at $z = 0$ and the other is at the depth d. In the upper layer there is no restriction that the temperature variation must remain finite for infinite values of z, since z cannot become infinite. Consequently the second solution of (4.5), the one with the plus sign in (4.13), which corresponds to an increasing amplitude for increasing z must now also be taken into account.

In the upper layer $0 \leqslant z \leqslant d$

$$\vartheta_1(z,t) = \vartheta_\mathrm{a} + {}^\mathrm{A}\vartheta'_1 \exp\left(-\frac{z}{D_1}\right)\sin\left(\omega t - \frac{z}{D_1}+\varphi'_1\right) + {}^\mathrm{A}\vartheta''_1\exp\left(+\frac{z}{D_1}\right)\sin\left(\omega t + \frac{z}{D_1}+\varphi\right)$$

(6.1)

in the lower layer $z \geqslant d$

$$\vartheta_2(z,t) = \vartheta_\mathrm{a} + {}^\mathrm{A}\vartheta_d \exp\left(-\frac{z-d}{D_2}\right)\sin\left(\omega t - \frac{z-d}{D_2}+\varphi_2\right),$$

(6.2)

in which $^A\vartheta'_1$ and $^A\vartheta''_1$ are the amplitudes of the two temperature waves in the upper layer at $z = 0$ and $^A\vartheta_d$ is the amplitude in the lower layer at $z = d$. In these formulas D is again the damping depth, $D = \sqrt{(2\lambda/C\omega)}$ and the φ's are phase constants. The phase constants and the amplitudes have such values that $\vartheta_1(0,t)$ is equal to the given surface temperature, that $\vartheta_1(d,t) = \vartheta_2(d,t)$ and that the same heat flux is calculated from both equations at $z = d$. The amplitude $^A\vartheta_d$ applies to the boundary $z = d$.

The phase constants and the amplitudes can be expressed in the damping depth, the depth of the upper layer, the ratio of λC in both layers and the amplitude and phase constant of the temperature variation at the surface. The expressions are somewhat complicated and cumbersome for use in actual calculations. They are represented in the graphs in Figs 6.1 and 6.2 (explanation in section 6.4). The full expressions are given in Table 6.1. A derivation is given in section 6.3.

TABLE 6.1

Amplitude and phase in a soil consisting of two layers

$$^A\vartheta'_1 = {}^A\vartheta_t[1 + r_l^2 \, e^{-4d/D_1} + 2 \, r_l \, e^{-2d/D_1} \cos(2d/D_1)]^{-\frac{1}{2}} \tag{6.3}$$

$$^A\vartheta''_1 = {}^A\vartheta_t[1 + r_l^{-2} \, e^{4d/D_1} + 2r_l^{-1} \, e^{2d/D_1} \cos(2d/D_1)]^{-\frac{1}{2}} = {}^A\vartheta'_1 r_l \, e^{-2d/D_1} \tag{6.4}$$

$$^A\vartheta_d = {}^A\vartheta'_t(1 + r_l) \, e^{-d/D_1} \tag{6.5}$$

$$\varphi'_1 = \mathrm{arctg}\left(\frac{r_l \, e^{-2d/D_1} \sin(2d/D_1)}{1 + r_l \, e^{-2d/D_1} \cos(2d/D_1)}\right) \tag{6.6}$$

$$\varphi''_1 = \mathrm{arctg}\left(-\frac{e^{2d/D_1} \sin(2d/D_1)}{r_l + e^{2d/D_1} \cos(2d/D_1)}\right) = \varphi'_1 - (2d/D_1) \tag{6.7}$$

$$\varphi_2 = \varphi'_1 + (d/D_1). \tag{6.8}$$

The dimensionless quantity r_l is an auxiliary variable defined by

$$r_l = \frac{\sqrt{(\lambda_1 C_1)} - \sqrt{(\lambda_2 C_2)}}{\sqrt{(\lambda_1 C_1)} + \sqrt{(\lambda_2 C_2)}}. \tag{6.9}$$

$^A\vartheta_t$ is the total amplitude at the surface.

The surface temperature is written as

$$\vartheta(0,t) = \vartheta_a + {}^A\vartheta_t \sin(\omega t). \tag{6.10}$$

d is the depth of the upper layer, D_1 and D_2 are the damping depths in the upper and lower layer respectively. The lower layer extends to infinity. The product of the thermal conductivity and the volumetric heat capacity λC, (equation (6.9)) is called the *contact coefficient*.

The amplitude of the heat flux density at the surface, $^AH_{so}$, depends primarily on the radiation flux density and on the distribution of heat between soil and air, eventually on other energy fluxes, but it also depends on the thermal properties of both layers and on the depth of the upper layer.

6.3. Derivation of the formulas in Table 6.1*

The differential equation of heat conduction (4.4) has to be solved for the following boundary conditions:
(i) The surface temperature is given by (6.10)
(ii) The temperature remains continuous at $z = d$, or

$$\vartheta_1(d,t) = \vartheta_2(d,t) \tag{6.11}$$

(iii) The heat flux density remains also continuous at $z = d$

$$_1H_{so}(d,t) = -\lambda_1\left(\frac{\partial\vartheta_1(z,t)}{\partial z}\right)_{z=d} = {}_2H_{so}(d,t) = -\lambda_2\left(\frac{\partial\vartheta_2(z,t)}{\partial z}\right)_{z=d} \tag{6.12}$$

(iv) The temperature fluctuation decreases towards zero for infinite depth or

$$\lim_{z\to\infty} \vartheta_2 = \vartheta_a. \tag{6.13}$$

The calculations are materially shortened if complex functions are used instead of real trigonometrical functions (cf. section 4.4). Thus the temperatures are considered as the real part of complex functions.

$$\vartheta(0,t) = \vartheta_a + {}^A\vartheta_l\sin(\omega t) = \vartheta_a + \text{Re}[(1/i)\,{}^A\vartheta_l e^{i\omega t}] \tag{6.14}$$

$$\vartheta_1(z,t) = \vartheta_a + \text{Re}\,[(1/i)[\,{}^A\vartheta'_1\exp\{i\varphi'_1 - (1+i)z/D_1\} \\ + {}^A\vartheta''_1\exp\{i\varphi''_1 + (1+i)z/D_1\}]\exp(i\omega t)] \tag{6.15}$$

$$\vartheta_2(z,t) = \vartheta_a + \text{Re}\,[(1/i)\,{}^A\vartheta_d\exp\{i\varphi_2 - (1+i)(z-d)/D_2\}\exp(i\omega t)]. \tag{6.16}$$

The symbol Re denotes the real part of the complex function between the brackets. If one writes for abbreviation ${}^{CA}\vartheta'_1 = {}^A\vartheta'_1\exp(i\varphi'_1)$,

$${}^{CA}\vartheta''_1 = {}^A\vartheta''_1\exp(i\varphi''_1) \quad\text{and}\quad {}^{CA}\vartheta_d = {}^A\vartheta_d\exp(i\varphi_2)$$

then the boundary conditions (i), (ii) and (iii) are expressed by the following equations between the *complex amplitudes*

$${}^{CA}\vartheta'_1 + {}^{CA}\vartheta''_1 = {}^A\vartheta_l, \tag{6.17}$$

---

* Reading of this paragraph may be omitted by the reader who is not interested in mathematical derivations.

$$^{CA}\vartheta'_1 \exp\{-(1+i)d/D_1\} + {}^{CA}\vartheta''_1 \exp\{(1+i)d/D_1\} = {}^{CA}\vartheta_d, \quad (6.18)$$

and

$$\frac{\lambda_1 \, {}^{CA}\vartheta'_1 e^{-(1+i)d/D_1}}{D_1} - \frac{\lambda_1 \, {}^{CA}\vartheta''_1 e^{(1+i)d/D_1}}{D_1} = \frac{\lambda_2 \, {}^{CA}\vartheta_d}{D_2}. \quad (6.19)$$

The fourth boundary condition is satisfied by $\vartheta_2(z,t)$ as it is given in (6.16). Solving for $^{CA}\vartheta'_1$, $^{CA}\vartheta''_1$ and $^{CA}\vartheta_d$ leads to

$$^{CA}\vartheta'_1 = \frac{{}^{A}\vartheta_l e^{2(1+i)d/D_1}}{e^{2(1+i)d/D_1} + r_l}, \quad (6.20)$$

$$^{CA}\vartheta''_1 = \frac{r_l \, {}^{A}\vartheta_l}{e^{2(1+i)d/D_1} + r_l}, \quad (6.21)$$

and

$$^{CA}\vartheta_d = \frac{(1+r_l)^{A}\vartheta_l e^{(1+i)d/D_1}}{e^{2(1+i)d/D_1} + r_l}, \quad (6.22)$$

in which r_l is given by (6.9).

Multiplying the numerator and the denominator of (6.20) by $\exp[2(1-i)d/D_1] + r_l$ one obtains

$$^{CA}\vartheta'_1 = \frac{{}^{A}\vartheta_l(e^{4d/D_1} + r_l e^{2(1+i)d/D_1})}{e^{4d/D_1} + r_l^2 + r_l e^{2d/D_1}(e^{2id/D_1} + e^{-2id/D_1})},$$

or, remembering $\exp(2id/D_1) = \cos(2d/D_1) + i\sin(2d/D_1)$ and $\exp(2id/D_1) + \exp(-2id/D_1) = 2\cos(2d/D_1)$ one has

$$^{CA}\vartheta'_1 = {}^{A}\vartheta'_1 e^{i\varphi_1} =$$

$$= \frac{{}^{A}\vartheta_l\{e^{4d/D_1} + r_l e^{2d/D_1}[\cos(2d/D_1) + i\sin(2d/D_1)]\}}{e^{4d/D_1} + r_l^2 + 2r_l e^{2d/D_1}\cos(2d/D_1)} = a + bi.$$

Equations (6.3) and (6.6) respectively, result from the relationships

$$^{A}\vartheta'_1 = \sqrt{(a^2 + b^2)} \quad \text{and} \quad \varphi_1 = \text{arctg}(b/a).$$

The other expressions in Table 6.1 follow immediately from this result in combination with (6.20) to (6.22).

The heat flux densities are calculated from (6.15) and (6.16) in a similar way

$$_1 H_{so}(z,t) = -\lambda_1 \frac{\partial \vartheta_1}{\partial z}$$

$$= \lambda_1 \text{Re} \frac{1}{i}\left[\frac{1+i}{D_1} {}^{A}\vartheta'_1 e^{i\varphi'_1 - (1+i)z/D_1} - \frac{1+i}{D_1} {}^{A}\vartheta''_1 e^{i\varphi''_1 + (1+i)z/D_1}\right] e^{i\omega t}$$

or, since $1 + i = \sqrt{(2)}\exp(\tfrac{1}{4}\pi i)$,

$$_1H_{so}(z,t) = \frac{\lambda_1\sqrt{2}}{D_1} \, \text{Re} \, \frac{1}{i} \left\{ {}^A\vartheta'_1 \exp\left[i\varphi'_1 + \tfrac{1}{4}\pi i - \frac{(1+i)z}{D_1} \right] \right.$$
$$\left. - {}^A\vartheta''_1 \exp\left[i\varphi''_1 + \tfrac{1}{4}\pi i + \frac{(1+i)z}{D_1} \right] \right\} e^{i\omega t}. \qquad (6.23)$$

Similarly

$$_2H_{so}(z,t) = \frac{\lambda_2\sqrt{2}}{D_2} \, \text{Re} \, \frac{1}{i} \left\{ {}^A\vartheta_d \exp\left[i\varphi_2 + \tfrac{1}{4}\pi i - \frac{(1+i)(z-d)}{D_2} \right] \right\} e^{i\omega t},$$
$$\qquad (6.24)$$

for $z \geqslant d$.

If the temperature at the surface of the layered soil contains a phase constant, thus if

$$\vartheta_l(0,t) = {}^A\vartheta_l \sin(\omega t + \varphi_0), \qquad (6.25)$$

$_{CA}\vartheta_l = {}^A\vartheta_l e^{i\varphi_0}$ must be substituted instead of $^A\vartheta_l$ in (6.17) to (6.19). Then $\varphi_1 - \varphi_0$ takes the place of φ_1 in Table 6.1.

In some applications the temperature regime of the layered soil will be compared with that of a homogeneous soil. The comparison which is of the most practical value concerns a homogeneous soil whose thermal constants are either equal to those of the upper layer of the layered soil or to those of the subsoil. The most general case of arbitrary values of λ_h and C_h will, however, be treated here. The heat flux density in the two soils is in general different under equal meteorological conditions, but it is often convenient to make first a comparison assuming equal heat flux densities H_{so} to the soils at the surface. This assumption is afterwards corrected by application of the heat balance.

If the amplitudes are equal one has

$$^{A_1}H_{so}(0,t) = {}^{A_h}H_{so}(0,t) = \frac{\lambda_h\sqrt{2}}{D_h} \, {}^A\vartheta_h. \qquad (6.26)$$

The amplitude $^{A_1}H_{so}(0,t)$ is calculated from (6.23) in which $z = 0$ is inserted. Writing the complex function in the right-hand side of that equation as $i^{-1}\varrho \exp[i(\varphi + \tfrac{1}{4}\pi + \omega t)]$, one obtains*

$$^{A_1}H_{so}(0,t) = \left(\frac{\lambda_1\sqrt{2}}{D_1}\right) \varrho,$$

in which ϱ is the modulus of the complex number

$$^A\vartheta'_1 \exp(i\varphi'_1) - {}^A\vartheta''_1 \exp(i\varphi''_1) = {}^{CA}\vartheta'_1 - {}^{CA}\vartheta''_1.$$

---

* The value of the phase constant φ is of no importance for the following discussion. It must be equal to φ_0 since
$$_hH_{so}(0,t) = {}^A_hH_{so} \sin(\omega t + \tfrac{1}{4}\pi + \varphi_0).$$

Introduction of the amplitude of the temperature at the surface of the layered soil, $^A\vartheta_l$, gives the result (see (6.20) and (6.21))

$$^{A_1}H_{so}(0,t) = \left(\frac{\lambda_1\sqrt{2}}{D_1}\right)^{A}\vartheta_l \times \text{ modulus of } \left[\frac{\exp\left[2(1+i)d/D_1\right] - r_l}{\exp\left[2(1+i)d/D_1\right] + r_l}\right],$$

or

$$^{A_1}H_{so}(0,t) = \left(\frac{\lambda_1\sqrt{2}}{D_1}\right)^{A}\vartheta_l \left[\frac{\exp\left(4d/D_1\right) - 2r_l\left[\exp\left(2d/D_1\right)\right]\cos\left(2d/D_1\right) + r_l{}^2}{\exp\left(4d/D_1\right) + 2r_l\left[\exp\left(2d/D_1\right)\right]\cos\left(2d/D_1\right) + r_l{}^2}\right]^{\frac{1}{2}}.$$

$$\tag{6.27}$$

6.4. The surface temperature

The distribution of heat between soil and air is generally different for a layered soil from that for a homogeneous soil. Consequently different surface temperatures are often observed for equal meteorological conditions or, expressed more precisely, for the same energy flux density towards the surface. The heat balance near the surface must be used to calculate the fraction of energy which enters the soil. The procedure is quite similar to that of section 4.9 where two homogeneous soils with different thermal constants were compared.

The expression (6.27) must be inserted for $^{A_1}H_{so}(0,t)$ in (6.26). One then obtains a relation between the surface amplitudes of the layered soil $^A\vartheta_l$ and of the homogeneous soil $^A\vartheta_h$ for equal heat flux densities to the soils. In the general case that the heat flux densities are not equal but $^{A_1}H_{so}(0,t) = m\,^{A_h}H_{so}(0,t)$ where m is a constant, which may be either smaller or greater than 1 depending on the thermal properties of the two soils under comparison, the relation between the temperature amplitudes $^A\vartheta_l$ and $^A\vartheta_d$ becomes

$$\frac{\lambda_1}{D_1}\,^{A}\vartheta_l \left[\frac{\exp\left(4d/D_1\right) - 2r_l\left[\exp\left(2d/D_1\right)\right]\cos\left(2d/D_1\right) + r_l{}^2}{\exp\left(4d/D_1\right) + 2r_l\left[\exp\left(2d/D_1\right)\right]\cos\left(2d/D_1\right) + r_l{}^2}\right]^{\frac{1}{2}} = m\left(\frac{\lambda_h}{D_h}\right)^{A}\vartheta_d.$$

$$\tag{6.28}$$

For the moment the temperature and heat flux densities will be compared in a two layer soil and a homogeneous soil assuming equal amplitude $^AH_{so}$ of the heat flux densities at the surface, thus $m = 1$ in (6.28). The heat flux density in a homogeneous soil at its surface is

$$H_{so}(0,t) = [(\lambda_h{}^A\vartheta_h\sqrt{2})/D_h]\sin(\omega t + \varphi_0 + \tfrac{1}{4}\pi). \tag{6.29}$$

It is shown in section 6.3 that equal $^AH_{so}$ at the surface leads to the following relation between the amplitudes of the surface temperature (see (6.26) and (6.27))

$$\frac{{}^{A}\vartheta_l}{{}^{A}\vartheta_h} = \left[\frac{\lambda_h C_h}{\lambda_1 C_1} \frac{\exp(4d/D_1) + 2r_l[\exp(2d/D_1)]\cos(2d/D_1) + r_l^2}{\exp(4d/D_1) - 2r_l[\exp(2d/D_1)]\cos(2d/D_1) + r_l^2}\right]^{\frac{1}{2}}, \qquad (6.30)$$

in which the indices l, h, 1, refer to the surface of the layered soil, to the homogeneous soil and to the upper layer of the layered soil, respectively. The auxiliary variable r_l has been given in (6.9).

Some conclusions can immediately be drawn from (6.30) without performing an actual calculation of the right-hand side.

For large values of d/D_1 the right-hand side approaches to $\sqrt{(\lambda_h C_h/\lambda_1 C_1)}$. This is equal to the ratio of the amplitudes of the surface temperature for two homogeneous soils possessing the thermal constants λ_h, C_h and λ_1, C_1, respectively, if ${}^{A}H_{so}$ is the same for both (equation.(6.29)). The result is not surprising. A large value of d/D_1 means that the temperature variation in the layered soil is practically restricted to the upper layer. The properties of the subsoil are of no importance in that case.

The same result is obtained for an arbitrary value of d/D_1, if the parameter

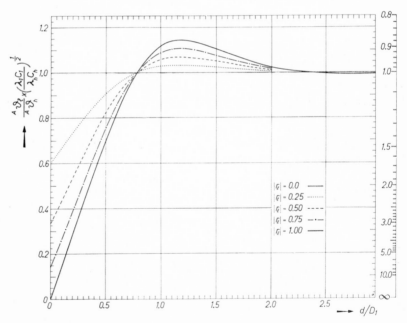

Fig. 6.1. Ratio of amplitudes in a layered soil and in a homogeneous soil. The ordinate is the right-hand side of equation (6.30) times the factor $\sqrt{(\lambda_1 C_1/\lambda_h C_h)}$. Each curve corresponds to a constant value of the parameter $r_l = [\sqrt{(\lambda_1 C_1)} - \sqrt{(\lambda_2 C_2)}]/[\sqrt{(\lambda_1 C_1)} + \sqrt{(\lambda_2 C_2)}]$. The right-hand vertical scale is to be used for positive r_l, the left-hand vertical scale corresponds to negative r_l.

$r_l = 0$. Now $r_l = 0$ when $\lambda_1 = \lambda_2$ and $C_1 = C_2$. This is a trivial case as it means that the layered soil is homogeneous in respect to its thermal properties. But $r_l = 0$ is also obtained if $\lambda_1 C_1 = \lambda_2 C_2$ though the λ's and C's themselves are not necessarily equal for the two layers. This is indeed a somewhat unforeseen conclusion from the mathematical treatment.

The discussion of (6.30) is facilitated by a graphical representation of the second factor between the brackets. This factor has been plotted in Fig. 6.1.

It is equal to one for $d/D_1 = \frac{1}{4}\pi$, $\frac{3}{4}\pi$, $1\frac{1}{4}\pi$ etc . . . and it approaches unity for infinite d/D_1, irrespective of the value of r_l.

The parameter r_l is positive if $\lambda_1 C_1 > \lambda_2 C_2$ (right-hand scale), which generally means that the upper layer is a better conductor for heat than the lower one. In comparison to a homogeneous soil with the same thermal properties as the upper layer the amplitude at the surface is increased for $r_l > 0$ thus by a subsoil with a lower contact coefficient $\sqrt{(\lambda C)}$. This applies to d smaller than $\frac{1}{4}\pi D_1$. The amplitude is, on the other hand, smaller than that of the homogeneous soil for $\frac{3}{4}\pi D_1 > d > \frac{1}{4}\pi D_1$.

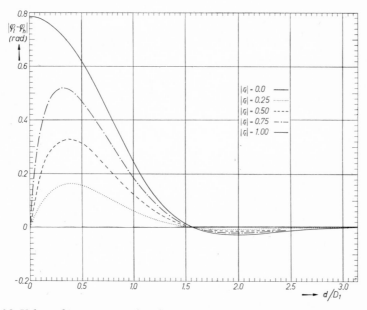

Fig. 6.2. Values of $|\varphi_l - \varphi_h|$ as a function of d/D_1 for different values of $|r_l|$. The sign of $\varphi_l - \varphi_h$ is opposite to the sign of r_l thus a positive value of r_l corresponds to a retardation in phase and a negative r_l to an advance in phase of the temperature in the layered soil as compared with the homogeneous soil.

The situation is reversed for a negative value of r_l. The subsoil is the one for which $\lambda_2 C_2$ is the greater one in this case. The same graphs can be used with a negative r_l if the ordinate is read at the left-hand vertical axis. Indeed, since the denominator and the numerator in the second factor on the right-hand side of (6.30) are interchanged when the parameter r_l takes the opposite sign, the factor changes into its reciprocal. The right-hand vertical scale corresponds to a negative r_l, it is reciprocal to the scale on the left.

Not only is the amplitude of the temperature wave influenced by the presence of a second layer, but the phase is also affected. The phase shift of the heat wave in respect to the temperature wave may now differ from $+\frac{1}{4}\pi$. It is again assumed that the heat flux density is the same in both soils as well as regards its amplitude as its phase. The temperature wave at the surface of the layered soil is then shifted in phase in respect to the temperature wave at the homogeneous soil by an amount

$$\varphi_l - \varphi_h = \text{arctg}\left[\frac{-2r_l\, e^{-2d/D_1}\sin(2d/D_1)}{1 - r_l^2 e^{-4d/D_1}}\right]. \tag{6.31}$$

A graph of this function is given in Fig. 6.2.

A positive value of r_l causes a lag of the temperature on the layered soil as compared with the homogeneous soil if $d < \frac{1}{2}\pi D_1$. A negative r_l results in an advance over the same angle. The difference $\varphi_l - \varphi_h$ converges rapidly towards zero for d/D_1 increasing towards infinity.

6.5. Temperature below the surface

The temperature at some depth under the surface can also be calculated though the formulas become more complicated. The layered soil is again compared with a homogeneous soil.

The formulas are given for a homogeneous soil which possesses the same thermal properties as the subsoil of the layered soil and equal heat flux density at the surface is assumed.

The amplitude at the depth z is denoted by $^A\vartheta_l(z)$ in the layered soil and by $^A\vartheta_h(z)$ in the homogeneous soil, thus

$$^A\vartheta_h(z) = {}^A\vartheta_h \exp(-z/D_2).^*$$

The phase factors are $\varphi_l(z)$ and $\varphi_h(z)$ respectively where the latter is equal to $(-z/D_h)$. The complete expressions are

---

* The notation $^A\vartheta_h$ is used instead of $^A\vartheta_h(0)$ for simplicity.

$$\frac{^A\vartheta_l(z)}{^A\vartheta_h} = \left[\frac{\lambda_2 C_2\,e^{-2z/D_1} + 2r_l e^{-2d/D_1}\cos(2d/D_1 - 2z/D_1) + r_l^2 e^{-4d/D_1+2z/D_1}}{\lambda_1 C_1\quad 1 - 2r_l e^{-2d/D_1}\cos(2d/D_1) + r_l^2 e^{-4d/D_1}}\right]^{\frac{1}{2}},$$

$$(6.32)$$

$$\varphi_l(z) - \varphi_h(z) =$$

$$\text{ctg}\left[-\frac{(e^{-z/D_1} + r_l^2 e^{-4d/D_1})\sin(z/D_1) + r_l e^{-2d/D_1}(e^{z/D_1} + e^{-z/D_1})\sin(2d/D_1 - z/D_1)}{(e^{-z/D_1} - r_l^2 e^{-4d/D_1+z/D_1})\cos(z/D_1) + r_l e^{-2d/D_1}(e^{z/D_1} - e^{-z/D_1})\cos(2d/D_1 - z/D_1)}\right].$$

$$(6.33)$$

Both formulas apply to the upper layer i.e. $0 < z < d$. In the subsoil, $z > d$, one has

$$^A\vartheta_l(z) = {}^A\vartheta_h(d)e^{-z/D_2}, \tag{6.34}$$

and

$$\varphi_l(z) = \varphi_l(d) - z/D_2. \tag{6.35}$$

The comparison with an arbitrary homogeneous soil is now simple. Let λ_{ah}, C_{ah} and D_{ah} refer to the arbitrary soil. The ratio of the amplitudes at a depth z in this soil, $^A\vartheta_{ah}(z)$, and in the homogeneous soil, with λ_2 and C_2, $^A\vartheta_h(z)$, respectively is

$$\frac{^A\vartheta_{ah}(z)}{^A\vartheta_h(z)} = \left(\frac{\lambda_2 C_2}{\lambda_{ah} C_{ah}}\right)^{\frac{1}{2}} e^{-z(D_{ah}-D_2)},$$

and

$$\varphi_{ah}(z) - \varphi_h(z) = -z\left(\frac{1}{D_{ah}} - \frac{1}{D_2}\right)$$

6.6. Tillage, properties of a tilled soil

The theory of heat conduction in a layered soil will now be applied to calculate the change in temperature caused by tillage. The problem has been studied by VAN DUIN [1956]. The soil before tilth is the homogeneous soil with which the layered soil will be compared. Thus it is assumed that the subsoil possesses the same properties as the homogeneous soil, but the top soil is different.

Tillage of the soil is practiced in view of the following objectives:
(i)   Killing of weeds,
(ii) Turning under stubble and manure,
(iii) Improving drainage of the soil,
(iv) Preparing a good seedbed,
(v)   Obtaining a favourable microclimate,
(vi) Facilitating harvesting.

Killing of weeds has apparently the most important effect on the growth, and on the yield of crops. The thermal effects come under the fourth and the fifth objective. We shall find that their influence is generally small though not always unimportant.

The structure of the upper soil layer is changed by ploughing and by cultivation, the more stable aggregates in the soil being rearranged such that the pore space is increased. The new pores are filled with air and both the heat conductivity and the volumetric heat capacity are in general smaller than in the original soil. Thus the product λC is smaller and in most cases the damping depth D is also reduced.* It is possible to calculate the thermal properties of a given type of soil if pore space and water content are known. These calculations are given in the next chapter. It is, however, not yet possible to calculate the increase of pore space caused by ploughing or by cultivation so this quantity must be experimentally determined. Empirical data are also needed to estimate the stability of the new arrangement of the aggregates after tilth.

From an extensive literature-study van Duin [1956] concluded that the structural change of the upper layer consists mainly of a mere loosening of the rather coarse aggregates that were already present in the original soil. This at least is the case when the cultivation is carried out on a soil which is not too wet. In a wet soil the aggregates can themselves be destroyed and a muddy soil may result. The best results appear to have been obtained for a surface with a moisture content somewhat below "field capacity".**

The pore space x_p of a soil is determined from the weight of a unit volume

---

* This need not be so if the soil was inhomogeneous before tilth, for instance, if a dry upper layer is ploughed under.

** *Field capacity* was defined by Veihmeyer and Hendrickson [1949] as: "The amount of water held in the soil after excess water has drained away, and the rate of downward movement of water has materially decreased, which usually takes place within two or three days after rain or irrigation in pervious soils of uniform structure and texture". It is, therefore, not an equilibrium property of a soil but a more or less arbitrarily chosen moisture content during the process of drainage.

Since, however, the rate with which a soil is drained decreases steeply when a certain fraction of the pore space is filled with air, the concept is nevertheless useful for roughly characterizing the soil. Field capacity corresponds approximately to the region in the drainage curve, considered as a function of the time, where the rate falls off steeply. An exceptional case occurs if the water table is so high that the moisture content of the soil exceeds the moisture content for which drainage takes place very slowly. Field capacity is no longer a useful concept under such circumstances (comp. also section 2.20).

of the dry soil, W_s, and the specific gravity of the solid fraction in it, W_m. We have

$$x_p = 1 - W_s/W_m, \tag{6.36}$$

in which x_p is the volume occupied by the pores per unit of volume of soil and W_s/W_m is the ratio of the weight of a unit volume of soil to the weight of a unit volume of the solid material.

The distribution function of the pore size is also an important factor since water is retained more firmly in the smaller pores.

The moisture curve of a soil, which gives the water content in the equilibrium state as a function of the height above a water table, is highly influenced by the pore size distribution. An approximate method of characterizing pore size distribution was introduced by KOPECKI [1914], who made a distinction between *capillary pore space* and *noncapillary pore space*. The amount of water remaining in a soil, after it had been allowed to drain for 24 hr under the action of gravity was considered to be contained in the capillary pore space. The soil was originally completely saturated with water.

The amount of water in the saturated soil above that present in the capillary pore space is by definition held in the noncapillary pore space.

The change of total pore space x_p or of W_s/W_m is used as a measure for structural changes.

6.7. The diurnal variation on a tilled soil

The calculation of the diurnal temperature wave at the surface of a tilled soil may serve as an illustration. The theory is applied to a soil whose properties are given in Table 6.2.

TABLE 6.2

Thermal properties of a sandy soil after tilth

	volume fraction		thermal conductivity λ (cal cm^{-1} sec^{-1} °C^{-1})	volumetric heat capacity C (cal cm^{-3} °C^{-1})
	solids	water		
upper layer	0.40	0.125	1.70×10^{-3}	0.31
lower layer	0.57	0.175	3.40×10^{-3}	0.44

	Damping depth D (cm)		λC (cal^2 cm^{-4} sec^{-1} °C^{-2})
	diurnal	annual	
upper layer	12.3	235	5.3×10^{-4}
lower layer	14.6	280	$15 \ \times 10^{-4}$

Equations (6.30) and (6.31) overestimate the influence of tillage since the heat flux density into the soil with a loose insulating top layer is actually smaller than before tilth if atmospheric conditions are equal.

The ratio $(\lambda_1 C_1/\lambda_2 C_2)^{-\frac{1}{2}} = 1.68$ in this case and $r_l = -0.254$. From this in combination with Fig. 6.1 it follows that ${}^A\vartheta_l(0)/{}^A\vartheta_h = 1.68$ for $d/D_1 = \frac{1}{4}\pi$, so for $d = 9.7$ cm. The maximum value of ${}^A\vartheta_l(0)/{}^A\vartheta_h$ is 1.735 which corresponds to $d = 15$ cm, and one concludes from the graph that the ratio is approximately 1.7 for d exceeding 10 cm. The temperature at the surface is advanced in phase with respect to the original soil, which has the properties of the lower layer in Table 6.2.

For a depth of 10 cm $d/D_1 = 0.81$ and the phase shift $= 0.10$ rad according to Fig. 6.2; the phaseshift decreases rapidly with increasing d.

The heat flux density into a homogeneous soil is $\frac{1}{4}\pi$ or 0.78 rad advanced in respect to the temperature wave. Consequently the heat flux density into the layered soil is $\frac{1}{4}\pi - 0.10$ rad $= 0.68$ rad advanced in respect to $\vartheta_l(0)$. This conclusion is independent of the assumption $_lH_{so} = {}_hH_{so}$.

Bare soil and equal evaporation are assumed in both cases so that the sum of the variable parts of the heat flux densities into the soil, into the air and of the net long wave radiation are equal. It will first be assumed that the net long wave radiation flux density is also equal though it is actually higher for a surface with a higher temperature. The difference will, however, be found of little importance (see section 6.8).

Let further, to fix ideas, ${}^A\vartheta_h = 18°C$. Then a value of ${}^A\vartheta_l(0) = 1.7 \times 18°C = 30.6°C$ results if $_lH_{so} = {}_hH_{so}$. But $_lH_{so}$ is not equal to $_hH_{so}$; their ratio will now be calculated using the heat balance (compare section 4.6).

Assuming $z_0 = 0.1$ cm and $b = 1.5 \times 10^{-3}$ cal cm^{-2} sec^{-1}°C^{-1}, thus the same roughness of the soil and the same apparent conductivity as in section 4.9, one has

$$^AH_{ai} = -{}^A\vartheta\, b/[2 \ln (\tfrac{1}{2}\gamma r_0)] = {}^A\vartheta\, (1.217 \times 10^{-4}),$$

since $r_0 = 2.37 \times 10^{-3}$.

Or for the homogeneous soil $^A{}_hH_{ai} = 2.19 \times 10^{-3}$ cal cm^{-2} sec^{-1}. The heat wave in air is advanced in phase by $\frac{1}{2}\pi + \operatorname{arctg} [(4/\pi)\cdot\ln (\tfrac{1}{2}\gamma r_0] = 0.13$ rad in respect to the surface temperature.

For the homogeneous soil one obtains (see (4.35))

$$\frac{^A{}_hH_{so}}{^A{}_hH_{ai}} = -\frac{2}{b}\Big[\sqrt{\lambda C\omega}\Big] \ln (\tfrac{1}{2}\gamma r_0) = -0.44 \ln (2.11 \times 10^{-3}) = 2.711.$$

$$(6.37)$$

Here λC pertains to the soil, $\lambda C = 15 \times 10^{-4}$ cal^2 cm^{-4} sec^{-1}°C^{-2}.

To calculate $^{A_l}H_{so}/^{A_l}H_{ai}$ after cultivation it is recalled that $^{A_l}H_{ai}$ is proportional to $^A\vartheta_l(0)$. Using the relation $^A\vartheta_l(0) = 1.7$ $^A\vartheta_h$ which holds for equal heat flux density into the soil as a first approximation, one obtains

$$\frac{^{A_l}H_{so}}{^{A_l}H_{ai}} = \left(\frac{^{A_l}H_{so}}{^{A_h}H_{so}}\right)\left(\frac{^{A_h}H_{so}}{^{A_h}H_{ai}}\right)\left(\frac{^{A_h}H_{ai}}{^{A_l}H_{ai}}\right)$$
$$= 1 \times 2.71 \times 1/1.70 = 1.59.$$

An improved estimate of the temperature can rapidly be made if phase shifts and infrared emission are ignored. The assumption $^A H_{so} + {}^A H_{ai} =$ constant is now substituted instead of $^A H_{so} =$ constant. Thus 1.7 times as much heat is then transferred into the air above the cultivated soil. With $^{A_l}H_{so} = {}^{A_h}H_{so}$ one obtains

$$^{A_l}H_{so}/^{A_l}H_{ai} = 2.71/1.70 = 1.59.$$

An improved estimate of the temperature can again rapidly be made if phase shifts and infrared emission are ignored and the assumption $^A H_{so} + {}^A H_{ai} =$ constant is substituted for the assumption $^{A_l}H_{so} = {}^{A_h}H_{so}$.
Before cultivation one has

$$^{A_h}H_{so} + {}^{A_h}H_{ai} = 3.71 \, {}^{A_h}H_{ai},$$

after cultivation

$$^{A_l}H_{so} + {}^{A_l}H_{ai} = 2.59 \, {}^{A_l}H_{ai}.$$

So the amplitude of the heat flux density into air has increased in a ratio $3.71/2.59 = 1.43$ and this corresponds to

$$^A\vartheta_l(0) = 1.43 \, {}^A\vartheta_h = 25.7 \, ^\circ C.$$

6.8. Phase shifts, net long wave radiation*

A more precise calculation will now be given (compare section 4.6). Slightly different results are obtained. Before cultivation $^A\vartheta_h = 18 \, ^\circ C$ from which the amplitude of the heat wave in air results as 2.19×10^{-3} cal cm^{-2} sec^{-1}. Thus (see equation (6.37))

$$_h H_{so} + {}_h H_{ai} = 2.19 \times 10^{-3} \times 2.71 \, [\sin(\omega t + \tfrac{1}{4}\pi) + \sin(\omega t + 0.13)]$$
$$= 7.78 \times 10^{-3} \sin(\omega t + \text{arctg } 0.703). \tag{6.38}$$

The net infrared emissivity will now be calculated using the temperatures at normal observation height ($z = 200$ cm), no clouds, hence $vm = 0$ in

---

* This paragraph may be omitted by the reader not interested in mathematical derivations.

(3.35), and $p_w = 10$ mm of mercury. The average air temperature is taken as 20 °C, the amplitude at a height z is $h_0(r)/h_0(r_0)$ times $^A\vartheta_h$ at $z = 0$ (section 8.11). The function $h_0(r)$, in which $r = (2/b)\sqrt{[\omega C_{aib}(z + z_0)]}$, is shown in Fig. 8.3; one has for $z = 200$ cm, $r/r_0 = \sqrt{(2001)} = 44.7$ or $r = 0.106$ cm and $h_0(0.106) = 1.62$. Since $h_0(r_0) = -(2/\pi)\ln(\tfrac{1}{2}\gamma r_0) = 3.92$ or $h_0(r)/h_0(r_0) = 0.41$, the amplitude at 200 cm in air is $0.41 \times 18 = 7.4$ °C.

The phase shift is $\tfrac{1}{2}\pi [\eta_0(r_0) - \eta_0(r)]$ which amounts to $0.196 - 0.229 = -0.033$ rad according to Fig. 8.3.

Hence the variable part of the net long wave radiation heat flux density becomes (equation (4.32))

$$_hH_{lo}^{net} = 4 \times (293)^3 \times 1.36 \times 10^{-12} \times 0.27 \times 7.4 \sin(\omega t - 0.033)$$
$$= 2.73 \times 10^{-4} \sin(\omega t - 0.033). \tag{6.39}$$

The amplitude of the variable part of the net long wave radiation heat flux density is only 3 per cent of that of the total heat flux into soil and air Seeing the large degree of uncertainty in the regression formula for $_hH_{lo}^{net}$, it seems doubtful whether it is of any practical value to carry out a correction for the infrared emission and it is the more questionable as the ratio of $^A\vartheta_l(0)$ to $^A\vartheta_h$ is influenced not by $_hH_{lo}^{net}$ itself but by the difference of $_hH_{lo}^{net} - {}_hH_{ev}$ in both cases. We shall yet take it into account in the present example and obtain from (6.38) and (6.39)

$$(1-\varrho)H_{sh} - H_{ev} = {}_hH_{so} + {}_hH_{ai} + {}_hH_{lo}^{net}$$
$$= 7.78 \times 10^{-3} \sin[\omega t + \text{arctg}(0.703)] + 2.73 \times 10^{-4} \sin(\omega t - 0.0\ldots$$
$$= 8.00 \times 10^{-3} \sin[\omega t + \text{arctg}(0.673)]. \tag{6.40}$$

The amplitude is 3 per cent larger than found when $_hH_{lo}^{net}$ is ignored and the phase shift = arctg $(0.673) = 0.59$ rad instead of arctg $(0.703) = 0.61$ rad.

After cultivation one has $^A{}_lH_{ai} = [-b/(2\ln(\tfrac{1}{2}\gamma r_0))]^A\vartheta_l = 1.217 \times 10^{-4}$ $^A\vartheta_l(0)$ and a surface temperature which is shifted in phase by $_l\varphi_0$, so

$$_lH_{so} + {}_lH_{ai} = 1.217 \times 10^{-4} \, ^A\vartheta_l(0)$$
$$[1.59 \sin(\omega t + \tfrac{1}{4}\pi - 0.033 + {}_l\varphi_0) + \sin(\omega t + 0.13 + {}_l\varphi_0)]$$
$$= 3.01 \times 10^{-4} \, ^A\vartheta_l(0) \sin(\omega t + \text{arctg } 0.56 + {}_l\varphi_0). \tag{6.41}$$

The phase shift is 0.514 rad. The net infrared emissivity is

$$^AH_{lo}^{net} = 4 \times (293)^3 \times 1.36 \times 10^{-12} \times 0.26 \times 0.41 \, ^A\vartheta_l(0)\sin(\omega t - 0.033 + {}_l\varphi_0)$$
$$= 1.46 \times 10^{-5} \, ^A\vartheta_l(0)\sin(\omega t - 0.033 + {}_l\varphi_0),$$

and the total absorbed short-wave irradiancy minus evaporation becomes

$$(1-\varrho)\,H_{sh} - H_{ev} = 3.136 \times 10^{-4}\,{}^{A}\vartheta_l(0)\sin(\omega t + \mathrm{arctg}\,0.533 + {}_l\varphi_0),$$
$$(1-\varrho)\,H_{sh} - H_{ev} = {}_lH_{so} + {}_lH_{ai} + {}_lH_{lo}^{net}$$
$$= 3.01 \times 10^{-4}\,{}^{A}\vartheta_l(0)\sin(\omega t + \mathrm{arctg}\,0.565 + {}_l\varphi_0)$$
$$+ 1.46 \times 10^{-5}\,{}^{A}\vartheta_l(0)\sin(\omega t - 0.033 + {}_l\varphi_0)$$
$$= 3.136 \times 10^{-4}\,{}^{A}\vartheta_l(0)\sin(\omega t + {}_l\varphi_0 + 0.19). \qquad (6.42)$$

Equating (6.42) to (6.40), a value ${}^{A}\vartheta_l(0) = 25.5\,°C$ results from this calculation. The advance of the temperature at the surface of the cultivated soil in respect to the original soil equals $0.59 - 0.49 = 0.10$ rad.

Summarizing the results we observe that, if both H_{lo}^{net} and the phase shifts are ignored, ${}^{A}\vartheta_l(0) = 25.7\,°C$. If only H_{lo}^{net} is taken into account, ${}^{A}\vartheta_l(0) = 7.78/0.301 = 25.8\,°C$ (see (6.38) and (6.41)) and the phase shift $= 0.61 - 0.51 = 0.10$ rad. If both quantities are taken into account, ${}^{A}\vartheta_l(0) = 25.5\,°C$ and the phase shift becomes 0.10 rad.

6.9. The annual variation on a tilled soil

The influence of tilth on the annual temperature variation is small. The reason is the same as discussed in the comparison of two homogeneous soils (section 4.9), i.e. the slow variation of the temperature results in a relatively large heat flux to the air. The condition that the local heat flux remains constant is then nearly equivalent to the condition that the heat flux into air must remain unchanged before and after tilth. The latter statement demands equal surface temperatures for equal meteorological conditions.

If again we insert $bz_0 = 1.5 \times 10^{-4}$ cal cm^{-1} sec^{-1} °C^{-1}, $b = 1.5 \times 10^{-3}$ cal cm^{-2} sec^{-1} °C^{-1} and $r_0 = 1.20 \times 10^{-4}$ (section 4.6) we obtain ${}^{A}_{h}H_{ai} = -{}^{A}\vartheta b/[2\ln(\tfrac{1}{2}\gamma r_0)] = 8.20 \times 10^{-5}\,{}^{A}\vartheta$ and the heat wave in air is advanced by $\tfrac{1}{2}\pi + \mathrm{arctg}\,[(4/\pi)\ln(\tfrac{1}{2}\gamma r_0)] = 0.09$ rad in respect to the temperature at the surface.

For the original soil ${}^{A}_{h}H_{so}/{}^{A}_{h}H_{ai} = -(2/b)\sqrt{(\lambda_h C_h \omega)}\ln(\tfrac{1}{2}\gamma r_0) = 0.21$.

Cultivation to a depth $d = 10$ cm now corresponds to $d/D_1 = 0.043$ and, for a value of $r_l = -0.254$ and of $\sqrt{(\lambda_1 C_1)}/\sqrt{(\lambda_2 C_2)} = 1.68$ as before, the ratio ${}^{A}\vartheta_l(0)/{}^{A}\vartheta_h = 1.68 \times 0.62 = 1.04$ results. The phase shift for the temperature is ${}_l\varphi_0 - {}_h\varphi_0 = {}_l\varphi_0 = 0.04$ rad (Figs. 6.1 and 6.2) assuming equal heat flux densities. The phase constant for the homogeneous soil has always been equalled to 0 in the following (${}_h\varphi_0 = 0$). The heat flux density to air is proportional to ${}^{A}\vartheta_l(0)$, thus it is 1.04 times the flux density into the homogeneous soil and so

$$^{A}_{l}H_{so}/{}^{A}_{l}H_{ai} = 0.21/1.04 = 0.20.$$

The total heat flux density before tilth ignoring net long wave radiation and phase shifts is

$$^A_hH_{so} + {}^A_hH_{ai} = 1.21 \, {}^A_hH_{ai}$$

in the case of the homogeneous soil and it is

$$^A_lH_{so} + {}^A_lH_{ai} = 1.20 \, {}^A_lH_{ai}$$

in the case of the tilled soil. Equating the left-hand sides of these equations, one obtains the result

$$^A\vartheta_l(0)/^A\vartheta_h = 1.01.$$

The conclusion from this calculation is that cultivation does not produce a significant change in the amplitude of the first harmonic of the annual temperature wave.

A calculation of the phase shifts (section 6.10) indicates that the phase shifts are of the order of a day or perhaps some days for the first harmonic. This is in accordance with observation (VAN DUIN [1956]). On the other hand under special weather conditions a marked difference in surface temperature can result from tillage. If, for instance, the temperature in the spring rises rapidly, strong harmonics of a high order are present in the Fourier development and these short period fluctuations cause an increase of the amplitude $^A\vartheta_l(0)$, which is much higher than the increase due to the first harmonic. If such an effect is observed it may easily be misinterpreted as a result from tillage whereas it is actually a combined effect from both tillage and the rapid rise of temperature.

6.10. The phase shift of the annual variation

The ratio of the surface amplitudes $^A\vartheta_l(0)/^A\vartheta_h$ and the phase shift $_l\varphi_0$ of the surface temperature of the layered soil in respect to the homogeneous soil will now be calculated for the annual variation. The method is similar to that in section 6.8 where it was applied to the diurnal variation. Net long wave radiation is ignored but the phase shifts are taken into account. It is assumed that the total absorbed heat flux density is the same on both soils. This assumption comes closest to reality when the reflection coefficients of the surface and the evaporation are equal. Thus inserting the numerical data of section 6.9

$$
\begin{aligned}
_lH_{so} + {}_lH_{ai} &= {}_hH_{so} + {}_hH_{ai} \\
&= 8.20 \times 10^{-5} \, {}^A\vartheta_h \, [0.21 \sin(\omega t + \tfrac{1}{4}\pi) + \sin(\omega t + 0.09)] \\
&= 9.59 \times 10^{-5} \, {}^A\vartheta_h \sin(\omega t + \text{arctg } 0.208).
\end{aligned}
\tag{6.43}
$$

The surface temperature of the homogeneous soil is represented by

$$\vartheta_h(0) = {}^A\vartheta_h \sin\omega t.$$

The surface temperature of the layered soil will in general show a phase shift $\iota\varphi_0$,

$$\vartheta_l(0) = {}^A\vartheta_l(0) \sin(\omega t + \iota\varphi_0). \tag{6.44}$$

The heat flux density to the layered soil was found to be advanced in phase in respect to the temperature by an amount $(\tfrac{1}{4}\pi - 0.04)$ rad, so it must be represented by

$$\iota H_{so} = 8.20 \times 10^{-5} \times 0.20 \, {}^A\vartheta_l \sin(\omega t + \tfrac{1}{4}\pi - 0.04 + \iota\varphi_0). \tag{6.45}$$

The factor 0.20 was found in section 6.9 as the ratio $\iota H_{so}/\iota H_{ai}$.

As the phase shift of the heat flux density in air in respect to the surface temperature is determined only by the properties of the air layer, which are the same above both soils, one has an advance in phase of 0.09 rad in either case. Or

$$\iota H_{ai} = 8.20 \times 10^{-5} \, {}^A\vartheta_l \sin(\omega t + 0.09 + \iota\varphi_0). \tag{6.46}$$

Substituting (6.45) and (6.46) in (6.43) gives

$$\iota H_{so} + \iota H_{ai} = 8.20 \times 10^{-5} \, {}^A\vartheta_l [0.20 \sin(\omega t + \tfrac{1}{4}\pi - 0.04 + \iota\varphi_0)$$
$$+ \sin(\omega t + 0.09 + \iota\varphi_0)]$$
$$= 9.55 \times 10^{-5} \, {}^A\vartheta_l \sin(\omega t + \mathrm{arctg}\,0.197 + \iota\varphi_0)$$
$$= 9.59 \times 10^{-5} \, {}^A\vartheta_h \sin(\omega t + \mathrm{arctg}\,0.208), \tag{6.47}$$

from which results ${}^A\vartheta_l/{}^A\vartheta_h = 1.004$ and $\iota\varphi_0 = \mathrm{arctg}\,0.208 - \mathrm{arctg}\,0.197 = 0.01$ rad.

When ${}^A\vartheta_h$ is, for instance, 10 °C an amplitude ${}^A\vartheta_l(0) = 10.04$ °C results at the surface of the layered soil. This is an entirely insignificant difference. The advance in phase corresponds to an advance in season of $(0.01 \times 365)/2\pi$ days $= 0.6$ day. Thus the conclusion is that the annual heat wave at the soil surface is practically not influenced by cultivation to 10 cm depth.

Even cultivation to 40 cm depth does not produce a significant change in the annual surface temperature. In that case $d/D_1 = 0.17$ from which follows ${}^A\vartheta_l(0)/{}^A\vartheta_h = 1.68 \times 0.71 = 1.19$ assuming equal heat flux densities into the soils, whereas $\iota\varphi_0 = 0.12$ rad. It is concluded that ${}^A\iota H_{so}/{}^A\iota H_{ai} = 0.21/1.19 = 0.176$ after cultivation. Thus the total heat flux density, ignoring net infrared emission, becomes

$$[0.176 \sin(\omega t + \tfrac{1}{4}\pi - 0.12 + \iota\varphi_0) + \sin(\omega t + 0{,}09 + \iota\varphi_0)] \times 8.20 \times 10^{-5} \, {}^A\vartheta_l$$
$$= 9.44 \times 10^{-5} \, {}^A\vartheta_l \sin(\omega t + \mathrm{arctg}\,0.175 + \iota\varphi_0), \tag{6.48}$$

from which one calculates $^{A}\vartheta_l(0)/^{A}\vartheta_h = 9.59/9.44 = 1.016$. The temperature is advanced by arctg $0.208 - $ arctg $0.175 = 0.205 - 0.173 = 0.032$ rad or nearly 2 days in respect to the homogeneous soil.

6.11. Temperature below the surface

The amplitude at the depth z in respect to that of the uncultivated soil is expressed by (6.32); the phase shift by (6.33).*

At the depth $z = d$ the cultivated soil has invariably the smaller amplitude. Inserting $z = d$ in (6.32) leads to

$$\frac{^{A}\vartheta_l(d)}{^{A}\vartheta_h} = \left[\frac{\lambda_2 C_2}{\lambda_1 C_1} \frac{e^{-2d/D_1}[1 + r_l^2 + 2r_l]}{1 + r_l^2 e^{-4d/D_1} - 2r_l e^{-2d/D_1} \cos(2d/D_1)}\right]^{\frac{1}{2}}. \quad (6.49)$$

The same result is obtained from Table 6.1, equations (6.3), (6.5) and (6.30).

6.12. Comparison with experiment

Here, as in many other fields of agriculture, it is very difficult to make a satisfactory *quantitative* comparison between theory and experiments described in the literature, owing to the fact that many quantities which enter into the calculation have not been measured, as their importance was not realized at the time when the experiments were performed. So, for instance, meteorological data are often lacking and it is in most cases also not possible to estimate the ratio $^{A}\vartheta_{so}/^{A}\vartheta_{ai}$ since records of the diurnal air temperature which could serve as an approximate indication of the variation of the total heat flux, are not available. Moreover, thermal data of the soil or other data such as moisture content and air filled pore space, from which λ and C could eventually be estimated are generally not given.

A *qualitative* agreement between theory and experiment does, however, exist. The temperature differences are of the expected order of magnitude and the greater effect of tilth on the diurnal temperature variation than on the annual temperature variation is confirmed.

The increased susceptibility for night frost on a cultivated soil is well known and so is the higher maximum temperature. This means that the amplitude of the diurnal variation is increased by some degrees centigrade.

---

* It is left to the reader to verify that if an infinite value of d is inserted in (6.32) it gives the ratio $^{A}\vartheta_1(z)/^{A}\vartheta_2(0)$ for two homogeneous soils, having the thermal constants λ_1, C_1, and λ_2, C_2 respectively and whose surface amplitudes are in a ratio $\sqrt{(\lambda_2 C_2)}/\sqrt{(\lambda_1 C_1)}$. The heat flux densities at the surface of both homogeneous soils are equal.

Schmidt, for instance, found an amplitude of 13.4 °C on a cultivated plot as compared with 9.7 °C on the untreated soil (cf. GEIGER [1960]). The difference in the annual variation is much smaller under comparable conditions.

Van Duin measured the temperature at $z = 0$, $z = 10$ and $z = 20$ cm in a clay soil which was ploughed in the fall to a depth $d = 20$ cm. The total porosity of the upper layer was increased from 0.56 to 0.70 as an average value for the winter. He calculated a difference of the order of 0.1 °C for the annual variation. It turned out, however, that in the winter a fluctuation with a period of one month was superposed upon the annual temperature wave. The corresponding difference in surface amplitude would be 3.5 times that of the annual variation. A Fourier analysis of the temperature records was carried out. The amplitudes and phase shifts given in Table 6.3 were obtained from this analysis for a period $\omega = 2.4 \times 10^{-6}$ sec^{-1} corresponding to one month.

TABLE 6.3

Comparison of uncultivated and ploughed clay soil (after VAN DUIN [1956])

	$z = 0$		$z = 10$ cm		$z = 20$ cm	
	uncult.	ploughed	uncult.	ploughed	uncult.	ploughed
$^A\vartheta(z)(°C)$	5.9	6.5	5.5	5.5	4.2	4.0
phase shift (rad)	0.0	+0.05	−0.09	−0.10	−0.25	−0.25
ϑ_a (°C)	−0.4	−0.9	−0.5	0.0	+0.4	+0.9
ϑ_{max} (°C)	+5.5	+5.6	+5.0	+5.5	+4.6	+4.9
ϑ_{min} (°C)	−6.3	−7.4	−6.0	−5.5	−3.8	−3.1
ϑ_a occurred	9 and 25 January	9 and 25 January	9 and 25* January	9 and 25 January	10 and 26 January	10 and 26 January

* At $z = 10$ cm the average temperature occurred between 9 and 10 and 25 and 26 January.

The table shows that, in agreement with the theory, the amplitude at the boundary $d = 20$ cm is higher in the uncultivated soil and that the minimum temperature is lower. At the surface the reverse situation holds. Similar results were obtained in a sandy soil.

Differences of the order of 0.1 °C have also been found by most other authors for the annual variation. The temperature near the surface increases more rapidly during a warm period in spring and in summer in the tilled soil and on the other hand the increase in temperature is lower at the boundary of the cultivated layer (Gade, Schwind, Keen, Holldack and von Nitsch quoted by

VAN DUIN [1956]). The fact that the influence of tilth is in an opposite direction at the surface to that at some distance below it may be an explanation of the inconsistency of the conclusions arrived at by several authors.

6.13. Attempt to a quantitative comparison

Van Duin has attempted to apply the theory to West's measurements in Australia which were made at several depths (WEST [1932]).
Unfortunately the properties of the soil before and after cultivation had to be assumed as they were not determined. This introduces a considerable uncertainty. The calculation is nevertheless given in full by way of example. The upper layer in West's experiments was 13 cm thick. It was formed by loosening a layer of 10 cm of the original soil. The experimental data together with the calculated curves are represented in Fig. 6.3.

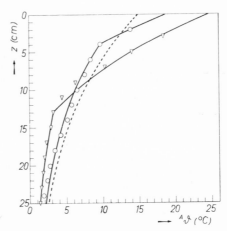

Fig. 6.3. Amplitudes of temperature waves as a function of depth.
$- \bigcirc - \bigcirc -$ = uncultivated soil
$- \triangledown - \triangledown -$ = cultivated soil
$------$ = calculated for homogeneous soil
    Measurements by WEST [1932] compared with calculations by VAN DUIN [1956].

The original soil was not homogeneous. This follows from the abnormal value of the amplitude at $z = 2$ cm. The ratio ${}^A\vartheta(2)/{}^A\vartheta(4)$ would lead to a highly improbable value of the damping depth in a homogeneous soil. Assuming a loose upper layer extending to 4 cm depth before cultivation and reasonable values for the thermal properties before and after cultivation the observations at $z = 2$ cm and $z = 4$ cm in the original soil and those

TABLE 6.4

Measured, assumed and calculated thermal data for the diurnal wave in a sandy soil (after West and van Duin)

	measured				assumed				
	z (cm)	$\Delta\theta(z)$ (°C)	d_1 (cm)	C_1 (cal cm⁻³)	C_2	λ_1 (cal cm⁻¹ sec⁻¹ °C⁻¹)	λ_2	$\sqrt{(\lambda_2 C_2/\lambda_1 C_1)}$	D_1 (cm)	D_2 (cm)
Uncult. soil	4	9.6	4	0.31	0.42	1.1×10^{-3}	3.0×10^{-3}	1.9	10.0	14.0
Cult. soil	13	3.2	13	0.33	0.42	0.8×10^{-3}	3.0×10^{-3}	2.2	8.2	14.0

$C_{ai} = 0.29 \times 10^{-3}$ cal cm⁻³ °C⁻¹, $z_0 = 0.4$ cm, $b = 2.47 \times 10^{-3}$ cal cm⁻² sec⁻¹ °C⁻¹, amplitude of $(H_{sh} - H_{1o}^{net}) = 7.6 \times 10^{-3}$ cal cm⁻² sec⁻¹.

TABLE 6.6

Properties of sand and peat both at field capacity

	x_m	x_w	C (cal cm⁻³ °C⁻¹)	λ (10^{-3} cal cm⁻¹ sec⁻¹ °C⁻¹)	$(\lambda C)^{\frac{1}{2}}$ (10^{-2} cal cm⁻² sec⁻¹ °C⁻¹)	D (diurnal) (cm)
sand	0.573	0.105	0.38	4.6	4.18	18.2
peat	0.100	0.500	0.56	0.68	1.95	5.8
mixture I	0.445	0.212	0.43	2.96	3.58	13.8
mixture II	0.337	0.303	0.469	2.12	3.15	11.1

Mixture I is a 0.73/0.27 mixture by volume of sand and peat. The composition of mixture II is 0.5/0.5.

made at $z = 3, 5, 7, 9, 11$ and 13 cm in the cultivated soil could be explained. His assumptions are collected in Table 6.4 together with the observed temperatures at 4 cm and at 13 cm respectively.

No surface temperatures were measured. First the daily temperature wave in a homogeneous soil with the properties of the subsoil is calculated. One has $\sqrt{(\lambda_2 C_2 \omega)} = 3.03 \times 10^{-4}$. Assuming a b-value for the average wind strength of 2.47×10^{-3}, with $r_0 = (2/b)\sqrt{(C_{ai} \omega b z_0)} = 3.70 \times 10^{-3}$, so $\ln \frac{1}{2} \gamma r_0 = -5.7$, one obtains

$$\frac{{}^A H_{so}}{{}^A H_{ai}} = \frac{-2[\sqrt{(\lambda_2 C_2 \omega)} \ln (\frac{1}{2} \gamma r_0)]}{b} = 1.40. \tag{6.50}$$

Ignoring evaporation the amplitudes and the phases of the various heat flux densities are calculated. For air

$$\varphi_{ai} = \tfrac{1}{2}\pi + \text{arctg} \left[(4/\pi) \ln \tfrac{1}{2} \gamma r_0 \right] = \tfrac{1}{2}\pi + \text{arctg}\,(-7.28) = 0.137 \text{ rad},$$

in the soil $\varphi_{so} = \frac{1}{4}\pi = 0.785$ rad. Inserting these values in (4.28) yields $\varphi_{sh} = \text{arctg}\,0.57 = 0.52$ rad. To calculate the amplitude of the temperature at the surface, the amplitude of the total heat wave must be known. It has been calculated from total solar radiation and the average cloudiness, (which was very low) and humidity. Multiplication of (4.27) by $\sin \varphi_{sh}$ and of (4.26) by $\cos \varphi_{sh}$ and addition yields

$${}^A H_{sh} = {}^A H_{so} \cos(\varphi_{so} - \varphi_{sh}) + {}^A H_{ai} \cos(\varphi_{ai} - \varphi_{sh}).$$

Since, according to (4.30) ${}^A H_{ai} = -{}^A\vartheta(0)\, b/(2 \ln \tfrac{1}{2} \gamma r_0)$ we have

$${}^A\vartheta(0) = \frac{-2\,{}^A H_{sh} \ln (\tfrac{1}{2} \gamma r_0)}{b\left[\cos(\varphi_{ai} - \varphi_{sh}) + \dfrac{{}^A H_{so}}{{}^A H_{ai}} \sin(\varphi_{so} - \varphi_{sh})\right]},$$

from which follows

$${}^A\vartheta_h(0) = 2035 \times 7.6 \times 10^{-3} = 15.5 \,°C.$$

For the uncultivated soil with a dry top layer, $r_l = -0.32$ and ${}^A H_{so}/{}^A H_{ai}$ is increased in the ratio ${}^A\vartheta_h(0)/{}^A\vartheta_l(0)$. The latter is the reciprocal value of the right-hand expression in (6.32). In this case one obtains ${}^A\vartheta_l(0)/{}^A\vartheta_h(0)$ $= 1.56$, and thus ${}^A H_{so}/{}^A H_{ai} = 1.40/1.56 = 0.898$.

The phase shift of the temperature at the surface in respect to the homogeneous soil is calculated from (6.31) as

$$\varphi_l - \varphi_h = \text{arctg} \frac{0.62 \exp(-0.8) \sin 0.8}{1 - 0.096 \exp(-1.6)} = 0.20 \text{ rad}.$$

With these data one obtains $\varphi_{so} = 0.58$ rad, $\varphi_{sh} = $ arctg $0.36 = 0.35$ rad and $^A\vartheta_l(0) = 2500 \times 7.6 \times 10^{-3} = 19.0\,°C$, whereas $\varphi_{ai} = 0.137$ rad as before.

For the *cultivated* soil, $r_l = -0.375$, $d = 13$ cm, resulting in $^A\vartheta_l/^A\vartheta_h = 2.27$ or $^AH_{so}/^AH_{ai} = 1.40/2.27 = 0.617$, whereas $\varphi_l - \varphi_h = -0.001$ rad. One then calculates $\varphi_{so} = 0.784$ rad, $\varphi_{sh} = $ arctg $0.40 = 0.38$ rad and $^A\vartheta_l(0) = 3010 \times 7.6 \times 10^{-3} = 22.9\,°C$.

The calculated amplitudes are now compared with the experimental amplitudes at $z = 4$ cm in the uncultivated soil, $^A\vartheta_h(4) = 9.6\,°C$, and at $z = 13$ cm in the cultivated soil, $^A\vartheta_h(13) = 3.2\,°C$. We have according to Table 6.1 (equations (6.5) and (6.3))

$$^A\vartheta(d) = {}^A\vartheta'_1(1 + r_l)\,e^{-d/D_1}$$
$$= {}^A\vartheta_l(1 + r_l)\,e^{-d/D_1}[1 + r_l^2\,e^{-4d/D_1} + 2r_l\,e^{-2d/D_1}\cos(2d/D_1)]^{-\frac{1}{2}},$$

which for $d = 4$ cm, $r_l = -0.31$ and $^A\vartheta_l = 19.0\,°C$ becomes $19.0 \times 0.510 = 9.7\,°C$, and for $d = 13$ cm, $r_l = -0.375$, $^A\vartheta_l = 22.9\,°C$ becomes $22.9 \times 0.126 = 2.9\,°C$.

The calculated curves drawn in Fig. 6.3 have been obtained by similar calculations. The agreement with experiment is fairly good. It could still be improved by adopting slightly different thermal properties, but it is not considered worth the effort. So many assumptions have to be made that the discussion must anyhow be considered as a qualitative check rather than as a quantitative one, though the assumed values are not improbable. The measurements would have permitted a much more satisfactory comparison with theory when the assumed quantities had been measured. This example may show how important a knowledge of the theoretical background is in performing field experiments.

6.14. Properties of a soil after tilth

Experience shows that the water content of the soil is not altered by cultivation. Thus the increase in volume is only caused by additional air and it is possible to calculate the volume fraction of minerals, of air and of water from the observed change in volume. If the cultivated layer had originally a thickness of l cm which is increased to d cm, one has $x_{m2}l = x_{m1}d$. The index 2 is used for the original soil, which is identical with the soil in the lower layer after tilth and the index 1 for the upper layer, x_m is the volume fraction of minerals. Similarly for the volume fraction of water-filled pores, $lx_{w2} = dx_{w1}$.

The air-filled pore space per unit of volume is

$$x_a = 1 - x_m - x_w.$$

The changes in the pore space brought about by tilth are, owing to these relations

$$x_{m1} = \frac{l}{d} x_{m2}, \tag{6.51a}$$

$$x_{w1} = \frac{l}{d} x_{w2}, \tag{6.51b}$$

and

$$x_{a1} = 1 - \frac{l}{d} [x_{m2} + x_{w2}] = 1 - \frac{l}{d} + \frac{l}{d} x_{a2}. \tag{6.51c}$$

If the soil contains organic material, its concentration changes in a similar way to that of the minerals, and then x_m represents the volume fraction of the total solid material present. It cannot be expected that such simple relations as (6.51) will quantitatively describe the properties of a system so complex as a soil, but the essential feature, i.e. the loosening of the upper layer, is taken into account by them and the intensity of the cultivation appears in the ratio d/l. The increase in air-filled pore space is according to (6.51c)

$$x_{a1} - x_{a2} = \left(1 - \frac{l}{d}\right)(1 - x_{a2}).$$

This quantity is always positive as x_{a2} is a fraction which is smaller than one.

Volumetric heat capacity and heat conductivity can be calculated from the volume fractions (cf. Chapter 7). The roughness of the soil surface differs with the method of cultivation which means that a different value of z_0 must be used for ploughing then in case of fine grain seedbed. One should use a value of z_0 which is of the same order, say 0.3 to 0.5 times the average height of the protruding soil parts; more precise advice cannot be given at present.

TABLE 6.5

Change of pore volume after tilth (after Nekrassov quoted by KRAUSSE [1931])

	before 30 May	30 May–3 July	3 July–7 Aug.	after 7 Aug.
Volume fraction of solid material	0.503	0.412	0.363	0.359
Noncap. pore space	0.126	0.265	0.357	0.331
Cap. pore space	0.371	0.323	0.280	0.310

Soil stability after tilth seems to vary considerably. In many cases the original porosity is practically restored after approximately six months, but the loose structure is sometimes preserved for more than a year. By way of example some data are given.

The soil to which Table 6.5 refers was ploughed on May 30, July 3 and August 7.

A further illustrative example is shown in Fig. 6.4 from which the instability of the loose structure follows.

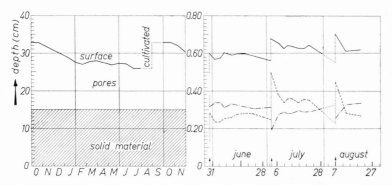

Fig. 6.4. Instability of loose structure of upper layer. (After von Nitzsch [1937].)

As an example for an exceptionally stable upper layer, Kloeppel's data may be mentioned (Kloeppel [1930]). No change in the volume fraction of solid matter was found after six months. It was approximately 0.39 after ploughing and 0.52 before it. The soil was ploughed to a depth of 22 cm. It is not stated what type of soil these figures refer to.

The water content, expressed in per cent by weight, is generally not altered by tilth as has been assumed in (6.51). An exception is sometimes formed by loam and other very densely packed soils, in which the water content expressed as volume fraction of water-filled pores changes less. The total water content of the upper layer has consequently increased.

6.15. Conclusions on thermal effects resulting from tilth

The aspects of the changes of soil temperature resulting from tilth in respect to plant growth may be summarized as follows:

Cultivation decreases the ratio $^A H_{so}/^A H_{ai}$ for the diurnal heat wave. In periods of increasing surface temperature the tilled soil is warmer at and near the surface. It is cooler than uncultivated soil from a certain depth on downwards. The air temperature above the tilled soil is then higher if evaporation is the same and provided that the areas which are compared are so extended that the air temperature is not mainly determined by advective air. The converse conclusions apply to a period of decreasing surface temperature.

The differences of the surface amplitudes are small for the annual temperature fluctuation. They are of the order of some tenths of a degree centigrade for Western Europe. Deep cultivation may perhaps advance the season by one or two days.

For the diurnal variation or with a rapid nonperiodic temperature variation several degrees centigrade difference may be expected, as for instance at the onset of a warm or a cold spell.

The influence on plant growth depends on the instant at which the soil is tilled. *Summer crops* are generally seeded when the temperature is increasing. The soil near the surface is then warmer in the average in the seedbed and germination and first growth are stimulated.

Risk of damage by night frost is enhanced on a tilled soil owing to higher diurnal temperature amplitude.

The high amplitude promotes germination with some crops.

Winter crops are sown in a period of decreasing temperature. The lower average temperature of a tilled soil which may occur in a period of an abnormal rapid fall of temperature retards germination and the risk of damage by night frost of the young plant is correspondingly increased. Thus it is concluded that intense and deep cultivation is not advisable if winter crops are sown.

Compressing the soil between the plant rows in the spring may promote the development of a winter crop owing to a slight increase of the average temperature in the root zone. It is, however, well known that in several cases soil compaction has an adverse effect on plant growth.

6.16. A sand layer on top of a peat soil

Application of a sand or of a clay layer on top of a peat soil is an old practice to improve the agricultural value of a peat soil (MITSCHERLICH [1954]). It is stated that a sand or clay layer prevents irreversible drying of the peat by preventing excessive evaporation and that the amplitude of the diurnal wave is reduced and consequently the risk of nightfrost decreased.

Irreversible drying is the phenomenon that water is extremely slowly absorbed by a peat soil when the peat has been dried below a certain water content. Under these circumstances rain causes a considerable runoff which may result in erosion and at any rate means uncontrolled loss of water. The surface layer of the peat soil obtains a very fine structure which is easily blown away by wind. Similar phenomena may even to a higher degree occur in a muck soil.

Evaporation is noticeably reduced when the upper three to four centimeters of a sandy soil are dried out. So a layer of that thickness on a peat soil would in general protect the latter against irreversible drying. In Germany a sand cover of some centimeters thickness is often applied to a peat soil which is used as grassland, but 10 to 15 cm of sand is common if arable crops are grown. The latter values are in agreement with the theory. For these depths the amplitude on the surface of the soil with a sand top soil is approximately equal to that on a sandy soil.

The experiment station at Bremen, Germany, has carried out systematic investigations on peat soils for more than eighty years (BADEN [1952]).
Application of a sand or clay layer on top decreases loss of moisture owing to evaporation and it also decreases frost danger; the latter could also be reduced by rolling the surface. The theory confirms this experience. The protection by a sand or a clay layer is due to its higher thermal conductivity as compared with peat; compression of a soil increases its thermal conductivity as the air-filled pore space is reduced. On the other hand the observed greater sensitivity to night frost of a deeply drained soil as compared with a soil in which a groundwater level at 50 cm is maintained, can be understood by the lower conductivity of the drier soil although evaporation is probably also an important factor in this case. A higher average summer temperature at the boundary layer between sand and peat as compared with uncovered peat at the same depth and a higher humidity of the air above the soil with the higher water level have been observed. This agrees with the theory although the observed difference of approximately two degrees centigrade seems too high unless it is due to a combined effect of reduction of evaporation and improved thermal properties. KREUTZ [1943] has made similar experiments and he arrived at materially the same conclusions.

Juusela reviewed practices in many countries from which follows that frost danger is decreased by a mineral cover of sufficient thickness and by rolling, though in the U.S.A. and in Ireland this effect is not considered as the main advantage of a clay cover. There the decrease of wind erosion is mentioned as the most important advantage (JUUSELA [1945, 1956]*.

---

* T. Juusela: private communication (1956).

The theory of the layered soil applied to a sand or to a clay covered peat soil leads to conclusions some of which are opposite as in case of tilth since now the upper layer is a better thermal conductor than the subsoil. The amplitude of the diurnal temperature wave at the surface is decreased, the phase is retarded. At the boundary layer a greater amplitude prevails than at the same depth of the soil without a mineral cover.

In the following calculations the same thermal properties of the air are adopted as in the previous examples. The thermal properties of the peat and the sand cover which will be used in the following discussion are given in Table 6.6 (see p. 193). The properties in the first and in the second row were determined on actual samples (DE VRIES and DE WIT [1954]).

The value of r_l is positive so the right-hand reciprocal scale must be used in Figs. 6.1 and 6.2. One has for the sand cover $r_l = 0.364$ and $(\lambda_2 C_2 / \lambda_1 C_1)^{\frac{1}{2}} = 0.47$. The indices 1 and 2 refer to the upper and to the lower layer respectively, as usual. For a sand layer of three cm thickness one has $d_1/D_1 = 0.16$ which corresponds to ${}^A\vartheta_l(0)/{}^A\vartheta_h(0) = 0.47 \times 1.7 = 0.80$. If $d_1/D_1 = 0.55$ ($d_1 = 10$ cm) and $d_1/D_1 = 0.72$ ($d_1 = 13$ cm) one obtains ${}^A\vartheta_l(0)/{}^A\vartheta_h(0) = 0.56$ and 0.49, respectively. Thus a layer of 13 cm thickness reduces the amplitude at the surface to practically the value prevailing on a sandy soil.

The above values pertain to equal heat flux densities. Ignoring the phase shift and the change in net infrared emissivity, one has for the homogeneous peat soil at field capacity (see section 4.9)

$$ {}^A H_{so}/{}^A H_{ai} = -2\frac{\sqrt{(\lambda C \omega)}}{b} \ln\left(\tfrac{1}{2}\gamma r_0\right) = -0.22 \ln\left(2.11 \times 10^{-3}\right) = 1.36. $$

At equal heat flux densities ${}^A\vartheta_l(0) = 0.80 \; {}^A\vartheta_h(0)$ if $d_1 = 3$ cm; the heat flux density into air is proportional to ${}^A\vartheta_l(0)$, so it is reduced to 80% of its value above the uncovered soil and ${}^A H_{so}/{}^A H_{ai} = 1.36/0.80 = 1.70$. Taking this change of the ratio ${}^A H_{so}/{}^A H_{ai}$ into account we have before the sand cover is applied ${}^A H_{so} + {}^A H_{ai} = 2.36 \; {}^A H_{ai}$, and after its application ${}^A H_{so} + {}^A H_{ai} = 2.70 \; {}^A H_{ai}$. The amplitude at the surface is thus altered in a ratio $2.36/2.70 = 0.87$, since ${}^A H_{so} + {}^A H_{ai}$ remains constant. Similar calculations for $d_1 = 10$ cm and $d_1 = 13$ cm give the results ${}^A\vartheta_l(0)/{}^A\vartheta_h(0) = 2.36/3.43 = 0.69$ and ${}^A\vartheta_l(0)/{}^A\vartheta_h(0) = 2.36/3.78 = 0.62$ respectively.

The reduction of the amplitude at the surface to just over 60 per cent by a sand cover of 13 cm thickness is certainly important in decreasing the risk of night frost damage. Using a value ${}^A H_{so} + {}^A H_{ai} = 7.55 \times 10^{-3}$ cal cm^{-2} sec^{-1}, one calculates with ${}^A H_{ai} = 1.22 \times 10^{-4} \; {}^A\vartheta(0)$ an amplitude ${}^A\vartheta(0) =$

$7.55 \times 10^{-3}/2.36 \times 1.22 \times 10^{-4} = 26\,°C$ (see section 6.7). This value is decreased to $16\,°C$ for a sand cover of 13 cm. Again equal evaporation (a very small value in this example) has been assumed.

The last two rows in Table 6.6 contain the thermal properties of mixtures of sand and peat. The values of x_m, x_w and C are additive, and the thermal conductivity has been calculated (see Chapter 7). A layer with intermediate properties is formed when the top layer becomes mixed with the subsoil in course of time. The layer will generally not have a uniform constitution in an actual case but the example gives a fair estimate of the effects of mixing. Tillage of the top layer promotes mixing.

If a sand layer 14.6 cm thick is mixed with 5.4 cm of peat to give a top layer for which $d = 20$ cm, the properties of that top layer are those of mixture I in Table 6.6. The value of $d/D_1 = 1.45$ and $r_l = 0.295$ which gives the result $^A\vartheta_l(0)/^A\vartheta_h(0) = 0.98 \times 0.54 = 0.53$. A sand layer extending to $d = 14.6$ cm before mixing would lead to $^A\vartheta_l(0)/^A\vartheta_h(0) = 0.47$. For a top layer of 14.6 cm height formed by a uniform mixture of 7.3 cm of sand and 7.3 cm of peat the ratio was $^A\vartheta_l(0)/^A\vartheta_h(0) = 0.60$.

The calculations of the mixed layers pertain to equal heat flux densities. Though the ratio $^A\vartheta_l(0)/^A\vartheta_h(0)$ must thus still be corrected for different heat flux densities, the results indicate that the gradual mixing of the top layer with the undersoil does not produce a rapid decrease of the improved thermal properties of the soil. Consequently application of a mineral cover will protect the soil during several years in succession. Deep cultivation must of course be avoided.

6.17. Dry upper layer

It will now be investigated to what extend the conclusions are altered when the top soil is dry. Approximating actually observed field conditions, DE VRIES and DE WIT [1954] have assumed the height of the dry layer in the soils under comparison to be 3.1 cm in sand and 2.4 cm in peat. The soil

TABLE 6.7

Thermal properties of dry sand and of dry peat

	x_m	C (cal cm^{-3} °C^{-1})	λ (10^{-3} cal cm^{-1} sec^{-1} °C^{-1})	$\sqrt{(\lambda C)}$ (10^{-2} cal cm^{-2} sec$^{-\frac{1}{2}}$ °C^{-1})	D (diurnal) (cm)
sand	0.573	0.27	0.60	1.27	7.8
peat	0.100	0.061	0.081	0.22	6.0

below these depths being at field capacity. For the thermal properties of dry sand and of dry peat we refer to Table 6.7.

The uncovered peat soil consists of two layers; an upper dry layer having a depth of 2.4 cm and the underlying peat at field capacity. The very high ratio $^A\vartheta_l^{pe}(0)/^A\vartheta_h^{pe}(0) = 5.5$ is calculated for the peat with dry upper layer in respect to the homogeneous peat soil at field capacity, for equal heat flux densities. For the same properties of the air as before one obtains a value $^AH_{so}/^AH_{ai} = 1.36/5.5 = 0.25$ for the dry peat soil or $^AH_{so} + ^AH_{ai} = 1.25\,^AH_{ai}$. This must be equal to the value $2.36\,^AH_{ai}$ which pertains to the peat at field capacity. The ratio $^A\vartheta_l^{pe}(0)/^A\vartheta_h^{pe}(0)$ thus becomes $2.36/1.25 = 1.89$ or, recalling that $^A\vartheta_h^{pe}(0) = 26\ °C$, one obtains $^A\vartheta_l^{pe}(0) = 49\ °C$. This latter value seems extremely high even for a bare dry peat soil.*

If the peat soil is covered with a sand layer which is partly dried out, one has a case of a soil consisting of three layers with different thermal properties. First there is a dry sand layer which in the present example is assumed to be 3.1 cm thick, secondly a sand layer at field capacity and thirdly the peat soil at field capacity. The three layer problem is discussed in section 6.19. It will be seen that the surface amplitude reaches practically the same value as for an infinite thickness, if the sand layer at field capacity is over 8 cm thick.

The ratio of the surface amplitudes of a sand soil consisting of two layers, an upper dry layer of 3.1 cm thickness and sand at field capacity underneath, in respect to a homogeneous sand soil at field capacity is calculated at $^A\vartheta_l^{sa}(0)/^A\vartheta_h^{sa}(0) = 2.36$, using $r_l = -0.53$ and $d/D_1 = 0.397$. This ratio applies to equal heat flux densities to the soils.

It is the object to calculate $^A\vartheta_l^{sa}(0)$ and compare it to $^A\vartheta_l^{pe}(0)$ under equal total heat flux densities, $(^AH_{so} + ^AH_{ai})$, for both. In order to perform this comparison the ratio $^A\vartheta_l^{sa}(0)/^A\vartheta_h^{pe}(0)$ will now be calculated, in which ϑ_h^{pe} pertains to the homogeneous peat soil at field capacity.

Since

$$\frac{^A\vartheta_l^{sa}(0)}{^A\vartheta_h^{pe}(0)} = \frac{^A\vartheta_l^{sa}(0)}{^A\vartheta_h^{sa}(0)}\,\frac{^A\vartheta_h^{sa}(0)}{^A\vartheta_h^{pe}(0)},$$

and the latter ratio is $(1.95/4.18) = 0.466$ (see Table 6.6) one obtains

$$^A\vartheta_l^{sa}(0)/^A\vartheta_h^{pe}(0) = 2.36 \times 0.466 = 1.10.$$

---

* For such high amplitudes the heat transport to air can probably no longer be described by a linearly varying apparent conductivity. As at present the laws of convective heat transfer in air are not well established, we shall still use the previous method to demonstrate how to calculate heat flux density into air.

The correction for different heat flux densities to both soils is now applied. We had $^AH_{so}/^AH_{ai}^{pe} = -2[\surd(\lambda C\omega)\ln(\tfrac{1}{2}\gamma r_0)]/b = 1.36$ for the homogeneous peat soil at field capacity. Thus the amplitude of the total heat flux density at the surface of the peat soil is $^AH_{so} + ^AH_{ai} = 2.36\,^AH_{ai}$.

The assumption of equal $^AH_{so}$ to the layered sand soil as to the peat soil gives the total heat flux density at the surface of the layered sand soil as $^AH_{so} + 1.10\,^AH_{ai}^{pe} = 2.46\,^AH_{ai}^{pe}$, in which $^AH_{ai}^{pe}$ is the amplitude of the heat flux density to air above the homogeneous peat soil. Since equality of the total heat flux densities will now be assumed instead of equal $^AH_{so}$, the latter two must be in a ratio $^A_lH_{so}^{sa}/^AH_{so}^{pe} = m$ such that $2.46\,m\,^AH_{ai}^{pe} = 2.36\,^AH_{ai}^{pe}$, or $m = 0.96$. From this value one obtains $^A\vartheta_l^{sa}(0)/^A\vartheta_h^{pe}(0) = 0.96 \times 1.10 = 1.06$. Since $^A\vartheta_h^{pe}(0)$ was 26 °C one now obtains $^A\vartheta_l^{sa}(0) = 27.6$ °C. This value must be compared with $^A\vartheta_l^{pe}(0) = 49$ °C for the peat soil with dry upper layer.

Thus the influence of a sand cover is very great in the case of a dry surface layer. If the soil is partly covered by plants the amplitude of the effective surface temperature is reduced and the more so if evaporation occurs. A higher value of z_0 must also be inserted in the equation for heat transfer to air in case of a vegetation cover. The ratio of the amplitudes at the two soils which are compared is not changed when evaporation occurs on both provided that the same fraction of available energy is consumed in evaporation in either case. The amplitudes themselves, however, are considerably smaller; the ratio decreases when z_0 increases.

Thus a sand or a clay layer on peat has a very marked effect on the surface temperature. A height of approximately 10 cm of sand is sufficient to obtain the maximum reduction of the amplitude of the diurnal temperature variation.

6.18. Other types of top layers

A mulch consisting of dry leaves, a dry sand mulch or a mulch of dry decomposed organic material on a soil at field capacity are examples of a layered soil of which the upper layer has the lower contact coefficient (λC). The parameter r_l is then negative. The temperature variation in the underlying soil is reduced. The amplitude at the boundary $^A\vartheta(d)$, i.e. at the soil surface under the mulch, can be calculated from (6.32) and (6.33). Below the depth d the attenuation of the temperature wave takes place as in a homogeneous soil. In a warm climate, a mulch keeps the soil temperature more uniform and prevents too high a maximum temperature. In a cold climate, it may be used to protect the seed from frost damage. In both cases the temperature variation is enhanced at the surface of the mulch, which means an increased risk for night frost damage to the young plants when they protrude out of the mulch layer.

The protection provided by a snow cover to plants buried under it is well known. If a shrub has only been partially buried under snow, severe frost damage has often been observed just above the snow surface. This is exactly what must be expected. In case of snow an extra factor comes into the picture since the reflection coefficient for solar radiation is very high; $1 - \varrho$ may become 0.2 or less in (4.18). Yet the emission coefficient for the long wave thermal radiation of 4μ and higher remains practically equal to 1, so that the snow radiates as a black body in those wave lengths. The energy flux available for heating the soil and the air is thus strongly reduced.

In Table 6.8 some characteristic values of the thermal properties of snow and of dry humic material are given.

We have seen that the surface temperature is practically equal to that on a

TABLE 6.8

Thermal properties of snow and of dry humus

	x_a	C (cal cm^{-3} °C^{-1})	λ (10^{-3} cal cm^{-1} sec^{-1} °C^{-1})	D (diurnal) (cm)
snow (fresh)	0.85	0.15	0.11	4.5
snow (old)	0.60	0.40	0.78	7.3
humus	0.90	0.061	0.08	6.0

homogeneous medium with the same thermal properties as the upper layer if $d = \frac{1}{4}\pi D_1$ or larger. This depth is 5.2 and 4.5 cm respectively for the media in Table 6.8.

The effect of a straw mulch on early growth of corn has been discussed by VAN WIJK, LARSON and BURROWS [1959]. The essential points of this discussion in which an empirical curve giving growth rate as a function of temperature is used to explain the influence of soil temperature will be repeated here.

Interstate experiments on early growth of corn in the U.S. had proved that a straw mulch has an unfavorable influence on dry matter production in Iowa and in Minnesota, it was slightly unfavorable in Ohio and no definite effect was found in South Carolina. Differences between mulched and unmulched soil were pronounced only during the early stage of development up to 6 to 7 weeks after germination.

Soil temperature was influenced in such a way that minimum temperatures were practically equal in mulched and in unmulched soil but maximum temperatures were lower in the mulched soil. This effect may be explained by the higher reflection coefficient for solar radiation of a mulched soil. The reflection coefficient for terrestrial radiation is not much different.

Thus the range of the diurnal temperature variation as well as the average temperature was decreased in the upper layers. The temperature at an arbitrary depth could be calculated from the maximum and minimum temperatures which were measured at two depths.

The average temperature was calculated as the mean value of maximum and minimum temperature.

At the 10 cm level the decrease of the average temperature was 0.6 to 1.1 °C under the mulch and the calculated depression at the 2.5 cm depth is approximately 2 °C.

HALL *et al.* [1953] have shown that early root growth of corn is mainly in a horizontal direction.

Thus the layers above approximately 10 cm depth are most important for the present discussion.

The most striking effects of the mulch can be explained on the basis of LEHENBAUER's [1914] growth curve shown in Fig. 6.5. In this curve corn growth is given as a function of temperature under laboratory conditions. It pertains to shoot growth of corn seedlings during a 9 hr period when both air and nutrient solution were maintained at the same temperature. It appears from other observations that the growth rate curve at a later stage of development will probably be not much different. The line segments in the figure indicate the ranges of the diurnal temperature variation at the 10 cm and 2.5 cm levels in unmulched soil.

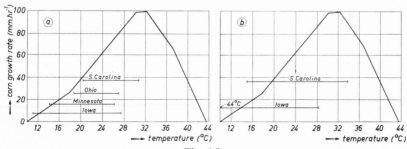

Fig. 6.5.

In Iowa maximum temperature at the 2.5 cm level is still in the range in which a temperature depression causes a depression in growth rate. Thus the decrease of the average temperature and that of the maximum temperature in mulched soil will cause a decrease of growth rate. This holds also for Minnesota. In both states at the 2.5 cm level temperatures occur at which growth stops.

In South Carolina maximum soil temperature at 10 cm is in the region of optimum growth rate but at the 2.5 cm level it is definitely in the range of falling growth rate with increasing temperature. A reduction of the maximum temperature has now a favorable effect in the layers above 10 cm depth. It has little or an adverse effect in deeper layers. A decrease of the average temperature retards growth. This situation explains why the straw mulch has little or no effect in South Carolina.

Soil temperatures at the experimental field in Ohio were lower than in South Carolina but higher than in Minnesota and Iowa. The response of dry matter production to mulching in Ohio is in agreement with this situation.

6.19. A soil consisting of three or more layers

The solution of the equation of propagation of heat in a soil consisting of three and more layers is derived in a similar way to that for a soil consisting of two layers. In the homogeneous subsoil, which is the nth layer in the general case when layers are present, one has

$$\vartheta_n(z) = \vartheta_{\text{ad}} + {}^{A}\vartheta_n \, e^{-z/D_n} \sin(\omega t + \varphi_n - z/D_n).$$

In the higher layers two solutions must be considered: one with an amplitude increasing with depth and the other with a decreasing amplitude. The amplitudes and phase constants must have such values that the temperature is continuous at each boundary layer, or $\vartheta_k(z = d_k) = \vartheta_{k+1}(z = d_k)$, and that the heat flux density is also continuous, i.e. $\lambda_k(\partial \vartheta_k/\partial z) = \lambda_{k+1}(\partial \vartheta_{k+1}/\partial z)$ for $z = d_k$. The calculation of the amplitudes and phase constants presents no essential difficulty, but the formulas become cumbersome to handle and it is recommended to insert numerical values directly at the beginning. As an example the calculation for the peat soil covered with a partially dry sand layer, which has been discussed in section 6.17, is now carried out.

The thermal properties of the three layers are given in Table 6.6 for sand and peat at field capacity and in Table 6.7 for the dry sand. They are again represented in Table 6.9, together with some other quantities used in the calculation.

TABLE 6.9

Data pertaining to a peat soil covered with sand

	C (cal cm^{-3} °C^{-1})	λ (10^{-3} cal cm^{-1} sec^{-1} °C^{-1})	D (diurnal) (cm)
layer 1 (dry sand)	0.27	0.60	7.8
layer 2 (sand at field cap.)	0.38	4.6	18.2
layer 3 (peat at field cap.)	0.56	0.68	5.8

The first layer extends from $z = 0$ to $d_1 = 3.1$ cm, the second from $d_1 = 3.1$ cm to $d_2 = 14.6$ cm; $d_1/D_1 = 0.40$; $d_1/D_2 = 0.17$; $d_2/D_2 = 0.80$; $d_2/D_3 = 2.52$.

It is of advantage to use complex numbers in order to keep the equations as simple as possible (see section 4.4.1).

According to (6.1)

$$\vartheta_k(z,t) - \vartheta_a =$$
$$^A\vartheta'_k \, e^{-(z-d_{k-1})/D_k} \sin(\omega t + \varphi'_k - z/D_k) + {}^A\vartheta''_k \, e^{+(z-d_{k-1})/D_k} \sin(\omega t + \varphi''_k + z/D_k),$$
$$(6.52)$$

where $\vartheta_k(z,t)$ denotes the temperature as a function of z and t between the boundaries d_k and d_{k+1}, i.e. in layer number k, whereas ϑ_a is the average temperature. Equation (6.52) may be written as

$$\vartheta_k(z,t) - \vartheta_a =$$
$$= \mathrm{Im}\,[^A\vartheta'_k \exp\{-z/D_k + i(\omega t + \varphi'_k - z/D_k)\}$$
$$+ {}^A\vartheta''_k \exp\{+z/D_k + i(\omega t + \varphi''_k + z/D_k)\}]$$

$$= \mathrm{Im}\,[^A\vartheta'_k \exp\{i\varphi'_k\} \exp\{-(1+i)z/D_k\} \exp\{i\omega t\}$$
$$+ {}^A\vartheta''_k \exp\{i\varphi''_k\}\exp\{+(1+i)z/D_k\} \exp\{i\omega t\}]$$

$$= \mathrm{Im}\,[(^{CA}\vartheta'_k \, \varepsilon^{-z/D_k} + {}^{CA}\vartheta''_k \, \varepsilon^{+z/D_k}) \exp i\omega t].\qquad(6.53)$$

In the last expression the abbreviations $\varepsilon = e^{(1+i)}$ and $^{CA}\vartheta_k = {}^A\vartheta_k \, e^{i\varphi_k}$ have been introduced (compare section 6.3).

One might call $^{CA}\vartheta_l$ the *complex amplitude* of the temperature variation at $z = 0$. Then $^{CA}\vartheta_k \, \varepsilon^{-z/D_k}$ is the complex amplitude at depth z. In this way a formal analogy with the case of a homogeneous soil is obtained. Thus all equations between temperatures or their derivatives at the boundaries can be written as equations between imaginary parts of exponential functions.

Two complex numbers can only be equal, if the real parts and also the imaginary parts are equal. Or $a = b$ implies $\mathrm{Re}(a) = \mathrm{Re}(b)$ and $\mathrm{Im}(a) = \mathrm{Im}(b)$. Therefore, if a solution of the differential equation of heat conduction satisfying the given boundary condition, is obtained as a complex exponential function, its imaginary part is also a solution of the same set of equations. The boundary conditions written as equations between complex exponential functions read:

(i) Continuity of temperature at $z = d_1 = 3.1$ cm, $\vartheta_1(z = d_1) = \vartheta_2(z = d_1)$ gives (see (6.53))

$$^{CA}\vartheta'_1\,\varepsilon^{-0.40} + {}^{CA}\vartheta''_1\,\varepsilon^{+0.40} = {}^{CA}\vartheta'_2\,\varepsilon^{-0.17} + {}^{CA}\vartheta''_2\,\varepsilon^{+0.17}. \qquad (6.53a)$$

(ii) Continuity of heat flux density at $z = d_1 = 3.1$ cm,

$$-\lambda_1\left(\frac{\partial\vartheta_1}{\partial z}\right)_{z=d_1} = -\lambda_2\left(\frac{\partial\vartheta_2}{\partial z}\right)_{z=d_1} \quad \text{gives}$$

$$\frac{0.60}{7.8}[^{CA}\vartheta'_1\,\varepsilon^{-0.40} - {}^{CA}\vartheta''_1\,\varepsilon^{+0.40}] = \frac{4.6}{18.2}[^{CA}\vartheta'_2\,\varepsilon^{-0.17} - {}^{CA}\vartheta''_2\,\varepsilon^{+0.17}]. \qquad (6.53b)$$

In the same way continuity of temperature at $d_2 = 14.6$ cm leads to (6.53c) and continuity of heat flux at d_2 to (6.53d).

$$^{CA}\vartheta'_2\,\varepsilon^{-0.80} + {}^{CA}\vartheta''_2\,\varepsilon^{+0.80} = {}^{CA}\vartheta_3\,\varepsilon^{-2.52} \qquad (6.53c)$$

$$\frac{4.6}{18.2}[^{CA}\vartheta'_2\,\varepsilon^{-0.80} - {}^{CA}\vartheta''_2\,\varepsilon^{+0.80}] = \frac{0.68}{5.8}\,^{CA}\vartheta_3\,\varepsilon^{-2.52}. \qquad (6.53d)$$

At the surface, $z = 0$, the temperature is $\vartheta_0 = {}^A\vartheta_0\sin(\omega t + \varphi_0)$. Thus

$$^{CA}\vartheta'_1 + {}^{CA}\vartheta''_1 = {}^{CA}\vartheta_0 = {}^A\vartheta_0\,e^{i\varphi_0}. \qquad (6.53e)$$

From these equations the complex amplitudes $^{CA}\vartheta'_1$, $^{CA}\vartheta'_2$, $^{CA}\vartheta'_3$, $^{CA}\vartheta''_1$, $^{CA}\vartheta''_2$ and $^{CA}\vartheta'_3$ can be solved when $^{CA}\vartheta_0$ is known.

Elimination of $^{CA}\vartheta_3\,\varepsilon^{-2.52}$ from (6.53c) and (6.53d) yields

$$-0.136\,^{CA}\vartheta'_2\,\varepsilon^{-0.80} + 0.370\,^{CA}\vartheta''_2\,\varepsilon^{+0.80} = 0,$$

or

$$^{CA}\vartheta''_2 = 0.367\,^{CA}\vartheta'_2\,\varepsilon^{-1.60}.$$

Substitution of this result in (6.53a) and (6.53b) gives the result

$$^{CA}\vartheta'_1\,\varepsilon^{-0.40} + {}^{CA}\vartheta''_1\,\varepsilon^{+0.40} = {}^{CA}\vartheta'_2\,\varepsilon^{-0.17} + 0.367\,^{CA}\vartheta'_2\,\varepsilon^{-1.60}\,\varepsilon^{0.17},$$

and

$$0.077[^{CA}\vartheta'_1\,\varepsilon^{-0.40} - {}^{CA}\vartheta''_1\,\varepsilon^{+0.40}] = 0.253[^{CA}\vartheta'_2\,\varepsilon^{-0.17} - 0.367\,^{CA}\vartheta'_2\,\varepsilon^{-1.43}].$$

Elimination of $^{CA}\vartheta'_2$ leads to

$$\frac{^{CA}\vartheta'_1\,\varepsilon^{-0.40} - {}^{CA}\vartheta''_1\,\varepsilon^{+0.40}}{^{CA}\vartheta'_1\,\varepsilon^{-0.40} + {}^{CA}\vartheta''_1\,\varepsilon^{+0.40}} = 3.29\,\frac{\varepsilon^{-0.17} - 0.367\,\varepsilon^{-1.43}}{\varepsilon^{-0.17} + 0.367\,\varepsilon^{-1.43}},$$

or

$$^{CA}\vartheta''_1 = {}^{CA}\vartheta'_1 \frac{1.57\,\varepsilon^{-2.06} - 2.29\,\varepsilon^{-0.80}}{4.29 - 0.84\,\varepsilon^{-1.26}} = -0.234\,{}^{CA}\vartheta'_1\,e^{-0.659\,i}.$$

After substitution in (6.53e) one obtains

$$^{CA}\vartheta'_1(1 - 0.234\,e^{-0.659\,i}) = {}^{CA}\vartheta_0,$$

or

$$^{CA}\vartheta'_1 = 1.21\,e^{-0.174\,i}\,{}^{CA}\vartheta_0$$

and

$$^{CA}\vartheta''_1 = -0.283\,e^{-0.833\,i}\,{}^{CA}\vartheta_0.$$

whereas the other amplitudes are found by substitution in (6.53a), (6.53b) and (6.53c).
They are

$$^{CA}\vartheta'_2 = 0.454\,e^{-0.458\,i}\,{}^{CA}\vartheta_0,$$
$$^{CA}\vartheta''_2 = 0.034\,e^{-2.058\,i}\,{}^{CA}\vartheta_0,$$

and

$$^{CA}\vartheta_3 = 3.476\,e^{1.262\,i}\,{}^{CA}\vartheta_0.$$

The calculations are valid for any complex value of $^{CA}\vartheta_0$. If we have $\varphi_0 = 0$ in (6.53e) $^{CA}\vartheta_0 = {}^A\vartheta_0$, thus it is a real and positive number. The imaginary parts of $^{CA}\vartheta'_1$ and $^{CA}\vartheta''_1$ must then cancel and the complex amplitudes are conjugate complex numbers. In this example $\varphi_0 = 0$ has been assumed and one has indeed $-0.283\sin(-0.833) = +0.210$ and $1.21\sin(-0.174) = -0.210$ for the coefficient of i in $^{CA}\vartheta''_1$ and $^{CA}\vartheta'_1$ respectively.

In Chapter 8 heat transfer in air is treated and solutions of the equation of heat conduction with λ variable with z are given. The results are also applicable to nonhomogeneous soil.

CHAPTER 7

THERMAL PROPERTIES OF SOILS

D. A. DE VRIES

Laboratory of Physics and Meteorology of the Agricultural University Wageningen,
The Netherlands

7.1. Introduction

It has already been shown in Chapter 4 that two independent thermal properties enter into a quantitative description of the heat transfer by conduction, viz. the thermal conductivity λ, and the heat capacity per unit volume $C = \varrho c$. In many equations the quotient of these two quantities appears; it is called the *thermal diffusivity* and denoted by the symbol a; thus $a = \lambda/C$.

The different substances that constitute a soil have widely different thermal properties as can be seen from Table 7.1.*

For the clay minerals and the organic matter the values given in this table are, of course, averages. The thermal properties of soil materials vary only slightly with temperature in the region of temperatures occurring in the field.

TABLE 7.1

Thermal properties and densities ϱ of some soil materials, water, and air at $10\,°C$ and of ice at $0\,°C$

Substance	λ (mcal cm^{-1} sec^{-1} $°C^{-1}$)	C (cal cm^{-3} $°C^{-1}$)	ϱ (g cm^{-3})
Quartz	21	0.48	2.66
Clay minerals	7	0.48	2.65
Organic matter	0.6	0.6	1.3
Water	1.37	1.00	1.00
Ice	5.2	0.45	0.92
Air	0.060	0.000 30	0.001 25

---

* Throughout this chapter the numerical values of the thermal conductivity λ are expressed as millical cm^{-1} sec^{-1} $°C^{-1}$, C as cal cm^{-3} $°C^{-1}$, ϱ as g/cm^3. The specific heat, c, can be found from the relation $C = \varrho c$.

7.2. The heat capacity of soils

The heat capacity per unit volume of soil can be found by adding the heat capacities of the different soil constituents in one cm³. Thus, if x_s, x_w and x_a denote the volume fractions of solid material, water (or ice) and air, respectively, one has

$$C = x_s C_s + x_w C_w + x_a C_a. \tag{7.1}$$

The third term in the right-hand side can usually be neglected. The value of $C_w = 1.00$ cal cm^{-3}°C^{-1} in case of water, 0.45 cal cm^{-3}°C^{-1} in case of ice at 0°C (cf. Table 7.1) and 0.43 cal cm^{-3}°C^{-1} at -20°C. The specific heats of twelve different mineral soils and soil materials were measured by KERSTEN [1949] (see Table 7.2). He found that the specific heat of most soil minerals varied linearly from 0.16 ± 0.01 cal cm^{-3}°C^{-1} at -18°C to 0.19 ± 0.01 cal cm^{-3}°C^{-1} at 60°C. Since the specific mass of these minerals is about 2.7 g cm^{-3} an average value of C_s of about 0.46 holds for a mineral soil at 10°C.

The specific heat of soil organic matter was determined by several authors (BRACHT [1949]; LANG [1878]; ULRICH [1894]; DE VRIES and DE WIT [1954]), the most probable value being 0.46 cal g^{-1}°C^{-1} (extremes are 0.42 and 0.48 cal g^{-1}°C^{-1}). An average value of the specific mass of the organic materials in soil is 1.3 g cm^{-3} and, therefore, $C_s = 0.60$ is a good average value in the case of organic soils.

If we denote the volume fractions of soil minerals and of organic matter by x_m and x_o resp., the heat capacity per unit volume equals

$$C = 0.46 \, x_m + 0.60 \, x_o + x_w \text{ cal cm}^{-3} \text{°C}^{-1}. \tag{7.2}$$

EXAMPLE

A soil with a total porosity of 49 volume per cents has a moisture content of 13 weight per cents on a dry weight basis. The solid material consists for 4 weight per cents of organic matter, the remaining 96% being soil minerals. Therefore the ratio of x_o and x_m equals $(0.04/1.3):(0.96/2.65) = 0.085$. Thus $x_o = (0.085/1.085) \times 0.51 = 0.04$ and $x_m = 0.47$. The weight of dry material per unit volume is $0.04 \times 1.3 + 0.47 \times 2.65 = 1.30$ g, from which it follows that $x_w = 0.17$. With (7.2) one finds consequently for C a value of 0.41 cal cm^{-3}°C^{-1}.

Experimental data on the specific heat of several soils obtained by KERSTEN [1949] are given in Table 7.2; Table 7.3 contains data pertaining to organic soils, while in Table 7.4 specific heats of several soil minerals and of rock materials are collected.

TABLE 7.2

Specific heat values c_s and densities ϱ_s of several
soils after KERSTEN [1949]

Soil	c_s (cal g^{-1} °C^{-1})	Mean temp. (°C)	ϱ_s (g cm^{-3})
Northway fine sand	0.197	61.0	2.76
Northway sand	0.171	− 6.7	2.74
	0.185	18.8	
	0.191	60.2	
Northway silt loam	0.168	−10.4	2.70
	0.176	20.4	
	0.193	60.4	
Chena river gravel	0.194	61.0	2.70
	0.196	60.4	
Fairbanks silt loam	0.164	− 8.4	2.70
	0.183	18.8	
	0.194	61.3	
Graded Ottawa sand	0.157	− 9.5	2.65
	0.164	18.5	
	0.176	37.7	
	0.189	60.3	
20–30 Ottawa sand	0.183	37.8	2.65
	0.189	59.9	
Lowell sand	0.159	− 9.5	2.67
	0.188	19.7	
	0.188	60.9	
Crushed quartz	0.190	60.9	2.65
Crushed trap rock	0.193	59.9	2.97
Crushed feldspar	0.190	59.3	2.56
Crushed granite	0.161	−13.3	2.67
	0.174	19.4	
	0.189	60.9	

TABLE 7.3

Specific heat values c_s and densities ϱ_s of several organic soils and soil materials

Material	c_s (cal g^{-1} °C^{-1})	Mean temp (°C)	ϱ_s (g cm^{-3})	Reference
Humus	0.477	—	1.26	LANG [1878]
	0.443	∼60		ULRICH [1894]
"Verwitterungserde"	0.416			BRACHT [1949]
"Bolster"	0.46	28	1.36	DE VRIES and DE-WIT [1954]

TABLE 7.4

Specific heat values c_s and densities ϱ_s of several soil minerals and rock materials

Material	c_s (cal g^{-1} °C^{-1})	Mean temp (°C)	ϱ_s (g cm^{-3})	Reference
Quartz	0.191	~ 60	2.65	ULRICH [1894]
Kaolin	0.224	~ 60	2.6	,,
CaCO$_3$	0.208	~ 60	2.71	,,
MgCO$_3$	0.246	~ 60	3.04	,,
CaSO$_4$	0.195	~ 60	2.45	,,
Fe$_2$O$_3$	0.165	~ 60	5.24	,,
Al$_2$O$_3$	0.217	—	3.7	LANG [1878]
Fe(OH)$_3$	0.226	~ 60	3.6	ULRICH [1894]
Orthoclase	0.194	~ 60	2.56	,,
Oligoclase	0.205	~ 60	2.64	,,
Potash mica	0.208	~ 60	2.9	,,
Magnesia mica	0.206	~ 60	2.9	,,
Hornblende	0.195	~ 60	3.2	,,
Apatite	0.183	~ 60	3.2	,,
Dolomite	0.222	~ 60	2.9	,,
Talc	0.209	~ 60	2.7	,,
Granite	0.192	56	2.6	LANDOLT-BÖRN-STEIN [1952]
Syenite	0.199	59	2.7	,,
Diorite	0.194	65	2.9	,,
Andesite	0.199	59	2.4	,,
Basalt	0.213	55	3.0	

7.3. The thermal conductivity of soils

In the foregoing section it has been shown that the heat capacity of a soil can be expressed as a linear function of the volume fractions and the heat capacities of the soil constituents. The problem of expressing the thermal conductivity as a function of the conductivities and volume fractions of the soil constituents is very intricate; it can be solved only approximately.

Mathematically the problem is analogous to expressing the electric conductivity or the dielectric constant of a granular material in the volume fractions and the respective physical properties of its constituents. A survey of the theoretical work on this problem has been given by DE VRIES [1952]. Here only the results which apply to soils will be treated.

7.4. Theory of the thermal conductivity of granular materials

In the simplest case the granular material consists of two substances only, viz. a continuous medium, with volume fraction x_0 and thermal conductivity λ_0, in which granules with a volume fraction $x_1 = 1 - x_0$ and thermal conductivity λ_1 are dispersed. This case corresponds for instance to a dry soil or a saturated soil consisting of particles which all have the same thermal conductivity, while the continuous medium is air or water respectively.

An average or apparent thermal conductivity λ of the granular substance as a whole can be defined as follows. Let us consider the cube of such material (see Fig. 4.1) with side l, where l is large in comparison with the dimensions of the granules. Let us assume that the upper face is kept at a temperature ϑ_2, the lower face at $\vartheta_1 < \vartheta_2$. Then a constant heat flux density H passes through the material, which is proportional to the temperature gradient, the factor of proportionality being λ. In formula

$$H = -\lambda \frac{\vartheta_2 - \vartheta_1}{l} = -\lambda \frac{d\vartheta}{dz},$$

which is equivalent to (4.1). The value of λ will be somewhere intermediate between λ_0 and λ_1. A theory developed by H. C. BURGER [1915], leads to the following expression for λ

$$\lambda = \frac{x_0 \lambda_0 + k_1 x_1 \lambda_1}{x_0 + k_1 x_1}, \tag{7.3}$$

where the quantity k_1 is the ratio of the average temperature gradient in the granules and the corresponding quantity in the medium:

$$k_1 = \frac{\overline{(d\vartheta/dz)_1}}{\overline{(d\vartheta/dz)_0}}, \tag{7.4}$$

the bar denoting a space average. The definition of λ requires that in taking these averages a volume is considered which contains a large number of particles.

The value of k_1 depends on the ratio λ_1/λ_0, on the size and the shape of the granules and on their relative positions. An exact mathematical expression for k_1 can only be given under the following restricting conditions: (a) the granules are of ellipsoidal shape, (b) the granules are so far apart they do not influence each other; this means that the temperature distribution in and around a granule is not markedly influenced by the presence of neighboring particles. In this case k_1 depends only on the shape and the orientation of the granules and on the ratio λ_1/λ_0. If the axes a, b and c of the ellipsoidal granules are orientated in a random way, k_1 can be found from the expression

$$k_1 = \tfrac{1}{3} \sum_{a,b,c} \left[1 + \left(\frac{\lambda_1}{\lambda_0} - 1 \right) g_a \right]^{-1}, \tag{7.5}$$

$$g_a = \tfrac{1}{2} a\,b\,c \int_0^\infty \frac{du}{(a^2 + u)^{\frac{3}{2}} (b^2 + u)^{\frac{1}{2}} (c^2 + u)^{\frac{1}{2}}}. \tag{7.6}$$

If the granules would have their a-axes in the direction of the average temperature gradient, k_1 would be given by the first term behind the summation sign in (7.5).

In the theory of the dielectric constant the quantity g_a is called the depolarisation factor of the ellipsoid in the direction of the a-axis. The quantities g_a, g_b and g_c depend on the ratios of the axes a, b and c, not on their absolute values. In other words they only depend on the shape of the ellipsoid and not on its size. The sum of these quantities is unity

$$g_a + g_b + g_c = 1. \tag{7.7}$$

Thus for spherical granules $g_a = g_b = g_c = \tfrac{1}{3}$.

For a spheroid with axes $a = b = nc$ the value of $g_a = g_b$ can be read from Fig. 7.1 for n-values varying from 0.1 to 100, while g_c follows from (7.7).

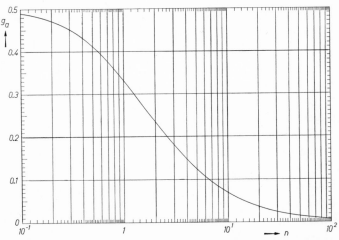

Fig. 7.1. Values of g_a in dependence of n for ellipsoids of revolution with axes $a = b = nc$.

Other special cases of practical importance are:

1. Elongated cylinders with elliptical cross section. Here
   $a = mb$, $c = \infty$; and $g_a = 1/(m + 1)$,
   $g_b = m/(m + 1)$, $g_c = 0$;
2. Lamellae (flat particles with a small thickness) where
   $b = c = \infty$; $g_a = 1$, $g_b = g_c = 0$.

In case there are several types of granules of different shapes and/or with different conductivities (7.3) can be extended to

$$\lambda = \frac{\sum_{i=0}^{N} k_i x_i \lambda_i}{\sum_{i=0}^{N} k_i x_i}. \tag{7.8}$$

$$k_i = \tfrac{1}{3} \sum_{a,b,c} \left[1 + \left(\frac{\lambda_i}{\lambda_0} - 1 \right) g_a \right]^{-1}. \tag{7.9}$$

Here N is the number of types of granules; all particles with the same shape and the same conductivity being considered as of one type. The summation can be extended over the medium as well if k_0 is taken equal to unity (cf. (7.4)).

The conditions mentioned under (a) and (b) above would at first sight seem to impede the application of (7.5) and (7.9) to soils. A theoretical investigation into the limits of the applicability of these equations, and a comparison of theoretical values with the results of a large number of experiments on the thermal conductivity of soils and other granular materials, have shown, however, that the thermal conductivity of moist soils with widely different compositions and moisture contents can be computed from the equations (7.8) and (7.9) with a fair degree of accuracy.

From the experiments it follows that in this respect the soil particles can be considered to a sufficient degree of approximation as spheroids (condition (a)). That this need not be a crude assumption can be seen from the fact that the influence of a given soil particle on the thermal conductivity of the granular substance will lie between the influence of an inscribed and a circumscribed spheroidal particle with the same conductivity as the actual particle.

Condition (b) implies that the distance between particles must be several times the size of the particles, a condition which is certainly not fulfilled in soils. It can be shown, however, that (7.5) or (7.9) may still be applied in certain cases, while in others a simple correction can be introduced for the influence of the proximity of the granules; the magnitude of this correction depending mainly on the values of the ratios λ_i/λ_0.

If for simplicity we confine the discussion to the case $N = 1$ it can be shown that the values of λ computed from (7.3) is too high, if $\lambda_1/\lambda_0 < 1$, and too low if $\lambda_1/\lambda_0 > 1$. It has been shown in a semiempirical way that the deviations between the true values and the values computed from (7.3) are less than 10%, if $0 \leqslant \lambda_1/\lambda < 10$. If λ_1/λ_0 is of the order of 100 the values derived from (7.3) are approximately 25% too low for values of x_1 ranging from 0.4 to 0.7, i.e. the region which is of most importance in soils.*

In moist soils water can be considered as a continuous medium, in which soil particles and air voids are dispersed, for moisture contents ranging from saturation to well below the field capacity. It can be seen from Table 7.1 that the value of λ_1/λ_0 is greater than unity for mineral particles and less than unity for organic materials and air. Therefore, the errors introduced by these different groups of "particles" are counteracting. Moreover, the values of λ_1/λ_0 (where λ_0 refers to water) are rather low, the largest value being about

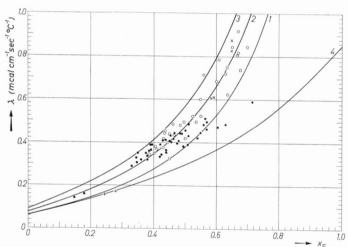

Fig. 7.2. Experimental and theoretical values of the thermal conductivity λ (in millical cm^{-1} sec^{-1} °C^{-1}) for dry soils in dependence on the volume fraction of solid material. Curves 1 and 4: theoretical values for $\lambda_1 = 7.0, \lambda_0 = 0.0615, g_a = g_b = 0.125$ and $\lambda_1 = 0.85$, $\lambda_0 = 0.0615, g_a = g_b = 0.5$ respectively. A curve with $\lambda_1 = 20.4$ (quartz) differs by less than 10% from curve 1 for $x_s < 0.7$. Curves 2 and 3 are obtained by multiplying the ordinates of curve 1 with 1.25 and 1.50 respectively.

● experimental values of Smith and Byers for oven-dry mineral soils.
○ experimental values of Smith for air-dry mineral soils.
+ experimental values of Smith and Byers for oven-dry peat.
× experimental values of Kersten for Ottawa sand.

_____

* It will be noted that (7.3) gives exact values for $x_1 = 0$ and $x_1 = 1$.

16 for quartz particles (see Table 7.1). This implies that the corrections are relatively small. Thus the thermal conductivity of moist soils can be calculated from (7.8) with an error which in most cases is less than 10%.

For dry soils λ_1/λ_0 is of the order of 100 (except for organic material). In this case a correction factor of 1.25 must be introduced in the right-hand side of (7.8) for mineral soils. Fig. 7.2 shows that in this way a reasonable agreement is obtained between computed and experimental values. The experimental data were taken from laboratory determinations, of SMITH and BYERS [1938], SMITH [1939, 1942] and KERSTEN [1949]. The average temperature of Kersten's measurements was 21 °C, the average temperature of the other measurements was not stated, but it must have been near room temperature. Therefore the value of the thermal conductivity for air at 20 °C, $\lambda_0 = 0.0615$ mcal cm^{-1} sec^{-1} °C^{-1} was used in the calculations.

7.5. The influence of moisture movement

In moist soils (not saturated with water) the transport of heat is complicated by the fact that temperature gradients cause moisture movement, so that the moisture will tend to redistribute itself when the temperature field changes. The moisture movement, which occurs both in the liquid and in the vapor phases, gives rise to a transport of sensible and latent heat, which again influences the temperature distribution.

A quantitative treatment of the combined transport of heat and moisture in porous media is very complicated. For a comprehensive discussion of this problem the reader is referred to monographs by KRISCHER [1956] and by LYKOW [1958], and to papers by PHILIP and DE VRIES [1957]. Here some of the aspects of the theory proposed by Philip and De Vries will be discussed.

The theory of combined heat and moisture transport leads to two simultaneous differential equations with two dependent variables, viz. the temperature $\vartheta(x,y,z,t)$ and the liquid moisture content, expressed for instance as the volume of liquid water per unit volume of soil, $x_w(x,y,z,t)$. The first of these equations follows from the conservation of mass, the second from the conservation of energy. The latter equation is an extension of the differential equation of heat conduction derived in Chapter 4 (see (4.4)).

Boundary conditions belonging to these equations describe conditions of temperature or heat flux, and of moisture content, moisture flux, or water potential at the boundaries of the porous medium.

Initial conditions describe the moisture distribution and the temperature field at time zero. In a stationary state both $\partial\vartheta/\partial t = 0$ and $\partial x_w/\partial t = 0$.

In extending the definition of average thermal conductivity λ given in section 7.4 to a moist porous material additional boundary conditions for the moisture flow must be specified. This implies that the value of λ will depend on these conditions and that λ has no longer a unique value for a given porous material at a fixed moisture content.

In experiments designed to measure the thermal conductivity, the sample is usually contained between walls that are impervious to moisture. In other words the boundary condition of zero moisture flux must hold at these walls. This does not mean that the outcome of an experiment is now uniquely determined; it will still depend on the initial conditions. For instance, the outcome of a stationary experiment will differ from that of a nonstationary experiment. In the former the moisture flux must be zero throughout the sample (this can, for instance, be due to equal but opposite fluxes of moisture in the liquid and the vapor phases); in the latter the moisture distribution will change continually during the experiment.

Fortunately, the influence of moisture movement on the heat transfer in in soils under natural conditions can be described to a good degree of approximation in a fairly simple way which was essentially first proposed by KRISCHER and ROHNALTER [1940].

In this simplified theory the transport of sensible heat due to moisture movement is neglected. This is usually not permissible when there is appreciable liquid movement under the influence of gravity or pressure differences.

The transport of latent heat is found in the gas-filled pores, where water vapor diffusion occurs under the influence of temperature gradients that give rise to gradients of (partial) vapor pressure. Since the vapor flux due to temperature differences is to a good degree of approximation proportional to the temperature gradient across the gas-filled pore, this transport can be described mathematically as an apparent increase of the heat conduction in the gas-filled pore. In other words, the apparent thermal conductivity of a gas-filled pore is composed of a part due to normal heat conduction λ_a and a part due to vapor movement λ_v. Hence

$$\lambda_{\text{apparent}} = \lambda_a + \lambda_v. \tag{7.10}$$

The following expression for λ_v was derived by KRISCHER and ROHNALTER [1940] for the case where the air in the pores is saturated with water vapor

$$\lambda_v{}^s = \frac{LDP}{R\Theta(P - p_w{}^s)} \frac{\mathrm{d}p_w{}^s}{\mathrm{d}\Theta}. \tag{7.11}$$

Here $\lambda_v{}^s$ is the value of λ_v for saturated vapor, L the latent heat of vaporization of water, R the gas constant for water vapor ($R = 4.615 \times 10^6$ erg $g^{-1}{}^\circ C^{-1}$), D the diffusion coefficient of water vapor in air, P the total pressure (atmospheric pressure in the case of soils), $p_w{}^s$ the saturation vapor pressure.

In the derivation of (7.11) it has been assumed that the total pressure P does not vary throughout the porous medium and is constant in time, that air and water vapor can be considered as ideal gases, and that thermodiffusion is negligible.

Numerical values of D for diffusion due to a temperature gradient were determined by KRISCHER and ROHNALTER [1940]. Their results can be represented in the range 20° to 70 °C by the expression

$$D = \frac{17.6}{P}\left(\frac{\Theta}{273}\right)^{2.3},\tag{7.12}$$

where D is expressed in cm^2 sec^{-1} and P in mm Hg. Data for isothermal conditions (see MACHE [1910]; SUMMERHAYS [1930]; SCHIRMER [1938]) differ appreciably from this (up to about 15%), especially at temperatures above 40 °C. The values of Krischer and Rohnalter are adopted here.

Values of $\lambda_v{}^s$ computed from (7.11) and (7.12) are shown in Fig. 7.4 in comparison with the thermal conductivities of dry air and liquid water in the range 0° to 75 °C.

PHILIP and DE VRIES [1957] have shown that when the soil air is not saturated with water vapor the value of λ_v is proportional to the relative humidity h; thus

$$\lambda_v = h\lambda_v{}^s.\tag{7.13}$$

The relative humidity is here expressed as a fraction and not in per cents. In the notation of Chapter 2 the relative humidity can be written as $h = p_w{}^s(\psi)/p_w{}^s(0)$.

DE VRIES [1958b] discussed the special case of zero moisture flux in the sample, where the moisture flow due to a temperature gradient is compensated by a return flow caused by a gradient of moisture content. In that case a factor $D_l/(D_l + D_v)$ must be added on the right-hand side of (7.13). D_l is the diffusivity for liquid moisture movement under the influence of gradients of the liquid moisture content (x_w), D_v is the diffusivity for vapor movement, also under the influence of gradients of x_w.* This factor differs very little from unity at the wet end of the moisture range ($x_w >$ the wilting percentage),

---

* In the original paper the symbols $D_{\theta l}$ and $D_{\theta v}$ are used.

where h is also close to unity (see sections 2.17 and 2.21). It diminishes rapidly at moisture contents below the wilting point and becomes practically zero at a small but finite moisture content. The reader is referred to the original paper for a further discussion of this case.

In coarse textured soils it has been found empirically that a decrease of the contribution of vapor movement to the heat transfer sets in at a moisture content corresponding to the field capacity. This can be explained by observing that in these soils the difference in moisture content between field capacity and wilting point is very small, while the hydraulic conductivity decreases very sharply below the field capacity. If at a certain spot the moisture content decreases due to movement under the influence of a temperature gradient, the liquid moisture content will decrease rapidly and the stage at which h starts to decrease will soon be reached. The magnitude of λ_v will depend, of course, on the magnitude of the temperature and moisture

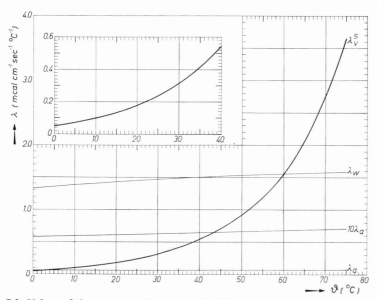

Fig. 7.3. Values of the apparent thermal conductivity due to vapor movement in air-filled pores, $\lambda_v{}^s$, in comparison with the thermal conductivities of water λ_w and air λ_a for temperatures between 0 °C and 75 °C. The lower part of the $\lambda_v{}^s$-curve is reproduced with a larger ordinate scale in the in-set figure.

gradients and on the boundary and initial conditions. The value found for λ in an experiment will therefore depend on the experimental procedure.

Summarizing the preceding discussion it can be said that in moist soils the contribution of vapor movement to the heat transfer leads to an increased value of the conductivity of the gas-filled pores. The apparent conductivity of the gas can be calculated from (7.10) to (7.13). It follows from Fig. 7.3 that at 0 °C the contribution of vapor diffusion is about equal to that of

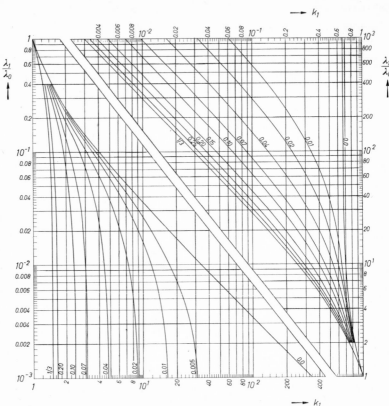

Fig. 7.4a. Values of k_1 in dependence of λ_1/λ_0 for various values of $g_a = g_b$ in the range $\frac{1}{3}$ to 0 (oblate spheroids). The g_a-values are indicated by the numbers adjacent to each curve.

normal heat conduction ($\lambda_a \approx \lambda_v{}^s$), provided that the relative humidity does not differ appreciably from unity. With increasing temperature $\lambda_v{}^s$ increases much more rapidly then λ_a and the influence of heat transfer by vapor movement becomes predominant in the gas-filled pores. At about 59 °C $\lambda_a + \lambda_v{}^s$ is equal to the thermal conductivity of water λ_w. By consequence the thermal conductivity of a moist granular material will be independent of its moisture content at this temperature in the moisture range where $h \approx 1$. This conclusion was already drawn by KRISCHER and ROHNALTER [1940]; it was confirmed experimentally by DE VRIES [1952] for a quartz sand (see Fig. 7.4a,b).

In calculations of the thermal conductivity of moist soils from (7.8) and (7.9) the proper value of the apparent conductivity must be substituted for the air-filled pores. A number of examples of such calculations are given in the next subsection.

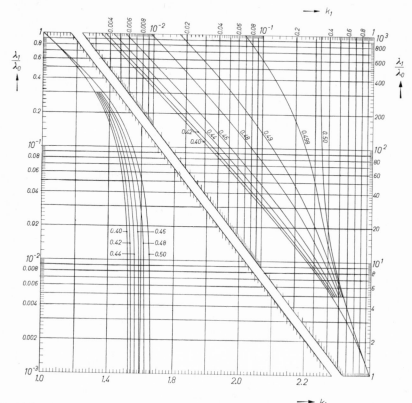

Fig. 7.4b. Values of k_1 in dependence of λ_1/λ_0 for various values of $g_a = g_b$ in the range 0.4 to 0.5 (prolate spheroids). The g_a-values are indicated by the numbers adjacent to each curve.

7.6. Examples of calculations of the thermal conductivity

7.6.1. QUARTZ SAND

As a first example a quartz sand is considered. The thermal conductivity of this sand in dependence of its moisture content was measured by DE VRIES at temperatures of 20°, 40°, 60° and 75 °C. The results are represented in Figs. 7.5 and 7.6. The accuracy of the experimental values is about $\pm$ 3%.

The sand used here consisted for 89 volume per cents of quartz and for 11% of feldspar and other mineral particles. The average specific mass was determined at 2.64 g cm^{-3}. The volume fraction of solid material was 0.573 in all measurements. The volume fraction of quartz particles x_1 thus equals $0.89 \times 0.573 = 0.510$ and the volume fraction of the other solid particles, $x_2 = 0.11 \times 0.573 = 0.063$. The moisture sorption curve of this sand is represented in Fig. 7.7. The field capacity corresponds to a moisture content $x_w = 0.09$.

The thermal conductivity of quartz was found from the International Critical Tables to 20.4, 19.0, 17.8 and 16.9 mcal sec^{-1}°C^{-1} at 20°, 40°, 60° and 75° resp.* For the other minerals the value 7.0 mcal cm^{-1} sec^{-1}°C^{-1} was adopted. This value holds for feldspar and according to the results of SMITH [1942] it also serves as a good estimate for many other soil minerals. The average of g_a for the solid particles was deduced from diffusion measurements to 0.144 which corresponds to a ratio of about 4 between the axes of an oblate spheroid (see Fig. 7.1).

The thermal conductivity of saturated soil $x_w = 0.427$, can be calculated directly from (7.9) and (7.8). For instance, at 20 °C one has $\lambda_0 = 1.42$ mcal cm^{-1} sec^{-1}°C^{-1} (water), $\lambda_1 = 20.4$ mcal cm^{-1} sec^{-1}°C^{-1} (quartz) and $\lambda_2 = 7.0$ mcal cm^{-1} sec^{-1}°C^{-1} (other materials) which leads to**

$$k_1 = \tfrac{1}{3}\left(\frac{2}{1+13.4\times 0.144} + \frac{1}{1+13.4\times 0.712}\right) = 0.259,$$

$$k_2 = \tfrac{1}{3}\left(\frac{2}{1+3.93\times 0.144} + \frac{1}{1+3.93\times 0.712}\right) = 0.514, \text{ and}$$

$$\lambda = \frac{0.427\times 1.42 + 0.259\times 0.510\times 20.4 + 0.514\times 0.063\times 7.0}{0.427 + 0.259\times 0.510 + 0.514\times 0.063} = \frac{3.54}{0.591}$$
$$= 6.0 \text{ mcal cm}^{-1}\text{ sec}^{-1}°C^{-1}$$

which is in excellent agreement with the observed value (see Fig. 7.5).

For dry soil, $x_w = 0$, the same procedure is followed, but now the correction factor 1.25 has to be introduced in the right hand side of (7.8). With $\lambda_0 = 0.0615$ mcal cm^{-1} sec^{-1}°C^{-1} (air) and λ_1, λ_2 as above, one obtains

---

* Quartz is anisotropic; the thermal conductivity in the direction of the main axis λ_α is different from that in a direction perpendicular to this axis λ_β. An average value of the thermal conductivity was computed from: $\lambda = \tfrac{1}{3}\lambda_\alpha + \tfrac{2}{3}\lambda_\beta$; this represents the average conductivity in the direction of the temperature gradient.

** To assist in numerical calculation values of k_i in dependence of λ_i/λ_0 and g_a can be read from Fig. 7.4a and 7.4b.

$$k_1 = \tfrac{1}{3} \left(\frac{2}{1 + 331 \times 0.144} + \frac{1}{1 + 331 \times 0.712} \right) = 0.0151,$$

$$k_2 = \tfrac{1}{3} \left(\frac{2}{1 + 113 \times 0.144} + \frac{1}{1 + 113 \times 0.712} \right) = 0.0427,$$

$$\lambda = 1.25 \times \frac{0.427 \times 0.0615 + 0.0151 \times 0.510 \times 20.4 + 0.0427 \times 0.063 \times 7.0}{0.427 + 0.0151 \times 0.510 + 0.0427 \times 0.063}$$

$$= 0.58 \text{ mcal cm}^{-1} \text{ sec}^{-1} \, {}^{\circ}\text{C}^{-1},$$

while the experimental value is 0.60.

To calculate the thermal conductivity for moisture contents in between absolute dryness and saturation additional suppositions must be introduced concerning the value of g_a of the air-filled pores. The following general procedure, which can be applied without any use of further experimental data was found to lead to an accuracy of about 10% of the calculated values except at very low moisture contents. If experimental values of the thermal conductivity at a few moisture contents are known, a more refined procedure leads to an accuracy of about 5%.

At first the range of x_w where the apparent thermal conductivity of the air-filled pores is equal to $\lambda_a + \lambda_v{}^s$ is considered. For the present sand this range lies between saturation and field capacity, as was discussed in the previous section. The value of $\lambda_v{}^s = 0.176$ mcal cm^{-1} sec^{-1} °C^{-1} at 20 °C as can be read from Fig. 7.3; hence the thermal conductivity of the air-filled pores equals $0.0615 + 0.176 = 0.238$ mcal cm^{-1} sec^{-1} °C^{-1} for $0.09 \leqslant x_w \leqslant 0.427$. In this range water can be considered as the continuous medium in the sence of section 7.4.

The effective value of g_a of the air-filled pores will diminish gradually with decreasing moisture content. This is so because with decreasing moisture content air will more and more replace water in the finer spaces between the soil granules. The influence of a certain volume fraction of air on the thermal conductivity of the soil will therefore increase with decreasing moisture content. This corresponds to an increase of k and a decrease of g_a for air as follows from (7.8) and (7.9).

At very small values of the volume fraction of air-filled pores, x_a, it is reasonable to suppose that the air voids will be nearly spherical, hence g_a approaches $\tfrac{1}{3}$ as x_a tends to 0. At very low values of x_w one would have a situation where the air is enclosed between the soil particles which are covered with a thin water film. In this case the value of k for particles with the same conductivity as water (e.g. 1.42 at 20 °C) and $g_a = 0.144$ dispersed in air with a conductivity of 0.238 is found from (7.5), to

$$k_1 = \tfrac{1}{3}\left(\frac{2}{1+4.96\times0.144} + \frac{1}{1+4.96\times0.712}\right) = 0.462.$$

Reversely air particles dispersed in water at the same conductivity of the medium as a whole should have a k_1-value equal to $1/0.462 = 2.16$, as follows from (7.3) and (7.4). This value of k_1 corresponds to a value of $g_a = 0.035$ according to (7.5) (cf. also Fig. 7.4a).

In the general procedure it is assumed that g_a varies linearly with x_a and x_w between the value $\tfrac{1}{3}$ at $x_a = 0$, corresponding to $x_w = 0.427$ in the present case, and the value 0.035 at $x_w = 0$, on the understanding that these values of g_a will be used only for moisture contents in the range where the apparent conductivity of the air-filled pores is equal to $\lambda_a + \lambda_v^s$, viz. $0.09 \leqslant x_w \leqslant 0.427$ in the present example. Hence

$$g_a = 0.333 - \frac{x_a}{0.427}(0.333 - 0.035) = 0.333 - 0.697\,x_a \ \text{ for } \ 0\leqslant x_a\leqslant 0.337.$$

For $x_a = 0.110$ one finds for instance $g_a = 0.257$ and $k_a = 1.41$. Substitution of these values in (7.8) leads to

$$\lambda = \frac{0.317\times1.42 + 0.259\times0.510\times20.4 + 0.514\times0.063\times7.0 + 1.41\times0.10\times0.2}{0.317 + 0.259\times0.510 + 0.514\times0.063 + 1.41\times0.110}$$

$= 5.38$ mcal cm^{-1} sec^{-1} °C^{-1}; for $x_a = 0.337$ one has $g_a = 0.098$, $k_a = 1.73$ and $\lambda = 3.82$ mcal cm^{-1} sec^{-1} °C^{-1}.

For moisture contents below 0.090 both g_a and the apparent conductivity of air will vary. For simplicity it will be assumed that λ_v varies linearly with x_w from λ_v^s at $x_w = 0.09$ to 0 at $x_w = 0$; thus the apparent conductivity of air becomes

$$\lambda_a + \lambda_v = 0.0615 + \frac{x_w}{0.090}(0.238 - 0.0615) = 0.0615 + 1.96\,x_w \text{ mcal cm}^{-1}\text{ sec}^{-1}\text{ °C}^{-1}$$

In order to find the value of g_a in the region $0 \leqslant x_w \leqslant 0.090$ a similar procedure is followed as in the range $0.090 \leqslant x_w \leqslant 0.427$. At $x_w = 0.090$ the value of g_a is taken equal to the value found before, viz. $g_a = 0.098$. The value at $x_w = 0$ is computed in the same way as above, but this time with the value for dry air of the thermal conductivity in the air-filled pores. Thus the value of k_1 for particles with $g_a = 0.144$ and the conductivity of water, $\lambda_1 = 1.42$ mcal cm^{-1} sec^{-1} °C^{-1} dispersed in air with $\lambda_0 = 0.0615$ mcal cm^{-1} sec^{-1} °C^{-1} becomes

$$k_1 = \tfrac{1}{3}\left(\frac{2}{1+22.1\times0.144} + \frac{1}{1+22.1\times0.712}\right) = 0.180.$$

The value of k_1 for air particles dispersed in water at the same conductivity is, therefore, $1/0.180 = 5.56$, which corresponds to $g_a = 0.013$. Assuming again a linear relation between g_a and x_w in the region under consideration, one has

$$g_a = 0.013 + \frac{x_w}{0.090}(0.098 - 0.013) = 0.013 + 0.944\,x_w, \text{ for } 0 \leqslant x_w \leqslant 0.090.$$

At $x_w = 0.030$ one obtains for instance $g_a = 0.041$, $\lambda_a + \lambda_v = 0.120$, $k_a = 2.78$ and $\lambda = 2.40$ mcal cm^{-1} sec^{-1} °C^{-1}.

At very low moisture contents it is obviously no longer permissible to consider water as the continuous medium. At $x_w = 0$ the present procedure would lead to $\lambda = 0.82$ instead of the value 0.58 obtained previously with dry air as the continuous medium. It is recommended, therefore, to discontinue the calculations with water as a continuous medium at an x_w-value of about 0.03 for coarse textured soils and at x_w equal to 0.05 to 0.10 for fine textured soils. The relation between λ and x_w for moisture contents below this critical value of x_w up to $x_w = 0$ can be obtained by graphical interpolation, since the value of λ for dry soil can be found from a calculation with air as the continuous medium. For peat soils at low moisture contents a slightly different procedure is recommended which will be discussed subsequently.

The calculations for the temperatures 40°, 60° and 75 °C are similar to those at 20 °C. The results are shown graphically in the Figs. 7.5 and 7.6 together with the experimental curves. The parts of the curves obtained by graphical interpolation between $x_w = 0.03$ and $x_w = 0$ are dotted. The agreement between theoretical and experimental values is satisfactory over the whole range of moisture contents and temperatures. Note the constancy of λ with moisture content at about 60 °C for values of x_w as predicted by KRISCHER and ROHNALTER [1940].

The measurements at 75 °C indicate that the value of the diffusion coefficient of water vapor in air deduced from (7.12) may be slightly too high.

For many practical applications, as e.g. calculations of temperature at different depths, the accuracy of the theoretical values of the thermal conductivity obtained in the manner outlined above is sufficient. The variations of λ in a given soil at a given depth due to the nonhomogeneity of the soil and to irregular changes in the moisture content will also be of the order of 5 to 10%.

A better agreement between theoretical and experimental values of λ can

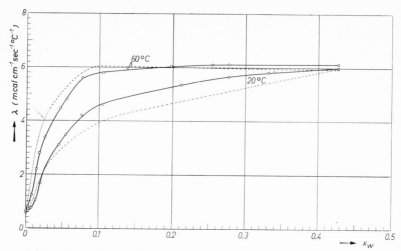

Fig. 7.5. Experimental values (open circles joined by full drawn curves) and theoretical values (broken curves) of thermal conductivity of a quartz sand at 20 °C and 60 °C in relation to the moisture content, x_w (volume fraction of moisture), ranging from 0 to saturation. The parts of the theoretical curves for $0 < x_w < 0.03$ (dotted lines) have been obtained through interpolation between the computed values at $x_w = 0$ and $x_w = 0.03$.

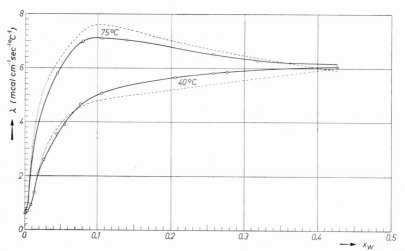

Fig. 7.6. Experimental values (open circles joined by full drawn curves) and theoretical values (broken curves) of thermal conductivity of a quartz sand at 40 °C and 75 °C in relation to the moisture content, x_w (volume fraction of moisture), ranging from 0 to saturation. The parts of the theoretical curves for $0 < x_w < 0.03$ (dotted lines) have been obtained through interpolation between the computed values at $x_w = 0$ and $x_w = 0.03$.

be obtained by a different choice of g_a and λ_v as functions of x_w. From a consideration of the moisture sorption curve of the sand, Fig. 7.7, it follows that for moisture contents between saturation and field capacity water is situated in pores with only slightly decreasing diameters (cf. section 2.21). At field capacity the water will be contained mainly in ring shaped volumes round the contact points of the soil grains. These rings will become smaller with decreasing moisture content.

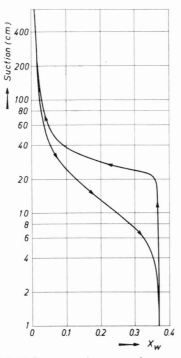

Fig. 7.7. Moisture sorption curve of a quartz sand.
(Thermal conductivities of the sand are given in Figs. 7.5 and 7.6).

From these considerations it follows that the effective value of g_a will decrease slowly with decreasing moisture content between saturation and field capacity. But a decrease of the water rings between the soil particles will have a large effect on the thermal conductivity, since the heat flow will pass mainly across these water bridges from one grain to another. Hence, g_a will decrease rapidly with decreasing moisture content below field capacity.

Moreover, it is probable that λ_v will show a more rapid decrease with moisture content than is given by a straight line relationship for moisture contents below the field capacity, since the hydraulic conductivity also decreases sharply in this region (cf. section 2.20).

As an example the values of g_a which correspond to the observed values of λ at 20 °C were calculated in the region $0.03 < x_w < 0.09$. For simplicity the values of λ_v^s were kept the same as in the preceding calculations. The results are represented in Fig. 7.8 together with the g_a-values according to the previous general method. It can be seen that the deviations are in the sense that follows from the preceding reasoning.

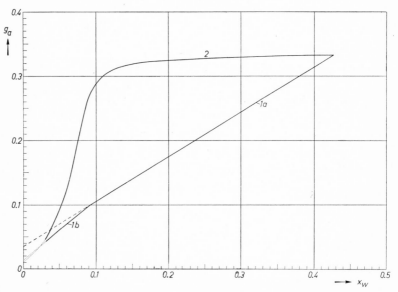

Fig. 7.8. Values of g_a found by linear interpolation (lines 1a and 1b) together with g_a computed from experimental thermal conductivity (curve 2) for a quartz sand (same as in Figs. 7.5, 7.6 and 7.7).

7.6.2. FAIRBANKS SAND

As a second example the thermal conductivity of Fairbanks sand is treated. Experimental values of λ at various dry densities and moisture contents were determined by KERSTEN [1949]. This sand consists for 59.4 weight per cents of quartz and for 40.6 weight per cents of feldspar and other minerals. The specific mass of the dry material is 2.72 g cm^{-3}. Since the specific mass of quartz equals 2.66 g cm^{-3}, the average specific mass of the other soil minerals is computed at 2.80 g cm^{-3}. From these figures it follows that the volume percentages of quartz and other minerals are 60.6 and 39.4 respectively.

Calculations were made for 4.4 °C (40 °F). Here $\lambda_1 = 21.6$ for quartz, $\lambda_w = 1.34$, $\lambda_a = 0.059$ and $\lambda_v{}^s = 0.066$, while for the other soil minerals an average value of $\lambda_2 = 7.0$ was adopted (all values expressed as mcal cm^{-1} sec^{-1} °C^{-1}). The value of g_a for the soil particles was taken as 0.125. This corresponds to a ratio of 5 between the long and the short axes of the ellipsoids, a value which is in accordance with the diffusion measurements on soils (cf. DE VRIES [1952]).

The calculations were analogous to those in the preceding chapter. It was assumed that λ_v decreased linearly from 0.066 to 0 in the moisture range $0.03 \geqslant x_w \geqslant 0$. Apart from this assumption the theoretical values were obtained exclusively from the thermal conductivities of the constituents and from their volume fractions.

The results are represented in Table 7.5; they are in excellent agreement with the experimental values. The accuracy of the latter is estimated at 5% on the average. Individual figures may have a larger error, especially in the

TABLE 7.5

Experimental (λ_e) and computed (λ_c) values of the thermal conductivity for Fairbanks sand

x_w	x_s	x_a	λ_e	λ_c	λ_e/λ_c
			(mcal cm^{-1} sec^{-1} °C^{-1})		
0.212	0.660	0.128	5.49	5.42	1.01
0.203	0.710	0.087	6.07	6.30	0.96
0.184	0.632	0.184	4.97	4.71	1.06
0.117	0.705	0.178	5.24	5.35	0.98
0.112	0.665	0.223	4.85	4.56	1.06
0.102	0.691	0.207	5.31	4.93	1.08
0.101	0.631	0.268	3.75	3.90	0.96
0.050	0.710	0.240	4.28	4.32	0.99
0.047	0.665	0.288	3.45	3.57	0.97
0.043	0.631	0.326	2.92	3.04	0.96
0.026	0.727	0.247	2.87	2.8*	1.02
0.025	0.705	0.270	2.20	2.5*	0.88
0.024	0.665	0.311	1.93	2.0*	0.97
0.021	0.631	0.348	1.38	1.7*	0.81
0.004	0.710	0.286	0.125	0.12*	1.04
0.004	0.665	0.331	0.90	0.95*	0.95
0.003	0.629	0.368	0.79	0.80	0.99

* These values are obtained by graphical interpolation.

range of moisture contents below $x_w = 0.03$, because Kersten used a stationary method for measuring λ. During long test runs the moisture accumulates at the cold side of the sample, especially when the hydraulic conductivity is low. This drawback was realized by Kersten from the start of the measurements. Its effect was kept as low as possible by taking a small value (10 °F) of the temperature difference between the warm side and the cold side of the sample. An uneven distribution of moisture in the sense indicated above will at low moisture contents result in an increase in the thermal resistance of the sample and thus the experimental value of λ will be lower than the value that corresponds to the average moisture content.

7.6.3. HEALY CLAY

This soil consists mainly of clay (55%), with additions of quartz (22.5%), coal (22%) and some other minerals (0.5%). The specific mass of the dry material equals 2.59 g cm^{-3}. All experimental data are again taken from Kersten's work.

To simplify calculations an average value of the thermal conductivity of the solid material has been adopted. This value, $\lambda_s = 6.0$ mcal cm^{-1} sec^{-1} °C^{-1}, was taken such that the theoretical value for saturated soil (first row in

TABLE 7.6

Experimental (λ_e) and computed (λ_c) values of thermal conductivity for Healy clay

x_w	x_s	x_a	λ_e λ_c (mcal cm^{-1} sec^{-1} °C^{-1})		λ_e/λ_c
0.359	0.641	0.000	3.68	3.66	1.01
0.450	0.499	0.051	2.93	2.85	1.03
0.402	0.444	0.154	1.97	2.34	0.84
0.334	0.579	0.087	3.22	3.07	1.05
0.304	0.517	0.179	2.18	2.51	0.87
0.270	0.671	0.059	3.89	3.59	1.08
0.256	0.581	0.163	2.84	2.82	1.01
0.231	0.519	0.250	2.27	2.28	1.00
0.163	0.581	0.256	2.11	2.32	0.91
0.144	0.519	0.337	1.53	1.96	0.78
0.095	0.575	0.330	1.42	1.83	0.78
0.091	0.525	0.384	1.00	1.66	0.60
0.041	0.521	0.438	0.71	0.85*	0.84
0.038	0.457	0.505	0.49	0.65*	0.75
0.033	0.396	0.571	0.38	0.48*	0.79

* These values are obtained by graphical interpolation.

Table 7.6) was approximately equal to the experimental value. The value of g_a for the soil particles was again taken as 0.125. Further it was assumed that a linear decrease of λ_v occurred between a moisture content of 15 weight per cents and zero.

The results are represented in Table 7.6. At moisture contents below $x_w = 0.15$ the computed values are systematically higher than the measured ones. This is partly due to the characteristics of the theoretical procedure, which tends to overestimate the value of the thermal conductivity in this region. On the other hand the experimental values will tend to be too low due to an uneven distribution of moisture.

7.6.4. FAIRBANKS PEAT

This soil is described by Kersten as "a fibrous brown peat". Since the value of the specific mass of the dry material is not given by Kersten, an attempt was made to estimate it from the measurement at the highest moisture content. Assuming that here the soil was saturated a value of 1.36 g cm^{-3} was found which comes close to the values obtained for other organic soils.

The temperature of the measurements was again 40 °F. A value of 0.6 mcal cm^{-1} sec^{-1} °C^{-1} was adopted for the conductivity of the dry material. The soil particles were considered as long cylinders with circular cross section, hence $g_a = g_b = 0.5$, $g_c = 0$. At values of $x_a < 0.5$ water was taken as the continuous medium. The air-filled pores were also considered as long circular cylinders.

At values of $x_a > 0.5$ air was considered as the continuous medium. Firstly the conductivity of the wet peat soil was calculated on the basis of peat cylinders dispersed in water. Secondly the conductivity of the soil as a whole was found for air with long circular cylinders of wet peat included. The conductivity of the air was taken as $\lambda_a + \lambda_v^s$ in all cases, except the two with $x_w < 0.1$, where λ_a was used.

The calculated values, represented in Table 7.7 are in good agreement with the experimental ones.

The calculations for two cases, one with $x_a = 0.142$ the other with $x_a = 0.777$ are given below as examples.

1. For $\lambda_s = 0.60$ mcal cm^{-1} sec^{-1} °C^{-1}, $\lambda_w = 1.34$ mcal cm^{-1} sec^{-1} °C^{-1} and $g_a = g_b = 0.5$, $g_c = 0$ one obtains

$$k_s = \tfrac{1}{3}\left(\frac{2}{1 - 0.552 \times 0.5} + 1\right) = 1.253.$$

Similarly for $\lambda_a + \lambda_v{}^s = 0.125$, $\lambda_w = 1.34$ and $g_a = g_b = 0.5$, $g_c = 0$

$$k_a = \tfrac{1}{3}\left(\frac{2}{1 - 0.907 \times 0.5} + 1\right) = 1.55.$$

TABLE 7.7

Experimental (λ_e) and computed (λ_c) values of thermal conductivity for Fairbanks peat

x_w	x_s	x_a	λ_e λ_c (mcal cm^{-1} sec^{-1} °C^{-1})		λ_e/λ_c
0.790	0.210	0.000	1.07	1.15	0.93
0.676	0.292	0.032	1.07	1.04	1.03
0.660	0.171	0.169	0.96	0.92	1.04
0.614	0.244	0.142	0.89	0.91	0.98
0.399	0.169	0.432	0.59	0.58	1.02
0.380	0.248	0.372	0.60	0.60	1.00
0.322	0.087	0.591	0.32	0.37	0.86
0.250	0.169	0.581	0.33	0.35	0.94
0.229	0.095	0.676	0.24	0.30	0.80
0.135	0.088	0.777	0.22	0.23	0.96
0.032	0.256	0.712	0.15	0.16	0.94
0.023	0.164	0.813	0.12	0.12	1.00

Thus at $x_w = 0.614$, $x_s = 0.244$ and $x_a = 0.142$

$$\lambda = \frac{0.614 \times 1.34 + 1.253 \times 0.244 \times 0.60 + 1.55 \times 0.142 \times 0.125}{0.614 + 1.253 \times 0.244 + 1.55 \times 0.142}$$
$$= 0.91 \text{ mcal cm}^{-1} \text{ sec}^{-1} \text{ °C}^{-1}.$$

2. Here $x_w = 0.135$, $x_s = 0.088$ and $x_a = 0.777$. The value of the conductivity for water and peat alone, where water is considered as the continuous medium, is found as follows

$$\lambda_{sw} = \frac{0.135 \times 1.34 + 1.253 \times 0.088 \times 0.6}{0.135 + 1.253 \times 0.088} = 1.01 \text{ mcal cm}^{-1} \text{ sec}^{-1} \text{ °C}^{-1}.$$

The value of k_1 for $\lambda_1 = \lambda_{sw} = 1.01$, $\lambda_0 = \lambda_a = 0.125$ and $g_a = g_b = 0.5$, $g_c = 0$ becomes

$$k_1 = \tfrac{1}{3}\left(\frac{2}{1 + 7.08 \times 0.5} + 1\right) = 0.480, \text{ and finally}$$

$$\lambda = \frac{0.777 \times 0.125 + 0.480 \times 0.223 \times 1.01}{0.777 + 0.480 \times 0.223} = 0.23 \text{ mcal cm}^{-1} \text{ sec}^{-1} \text{ °C}^{-1}.$$

7.6.5. CONCLUDING REMARKS

It follows from the preceding examples that a theoretical estimate of the thermal conductivity of a soil can be made if its mineral composition, its porosity and its water content are known. The accuracy of this estimate is better than ten per cent in most cases. This degree of accuracy will be sufficient for many applications, e.g. those where estimates are required of the heat flux into the soil, or where the influence of soil thermal properties on the temperature regime near the surface is calculated.

When the moisture sorption curve of the soil is known even a better theoretical estimate of the thermal conductivity, with an accuracy of about five per cents, can be made.

When it is desired to determine the moisture content of the soil from its thermal conductivity an experimental determination of the relation between λ and x_w will be necessary. The experimental procedure applied in the field should resemble as closely as possible that used in calibrating the soil, so that the influence of moisture movement is approximately the same in both cases.

CHAPTER 8

TURBULENT TRANSFER IN AIR

W. R. VAN WIJK AND A. J. W. BORGHORST

*Laboratory of Physics and Meteorology of the Agricultural University Wageningen,
The Netherlands*

8.1. Turbulence, mixing length

Turbulence is a state of movement of a fluid in which the velocity, direction as well as magnitude, in the fluid varies in a more or less random way. The various parts of the fluid are thereby mixed. On windy days smoke from a chimney is carried off in the general direction of the wind but irregular protuberances on the plume evince the mixing with the surrounding air. The motion of light objects, as dry leaves blown by the wind, and the gustiness of the wind also show the existence of unsystematic or eddy velocity components. Records of wind velocity and wind direction show fluctuations superposed on the average magnitudes (Fig. 8.1).

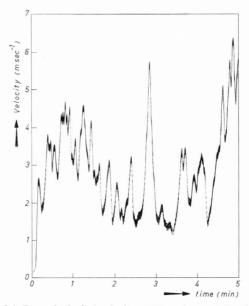

Fig. 8.1. Record of wind velocity at Wageningen at 2 m height

The velocity at a certain point is usually written as

$$u(t) = \bar{u} + u'(t) \tag{8.1}$$

for the x direction, while similar equations hold for the components v and w in the y and z directions. According to (8.1) the component u is the sum of an average velocity $\bar{u}$ and a fluctuating velocity u'. The average velocity is generally a function of the time as well but it varies slowly compared with u'. In an interval of time Δt which is large in comparison to the periods of fluctuation of u' but small with respect to the time in which $\bar{u}$ varies appreciably, one has

$$\frac{1}{\Delta t} \int_{t-\Delta t/2}^{t+\Delta t/2} u(t)\,\mathrm{d}t = \frac{1}{\Delta t} \int_{t-\Delta t/2}^{t+\Delta t/2} \bar{u}\,\mathrm{d}t + \frac{1}{\Delta t} \int_{t-\Delta t/2}^{t+\Delta t/2} u'\,\mathrm{d}t = \bar{u}. \tag{8.2}$$

Equation (8.2) contains the definition of $\bar{u}$. Similar equations hold for v and w. For the present, constant $\bar{u}$ will be assumed.

A qualitative description of turbulence can be based on the concept of parcels of air moving in various directions owing to their irregular velocity components. The motion, the size and the shape of these parcels change continually due to friction with the neighboring fluid. They may even merge and thereby lose their individuality or on the other hand a mass of air may be torn off by frictional forces and give rise to the formation of a new parcel. The properties of air are transferred from one location to another by these parcels.

The picture bears some resemblance to the irregular thermal motion of molecules in the kinetic theory of matter. Particularly for a gas at a moderate pressure many phenomena are explained by the fact that the molecules cover in the average a certain distance, the mean free path, between two collisions. The properties of the molecule acquired at the last collision are transferred to the region where the next collision takes place (KRONIG [1959]).

This method of approach has the merit that its concepts are easily visualized. It is, however, difficult to use the mean free path as a basic concept in a theory which has to meet modern standards of exactness when interaction of the molecules between collisions becomes important. This holds obviously also for a medium consisting of irregularly moving parcels. The magnitude corresponding to the mean free path is called *mixing length* in the case of turbulence (PRANDTL [1931]). It is defined as the average distance which a parcel has covered between breaking away and losing its individuality by mixing with its environment.

Since the parcel is strongly influenced by its environment during its motion, the definition of the mixing length must remain vague. Therefore, a statistical approach (TAYLOR [1915]) is preferred in theories on turbulence.

Yet the transfer properties will be discussed here, using the concept of mixing length. This approach makes it easy to derive the type of equations which will be used to calculate turbulent exchange by parcels in the air near the ground. Calculation of the exchange coefficients themselves will not be attempted. They will be considered as empirical magnitudes, about which the theory can only provide information in a very general way.

8.2. Equation of molecular exchange

As an introduction the classical method of treating molecular exchange in a gas by molecular movement will be briefly discussed (Fig. 8.2). The axis of x is in the direction of the systematic velocity $\bar{u}$. Assuming that half of the molecules possess a velocity with a component in the positive z direction, the number of molecules passing per second one cm^2 of the plane in an upward direction is $\frac{1}{2}Nw'_+$, N being the number of molecules per cm^3 and w'_+ the average velocity of the molecules moving in the positive z direction. Let l be the mean free path in the z direction; then these molecules transfer the properties of the layer at $z - l$ to the air above the plane z, in the average.*
Thus

$$\tfrac{1}{2}Nw'_+ \, P(z - l) = \tfrac{1}{2}Nw'_+ \left[P(z) - l\frac{dP}{dz} \right] \tag{8.3}$$

is transferred of the molecular property denoted by $P(z)$.

A similar expression holds for the transfer across the plane by molecules moving downward across the chosen plane

$$\tfrac{1}{2}Nw'_- \, P(z + l) = \tfrac{1}{2}Nw'_- \left[P(z) + l\frac{dP}{dz} \right]. \tag{8.4}$$

---

* The reader might expect that the molecules would transfer the properties of the layer at $z - \frac{1}{2}l$ since not all of them collide immediately above z. It can, however, be shown that though the argument is correct, yet the mean free path l must be inserted. This follows from the fact that the distance between successive collisions is not the same for all molecules. The longer the individual free path, the higher is the probability that the molecule crosses the plane. When the proper distribution function of the free path is used in the calculation of the transfer coefficient, more statistical weight is given to the greater path length.
The above result is obtained in the elementary version of the kinetic theory. A more advanced theory leads to correction factors owing to the fact that the effects of previous collisions persist to some extent and to interaction between collisions.

Assuming symmetry of the unsystematic velocity, $w'_+ = -w'_-$, and N independent of z, the flux density of P becomes

$$- N w'_+ \, l \frac{\mathrm{d}P}{\mathrm{d}z}. \tag{8.5}$$

As N, w'_+ and l are positive quantities, the net transfer possesses the opposite sign to $\mathrm{d}P/\mathrm{d}z$, thus it is negative or downwards when P increases with z and upwards when $\mathrm{d}P/\mathrm{d}z$ is negative.*

To illustrate the use of (8.5) let us calculate momentum transfer. The momentum of a molecule in the x direction is $m(\bar{u} + u')$ with m the mass of a molecule. Its average value is $m\bar{u}$ (cf. (8.2)). So the transfer in the z direction of momentum directed along the positive axis of x is

$$\tau_{xz} = - N w'_+ \, lm \frac{\mathrm{d}\bar{u}}{\mathrm{d}z} = - \eta \frac{\mathrm{d}\bar{u}}{\mathrm{d}z}. \tag{8.6}$$

The symbol η denotes the *dynamic viscosity*; in the elementary kinetic theory of gases it is shown that $\eta = N' w'_+ \, lm = \frac{1}{3} \varrho c l$ with ϱ the specific mass of the gas (g cm^{-3}) and c the average absolute value of the thermal velocities of the molecules. Equation (8.6) expresses the fact that the air above z loses momentum in the positive x direction if $\bar{u}$ increases with z; thus the air above the plane z is retarded by the air below that plane. The motion must be sustained by a continuous supply of momentum from higher air layers. Since a gain of momentum is equivalent to the action of a force, the quantity τ_{xz} may be interpreted as a force in the positive x direction, exerted per unit of area of the plane z, by the air above z on the air below z. Such a force is called a shearing stress. It is counted positive if the medium below z accelerates the medium above z in the positive x direction, corresponding to transfer in the positive z direction. Thus τ_{xz} is negative in case of positive $\mathrm{d}u/\mathrm{d}z$.

In fluid dynamics the quantity $v = \eta/\varrho$ occurs in many equations. It is called the *kinematic viscosity*. Its dimension is cm^2 sec^{-1}, which is the same dimension as of the thermal diffusivity. From equation (8.6)

$$v = w'_+ \, l \tag{8.7}$$

since $Nm = \varrho$.

---

* If, of the quantities N, w'_+ and l, two or more are correlated, the average value of their product should appear in (8.5) instead of the product of their average values.

8.3. Equations of turbulent exchange

Substitution of the number of parcels per unit of volume for the number of molecules in the previous section and of mixing length and velocity of a parcel for mean free path and molecular velocity respectively, leads to an equation of turbulent transfer which is analogous to (8.5). The number of parcels per unit of volume is difficult to establish. It is even difficult to give a rigorous definition of a parcel itself.

It is for that reason more practical to consider a property per unit of volume P_{vol} instead of per parcel. The quantity P_{vol} corresponds to NP in the molecular case. One has for the total, turbulent and molecular, transfer flux density of P:

$$-(K+\nu)\frac{dP_{vol}}{dz}. \tag{8.8}$$

The symbol K denotes the *exchange coefficient*, sometimes called *eddy viscosity*, which corresponds to $w'_+ l$ in (8.5). It has the same dimension as ν, $cm^2 \, sec^{-1}$. In the atmosphere the contribution of molecular transfer is usually negligible, except in a layer of a few mm immediately above the earth's surface. At greater heights above the ground K is large as compared to ν.

The analogue of the dynamic viscosity is the mass exchange or the mass "*Austausch*" *coefficient* (SCHMIDT [1918]).

$$A_m = \varrho K \; (g \, cm^{-1} \, sec^{-1}).$$

In using these names one should recall that net mass transfer is always zero when the mass per unit of volume is constant with height ($d\varrho/dz = 0$).

The flux density of the property P_{vol} is analogous to the heat flux density in heat conduction. In a similar way to that shown in section 4.3 for heat conduction in a soil,

$$\frac{\partial P_{vol}}{\partial t} = \frac{\partial}{\partial z}\left(K\frac{\partial P_{vol}}{\partial z}\right) \tag{8.9}$$

is obtained as the equation of nonstationary turbulent exchange of the property P_{vol}. This equation can only be expected to hold for the average flux density. The air parcels are of dimensions comparable with the mixing length and often also with the distance over which a sizeable variation of P_{vol} occurs. Moreover, (8.9) treats the medium as if it were homogeneous. This may be an allowable approximation with strong winds when intensive mixing takes place in the air but it remains questionable when the air rises and descends in spacially separated columns as is the case when free convection is strongly developed. Though the spots where columns of warm air ascend shift in course of time, one may question the homogeneity of the medium even when a long time average is considered. Since the object of this book is not to give a critical appraisal of the fundamental equation of turbulent transfer in the lower atmosphere, this point will be discussed no further. Equation (8.9) will be used in the following but it is emphasized that future refinements of the theory of turbulence in the air near the ground may result in a partial revision of some of the conclusions drawn from (8.9).

An indication for an influence of inhomogeneity may be seen in the occasionally reported different values of the exchange coefficients in respect to transfer of heat, of momentum and of water vapor, respectively (RIDER [1954]; SWINBANK [1951]). An ascending air parcel containing much water vapor must have a relatively low temperature owing to the heat consumed in the vaporization of water from the ground surface or vegetative cover. Under the same circumstances of energy supply, an air parcel rising from a spot where no water is present will acquire a higher temperature and thus ascend more rapidly but carry less water vapor. RIDER [1954] reported for a lawn near Cambridge, England, $K_{he} = 1.14\ K_{ev} = 1.48\ K_{mo}$, in which the subscripts he, ev and mo denote heat, evaporation and momentum, respectively. The ratio will depend on the stratification and degree of turbulence in the air (PRIESTLEY [1959]).

Several authors assume equality of the transfer coefficients as a first approximation.

The exchange coefficient increases with wind velocity. It also increases with height. It is small at the earth's surface owing to the suppression of turbulence by friction. Some laws of variation of K with height will be discussed later.

8.4. Bowen's ratio

In case of equality of K_{he} and K_{ev}, the ratio of heat flux density and moisture flux density can be expressed as a ratio of temperature and vapor pressure differences.

Consider two air layers at different heights whose temperatures are $^1\vartheta$ and $^2\vartheta$ respectively and in which the vapor pressures of water are p_1 and p_2. The total pressure of moist air p_{ai} is the same at both heights. If a unit volume of air is exchanged, a net transfer of sensible heat $\phi_{he} = C(^1\vartheta - {}^2\vartheta)$ has taken place from layer 1 to layer 2, with $C = \varrho c$, the volumetric heat capacity of moist air (cal cm^{-3} °C^{-1}).

Let V be the volume of one grammole of moist air at p_{ai} mbar and $\frac{1}{2}(^1\vartheta + {^2\vartheta})$ °C. The mass of water vapor per unit of volume and per unit of water vapor pressure is $18/(Vp_{ai})$ at that temperature. Thus the net water vapor transfer is $\phi_{mw} = 18(p_1 - p_2)/(Vp_{ai})$

The ratio of the two transferred quantities is

$$\frac{\phi_{he}}{\phi_{mw}} = \frac{(CVp_{ai}/18)(^1\vartheta - {^2\vartheta})}{p_1 - p_2}. \tag{8.10}$$

Now CV is the heat capacity of one grammole of moist air. Taking the average value of the specific heat capacity of the air as 0.24 cal g^{-1} °C^{-1} one has $CV = 29 \times 0.24 = 7.0$ cal °C^{-1}. Or

$$\frac{\phi_{he}}{\phi_{mw}} = b_m = 0.389 \frac{(^1\vartheta - {^2\vartheta})p_{ai}}{p_1 - p_2}. \tag{8.11}$$

The ratio b_m is called *Bowen's ratio* after I.S. BOWEN [1926] who discussed sensible and latent heat transfer from a lake.

Instead of the ratio b_m of the sensible heat flux density to the mass flux density, the ratio b_h between sensible and latent heat flux density is often required in problems concerning plant environment. The latent heat flux density is obtained by multiplication of ϕ_{mw} by the latent heat of vaporization of water L. At 15 °C under atmospheric pressure $L = 587.6$ cal g^{-1}. The ratio between sensible and latent heat flux then becomes

$$b_h = 0.000659 \frac{(^1\vartheta - {^2\vartheta})p_{ai}}{p_1 - p_2}. \tag{8.12}$$

This ratio is also called Bowen's ratio. In the standard wet and dry bulb psychrometric theory without correction for radiation, all the latent heat of vaporization is supplied by the sensible heat of the air flowing past the wet bulb. Thus ϕ_{he} from the air to the wet bulb equals the latent heat flux density from the bulb into the air and consequently $b_h = -1$. The index 1 now refers to the air at a great distance of the wet bulb (or to the air before contact with the wet bulb) and the index 2 refers to the thin air layer in direct contact with the wet bulb.

The psychrometer constant $\gamma = 0.000659\, p_{ai}$. It is 0.668 mbar °C^{-1} at atmospheric pressure (1013 mbar) and 15 °C; $\gamma = 0.501$ if pressures are expressed as mm of mercury. The value of γ depends on the temperature. At 10 °C and 1 atm one has $\gamma = 0.665$ mbar °C^{-1} or $\gamma = 0.499$ mm Hg °C^{-1}.

8.5. Some experiments on turbulence in the atmosphere

As a model of convection in the air near the ground Ramdas and associates

(RAMDAS [1948, 1953]) studied convection above a hot plate. The hot air rises in a single column near the center when the hot plate is small, e.g. 2.5 cm². The cross section of the column decreases rapidly with height. The hot air flows in a thin layer with a thickness of the order of 0.1 mm over the plate's surface towards the column. This pattern remains fairly steady. This is not so with a hot plate of larger dimensions, say 30 cm² or more. A number of columns are then observed which develop and move over the plate's surface in an apparently random manner. They persist in moderate winds but are then inclined instead of vertical. The columns were observed to extend up to several cm in height above the plate in the experimental setup. Cold air descends between the columns. The ascending hot air in a mass of cold air causes the "shimmering" of distant objects when viewed through the air near the ground.

Ramdas and associates investigated the extension of the shimmering layer in the atmosphere above bare soil using the existence of fluctuations of the air temperature as an indication. They found that the shimmering layer could reach a height of 30 to 60 m at the time of maximum insolation at Poona (India). It decreased after that time to a very low level before daybreak when it again started to increase. A nocturnal inversion was formed on nights with slight or no wind, which started at some height above the ground and not at the earth's surface as one might expect. These investigations indicate a strong variation of the exchange coefficient with insolation under conditions of slight winds. A diurnal as well as a seasonal variation of the exchange coefficient is therefore to be expected. The ratio of the maximum during the day and the minimum at night may be of the order of 10 or more (BUDYKO [1956]; POPPENDIECK [1952]).

Investigation of the spectrum of turbulence is a more fundamental approach to the structure of air movement in the lower atmosphere. The degree of correlation between fluctuations of temperature, and of wind velocity or wind direction at different measuring points is studied. With specially constructed thermocouples, thermistors or hot wire anemometers, fluctuations of a period of less than a second are recorded. The analysis of the fluctuations, performed with computers, gives the frequency of the occurrence of fluctuations of a given duration (SWINBANK [1951]; PRIESTLEY [1954]).

A discussion of these techniques and the results obtained with them falls outside the scope of this book. Reference is made to PRIESTLEY's monograph [1959].

8.6. Constant thermal conductivity, sinusoidal variation

As early as 1915 Taylor analysed the temperature distribution above the Grand Banks of Newfoundland. The warm advected air is cooled during its passage over the cold sea. If the initial air temperature is represented by $\vartheta = {}^0\vartheta - \beta z$, and ${}^1\vartheta$ is the constant temperature of the sea surface (${}^1\vartheta < {}^0\vartheta$), one obtains

$$\vartheta(z,t) = {}^0\vartheta - \beta z + ({}^1\vartheta - {}^0\vartheta) \text{ erfc } [z/\sqrt{(4Kt)}] \qquad (8.13)$$

for the temperature distribution in a column of air whose ground surface has been kept at ${}^1\vartheta$ since $t = 0$. Taylor found K roughly proportional to the wind velocity.

SCHMIDT [1918] presented a treatment of the temperature wave in air assuming constant apparent thermal conductivity λ, which is the turbulent analogue of the ordinary thermal conductivity. One has $\lambda = C_{ai} K$ where C_{ai} is the volumetric heat capacity of the air (cal cm^{-3} °C^{-1}) and K the exchange coefficient (cm^2 sec^{-1}). Though we now know that an apparent conductivity which is variable with height follows from theory and experience, and that Schmidt's theory leads to incorrect results on vital points such as the temperature distribution close to the earth's surface and the distribution of heat between air and soil, it is still of importance to discuss some of his conclusions and to compare them with newer ones based upon variable apparent conductivity.

Using (4.7), Schmidt calculated the thermal diffusivity or the exchange coefficient of the air above Paris from temperature measurements by ANGOT [1883, 1907] on the Eiffel tower. Actually Schmidt calculated the "Massenaustausch" coefficient $A = \varrho K$. The values of K in the present text have been obtained by dividing Schmidt's data by $\varrho = 0.0012$ g cm^{-3}. An exchange coefficient or thermal diffusivity K of the order of 8000 cm^2 sec^{-1} was found for the air below 100 m and of the order of 16000 cm^2 sec^{-1} for the air between 200 and 300 m. We have seen before that it is not allowed to apply (4.7) to a situation where K varies with height. Yet this result shows that the thermal diffusivity increases with height and that heat transfer in air is caused by turbulence and not by molecular conduction. Since at 20 °C, $\lambda = 6.15 \times 10^{-5}$ cal cm^{-1} sec^{-1} °C^{-1} for absolutely still air and $C_{ai} = 0.287 \times 10^{-3}$ cal cm^{-3} °C^{-1} the thermal diffusivity for molecular transfer is 0.214 cm^2 sec^{-1}.

Even below screen height turbulent transfer largely exceeds molecular transfer. For instance, a damping depth of the diurnal variation $D = 640$ cm is calculated from the recorded temperature at 10 and 200 cm in Fig 4.6a, whereas $D = 76.6$ cm follows from the molecular thermal conductivity. Schmidt also found a seasonal variation. Average values, which he considered to be representative for the air above Paris, are given in Table 8.1.

TABLE 8.1

Approximate values of apparent thermal diffusivity of air above Paris (cm² sec⁻¹) (after SCHMIDT [1918])

Jan.	Febr.	March	April	May	June	July	Aug.	Sept.	Oct.	Nov.	Dec.
5000	6400	10000	10500	11600	13400	13800	12500	8400	7000	5400	6100

A constant apparent conductivity in both air and soil would lead to a distribution of the heat flux between both media, which is independent of the frequency of the temperature variation. In consequence the surface amplitude should be approximately 19 times as high for the diurnal variation than for the annual one at such latitudes where the amplitudes of the diurnal and of the annual heat flux density are equal (cf. (4.17)). The fact that such an extreme ratio has not been found in middle latitudes was an argument for LETTAU [1952] to assume a linear increase of λ with height. A maximum ratio of 3 to 4 is observed on a continent and a ratio of about 10 on the Atlantic Ocean, where the diurnal variation is very small, e.g. of the order of 0.2 °C (SCHMIDT [1918]). But in the ocean, heat transfer is also effected by turbulence. Thus we may conclude that the determinations of the apparent thermal conductivity of air and the distribution of heat flux over air and soil provide arguments for the assumption of an apparent thermal conductivity which increases with height at least in the air near the ground. This implies that a lower average value of the apparent thermal conductivity is effective in a rapid temperature variation when the heat does not penetrate to a considerable height, than in a slow variation.

8.7. Advective air over a surface at constant temperature

Advective air is air which is transported from other regions. The name is in particular used when the air flows over a surface to whose thermal or moisture conditions it has not yet become adjusted.

For the present book the most important phenomena in connection with advective air are the transfer of heat from a body of air to a body of soil or conversely, the evaporation caused by it and the readjustment of the temperature and humidity as a function of height. Generation of heat by absorption of radiation at the soil surface will not be considered in the following discussion.

SCHMIDT [1918] considered the change of temperature as a function of height in a moving air column when the column passes a line at which the temperature of the soil surface changes abruptly from $^1\vartheta$ to $^2\vartheta$. Uniform air temperature equal to $^1\vartheta$ is assumed before the boundary. The velocity v is the same at all heights. With these assumptions heat transfer takes place in the same way as in an air column at rest in which the initial temperature is $^1\vartheta$ and whose ground surface is kept at $^2\vartheta$ from $t = 0$ on. This problem has been treated in Chapter 5. One has (equation (5.17))

$$\vartheta(z,t) - {}^1\vartheta = ({}^2\vartheta - {}^1\vartheta)[1 - \text{erf}(z/2\sqrt{(Kt)})]. \tag{8.14}$$

Thus the height at which a given temperature occurs t seconds after passage of the boundary, increases proportionally to $\sqrt{t}$. Since the column moves with the constant velocity v, a distance vt is covered after t seconds. The isotherms in air are shown in Fig. 8.2.

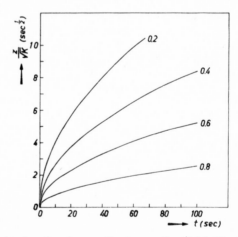

Fig. 8.2. Isotherms in advective air according to equation (8.14). The figures at the curves are the fractions $[\vartheta(z,t) - {}^1\vartheta]/[{}^2\vartheta - {}^1\vartheta]$.

To illustrate the effect of the change of surface temperature the distance is now calculated at which the temperature at 200 cm height, $\vartheta(200)$, equals $^1\vartheta + 0.90\,({}^2\vartheta - {}^1\vartheta)$. Since erf (0.089) = 0.10 one has $2\sqrt{(Kt)} = 200/0.089$ or $Kt = 1.26 \times 10^6$ cm^2. For a value of $K = 10^4$ cm^2 sec^{-1} one has $t = 1.26 \times 10^2$ sec which corresponds to a distance of 378 m if v is 3 m sec^{-1}.

In many problems of advective air the heat flux density at the soil surface is an important quantity. It follows from (8.14) that

$$H_{ai} = -\lambda \left(\frac{\partial \vartheta}{\partial z}\right)_{z=0} = \frac{(^2\vartheta - {}^1\vartheta)\,C_{ai}\,K}{\sqrt{(\pi K t)}}. \qquad (8.15)$$

for $t > 0$.

8.8. Advective air, air temperature constant

A soil surface which should remain at $^2\vartheta$ °C may seem an unrealistic assumption since the heat capacity of the upper soil layers taking part in the exchange of heat is small compared with that of an overflowing air mass (see, however, section 8.9). PRIESTLEY [1957] has pointed out that the condition may apply to an ocean, which can be considered as a heat reservoir of unlimited capacity owing to a high turbulent exchange coefficient and the large mass of water involved. Over land surfaces, however, the assumption that air temperature above a certain level z_1, $\vartheta_{ai}(z_1)$, remains practically constant is probably a better approximation than the former one. In this model the exchange coefficient in air is assumed to be very high above the "certain level" so that the air above it is considered as a large heat reservoir whose temperature is not affected by heat exchange with the ground.

The rate of heat exchange between soil and air will depend upon the air velocity v and the thermal diffusivities of the soil and the air near the ground. Instead of making assumptions about the thermal diffusivity in the air near the ground, Priestley introduces a boundary condition for the heat flux density into air at the soil surface

$$H_{ai} = C_s\,v\,[\vartheta(0,t) - \vartheta_{ai}(z_1)] \qquad (8.16)$$

in which $\vartheta(0,t)$ is the surface temperature and C_s an empirical factor which has the dimension of volumetric heat capacity (cal cm^{-3} °C^{-1}); $C_s\,v$ is the surface heat transfer coefficient. The temperature in the soil, which is assumed to be originally at the uniform temperature $^1\vartheta$ is then given by

$$\frac{\vartheta_{so}(z,t) - \vartheta_{ai}(z_1)}{^1\vartheta - \vartheta_{ai}(z_1)} = \operatorname{erf}\xi + \exp(2\xi\tau + \tau^2)[1 - \operatorname{erf}(\xi + \tau)] \qquad (8.17)$$

in which $\xi = z/[2\sqrt{(at)}]$, $\tau = (C_s\,v\sqrt{t})/(\varrho c\sqrt{a})$, a is the thermal diffusivity, ϱ the specific mass and c the specific heat of the soil.

Equation (8.17) also satisfies the boundary condition (8.16) which can be proved by calculating $-H_{so} = \varrho c a(\partial\vartheta/\partial z)$ at $z = 0$ and remembering that $-H_{so} = +H_{ai}$ in this case. At the surface, $\xi = 0$, and (8.17) becomes

$$\frac{\vartheta_{so}(0,t) - \vartheta_{ai}(z_1)}{{}^1\vartheta - \vartheta_{ai}(z_1)} = \exp(\tau^2)[1 - \text{erf}(\tau)]. \tag{8.18}$$

Differentiation of (8.17) gives the result

$$\frac{H_{ai}}{C_s v[{}^1\vartheta - \vartheta_{ai}(z_1)]} = \exp(\tau^2)[1 - \text{erf}(\tau)]. \tag{8.19}$$

The denominator in the left hand side of (8.19) is the initial heat flux density. For large values of τ its right hand expression approaches $1/(\tau\sqrt{\pi})$. Thus the rate of heat exchange decreases asymptotically proportionally to $1/\sqrt{t}$ as in the previous case.

In many applications it is more useful to know the total amount of heat transferred in a given interval of time $0 - t$.

Integration of (8.19) gives the result

$$\int_0^t H_{ai}\, dt = -\int_0^t H_{so}\, dt$$
$$= 2[{}^1\vartheta - \vartheta_{ai}(z_1)] \frac{(\varrho c)^2 a}{C_s v} \left[\tfrac{1}{2}\exp(\tau^2)(1 - \text{erf}\,\tau) - \tfrac{1}{2} + \frac{\tau}{\sqrt{\pi}} \right] \tag{8.20}$$

which approaches asymptotically

$$\int_0^t H_{ai}\, dt \to \frac{2}{\sqrt{\pi}}[{}^1\vartheta - \vartheta_{ai}(z_1)]\, \varrho c\sqrt{(at)}. \tag{8.21}$$

This equation would also follow from (8.15) except that in this case the thermal constants of the soil appear.

PRIESTLEY [1959] has applied (8.19) and (8.20) to various surfaces. As an example some of his results are shown in Table 8.2.

TABLE 8.2

Evolution of heat flux as dependent on the underlying medium (after PRIESTLEY [1959])

Medium	$\varrho c\sqrt{a}$	Time for H_{ai} to fall to fraction of initial value			Heat transfer cal cm^{-2} first		second
		0.5	0.25	0.1	12 hr	24 hr	24 hr
New snow	0.002	4 sec	35 sec	3 min	5	7	3
Old snow	0.01	100 sec	19 min	80 min	22	32	14
Dry snow	0.01	100 sec	19 min	80 min	22	32	14
Wet soils	0.04	26 min	15 hr	22 hr	75	110	55
Ice	0.05	40 min	8 hr	35 hr	90	140	70

A wind speed of 10 m sec^{-1} and an initial temperature difference of 10 °C are assumed and unstable air.

8.9. Advective air, thermal diffusivity finite in both media

The same problem will now be treated using a finite thermal diffusivity in both media (a and K for soil and air respectively). The conditions prevailing after $t = 0$ at the surface are $\vartheta_{ai} = \vartheta_{so} = {}^2\vartheta$ and, remembering $-H_{so} = +H_{ai}$

$$\lambda_{ai}\frac{\partial \vartheta_{ai}}{\partial z} + \lambda_{so}\frac{\partial \vartheta_{so}}{\partial z} = 0 \tag{8.22}$$

where as usual the indices denote air and soil respectively. The temperatures of soil and air are both assumed to be constant before $t = 0$ and equal to ${}^1\vartheta_{so}$ and ${}^1\vartheta_{ai}$ respectively. In both media the temperature is a function of z of the "impulse" type

$$\vartheta(z,t) = W_1 + W_2 \operatorname{erf}\left[\frac{z}{2\sqrt{(at)}}\right]$$

in which W_1 and W_2 are constants which are determined by the boundary conditions. One obtains

$$\vartheta_{ai}(z,t) = {}^2\vartheta + \frac{{}^3\vartheta\,\lambda_{so}}{\sqrt{a}}\operatorname{erf}\left[\frac{z}{2\sqrt{(Kt)}}\right] \tag{8.23}$$

$$\vartheta_{so}(z,t) = {}^2\vartheta + \frac{{}^3\vartheta\,\lambda_{ai}}{\sqrt{K}}\operatorname{erf}\left[\frac{z}{2\sqrt{(at)}}\right] \tag{8.24}$$

in which

$$^2\vartheta = \frac{{}^1\vartheta_{ai}(\lambda_{ai}/\sqrt{K}) + {}^1\vartheta_{so}(\lambda_{so}/\sqrt{a})}{\lambda_{ai}/\sqrt{K} + \lambda_{so}/\sqrt{a}}$$

$$^3\vartheta = \frac{{}^1\vartheta_{ai} - {}^1\vartheta_{so}}{(\lambda_{ai}/\sqrt{K}) + (\lambda_{so}/\sqrt{a})}$$

and $\lambda_{ai}/K = C_{ai}$, $\lambda_{so}/a = C_{so}$, the volumetric heat capacities of air and soil respectively. Thus at $z = 0$ the temperature ${}^2\vartheta$ remains constant as was assumed in the simplest case treated by Schmidt. At infinity one has ${}^1\vartheta_{so}$ and ${}^1\vartheta_{ai}$ in soil and air respectively, at all times.
The heat flux density at the surface is

$$H_{ai} = -H_{so} = -\lambda_{ai}\left(\frac{\partial \vartheta_{ai}}{\partial z}\right) = -\frac{{}^3\vartheta\,\lambda_{ai}\lambda_{so}}{\sqrt{(\pi a K t)}}$$
$$= -({}^1\vartheta_{ai} - {}^1\vartheta_{so})\frac{(\lambda_{ai}/\sqrt{K})(\lambda_{so}/\sqrt{a})}{(\lambda_{ai}/\sqrt{K}) + (\lambda_{so}/\sqrt{a})}\cdot\frac{1}{\sqrt{(\pi t)}}. \tag{8.25}$$

Evidently the different models all lead to a heat flux density at the surface which (except for an initial period in (8.20)) decreases as $1/\sqrt{t}$. Though the exchange coefficient of air near the ground varies with height, it becomes more or less constant above a certain level, which level varies with weather and other conditions. The models are, therefore, probably useful for an approximate calculation of heat transfer and temperature propagation to higher levels. Temperatures in air near the ground cannot be predicted from them.

It has been said before that the results obtained for heat transfer in air are applicable to transfer of water vapor or of carbon dioxide.

8.10. Exchange coefficient increases as $(z + z_0)$, wind profiles

Several authors have studied transfer phenomena, assuming a linear increase of the exchange coefficient with height. HAURWITZ [1936] attempted to explain the phase shift of the temperature wave in air and its attenuation as a function of height. LETTAU [1952] has particularly drawn attention to the distribution of heat between air and soil. Solutions of the equation of heat conduction when the exchange coefficient varies as some power of z were given by KÖHLER [1932]. BUDYKO [1956] reviewing his own and others' investigations (LAICHTMAN [1957], TIMOFEEV [1951]) gives a graphical representation of the exchange coefficient as a function of wind velocity and temperature difference at two heights. A large variation of the exchange coefficient in 24 hr and in a year has been found, corresponding to the variation of air stability. Budyko proposed a semiempirical expression for the exchange coefficient

$$K = \frac{k^2 \, \Delta \bar{u}}{\ln(z_2/z_1)} \frac{1 + [\ln(z_2/z_1)] \, \Delta \vartheta}{(\Delta \bar{u})^2} z \qquad (8.26)$$

in which $\Delta \vartheta$ and $\Delta \bar{u}$ are the differences of the temperature and wind velocity, respectively, at the two heights z_1 and z_2, and k is von Karman's constant (0.40). Similar formulas for the calculation of K have also been given by Laichtman and Timofeev (BUDYKO et al. [1953]).

Experimental and theoretical studies of the exchange coefficient have been published by SWINBANK [1951], POPPENDIECK [1952], BERLIAND [1950] OBUKHOV [1946], MONIN and OBUKHOV [1954], and other authors.

Under conditions of neutral stability a logarithmic wind profile in the air near the ground has been observed. It can be derived if the exchange coefficient varies linearly with height and if the shearing stress in air remains constant in the lower air layers.

If the pressure gradient is the driving force, the rate of increase of momentum in the x direction of a certain quantity of air caused by it must be equal to the rate of loss of momentum due to viscous forces, or

$$\frac{\partial \tau}{\partial z} = \frac{\partial p}{\partial x}. \tag{8.27}$$

Pressure gradients in the atmosphere near the earth's surface are of the order of some mb per 100 km. Thus $\partial \tau / \partial z$ must be of that order too and

$$\tau(z) = \tau_0 + \int_0^z (\partial p / \partial x) \, dz$$

is approximately constant near the ground, since τ_0 is much larger (comp. Table 8.3). The equation in turbulent transfer corresponding to (8.6) is $\tau_{xz} = -\varrho w'_+ \, l \, (d\bar{u}/dz) = -\varrho K (d\bar{u}/dz)$. The average value w'_+ of the eddy velocities in the direction of positive z must depend on the velocity gradient, as no turbulence is produced in a uniformly moving fluid. It must also depend on the mixing length. One generally assumes $w'_+ = l |\partial \bar{u}/\partial z|$, in which the vertical bars indicate the absolute value of the velocity gradient. Thus one has

$$\tau_{xz} = \varrho l^2 (\partial \bar{u}/\partial z)^2. *$$

The assumption $l = k(z + z_0)$ and $\tau_{xz} = \tau_0$ now leads to

$$\frac{d\bar{u}}{dz} = \left(\frac{\tau_0}{\varrho}\right)^{\frac{1}{2}} [k(z + z_0)]^{-1} \tag{8.28}$$

which on integration gives the logarithmic wind profile

$$\bar{u} = \frac{1}{k} \left(\frac{\tau_0}{\varrho}\right)^{\frac{1}{2}} \ln \left(\frac{z + z_0}{z_0}\right) + \text{constant}, \tag{8.29}$$

where k is von Karman's constant for which values ranging from $0.36 - 0.40$ are found in the literature; z_0 is the roughness parameter of the underlying surface. Some values of it together with values of $(\tau_0/\varrho)^{\frac{1}{2}}$ characteristic for natural surfaces are given in Table 8.3.

The constant in (8.29) equals zero since $\tau_0 = 0$ corresponds to zero wind velocity, $\bar{u} = 0$.

With the foregoing equations, and $\lambda = b(z + z_0)$ and $K = \lambda/C_{ai}$, is found

$$\bar{u} = bk^{-2} C_{ai}^{-1} \ln \left(\frac{z + z_0}{z_0}\right). \tag{8.30}$$

It should be kept in mind that the logarithmic wind profile holds only for

---

* This equation may be considered to contain a definition of the mixing length.

TABLE 8.3

Representative values of z_0 and $\sqrt{(\tau_0/\varrho)}$ for natural surfaces (neutral stability). The values of $\sqrt{(\tau_0/\varrho)}$ corresponding to $\bar{u} = 5$ m sec^{-1} at 2 m height were calculated by Sutton from data published by SHEPPARD [1947].

Type of surface	z_0 (cm)	$\sqrt{(\tau_0/\varrho)}$ (cm sec^{-1})	author
very smooth (mud flats, ice)	0.001	16	SHEPPARD [1947]
lawn grass up to 1 cm high	0.1	26	,,
downland thin grass up to 10 cm high	0.7	36	,,
thick grass up to 10 cm high	2.3	45	,,
thin grass up to 50 cm high	5	55	,,
thick grass up to 50 cm high	9	63	,,
smooth snow	0.5		PAESCHKE [1937]
smooth lawn	0.5		HELLMANN [1919]
fallow field	2.1		PAESCHKE [1937]
open field	3.2		SHAW [1930]
low grass	3.2		PAESCHKE [1937]
high grass	3.9		,,
sea surface (swell no breakers)	4.0		WÜST [1920]
wheat field	4.5		PAESCHKE [1937]

neutral stability. In stable weather of the inversion type a more rapid increase of wind velocity with height has been observed and, conversely, a slower increase in an unstable atmosphere.

Often a formula of the type

$$\bar{u} = u_1 z^n \tag{8.31}$$

is used under such circumstances. The value of the exponent n depends on air stability, u_1 is the extrapolated velocity at 1 cm height. The formula can only be applied to a height well above the roughness height.

An extension of this formula is

$$\bar{u} = c(z - d)^n \tag{8.32}$$

in which c, n and d are constants. The wind velocity is zero at $z = d$ owing to friction by obstacles on the earth's surface. The zero velocity plane is at a height comparable with the height of the obstacles. In a citrus orchard $d = 3$ m was found from wind velocity measurements by Kepner et al. (BROOKS [1959]).

Brooks gives some examples of actual wind profiles above and inside an orange tree orchard and the determination of p and d from the data by plotting them on a log scale as a function of log $\bar{u}$.

In (8.27) only the pressure gradient and the viscous shearing stress have been taken into consideration. The coriolis force causes a deviation of a moving parcel of air from the direction of the pressure gradient. It is of little importance for the type of problems we are interested in.

On the other hand, buoyancy is highly important. It causes an acceleration along the vertical and induces convective motions. The upward force per unit of volume is equal to $g(\varrho - \varrho_0)$ with ϱ_0 the density of the surrounding air and ϱ that of the parcel. The heating of the earth's surface does not take place uniformly, this fact together with other causes results in a strong nonhomogeneity in a horizontal plane in the air under conditions of free convection. The theory given in this chapter does not take such nonhomogeneities into consideration. The mathematical theory has not yet reached the stage that it can be applied to plant environment.

Free convection becomes important only at some (low) height above the surface.

Thus the objection of nonhomegeneity is less important for the air near the ground. The fact that the mixing length turns out to be of the same order as the distances over which the magnitudes involved in the transfer phenomena change, constitute an other difficulty as the validity of equations such as (8.3) is based upon the assumption that l is small compared with the distance over which P changes appreciably.

It is hoped that further study of the air layer near the ground will lead to a more satisfactory situation. For the present the theory given is this chapter has to be applied. Fortunately this still enables a better understanding of the interactions between a plant and its surroundings and of the structure of plant environment than is possible from the empirical data as such.

Though wind is an important factor in microclimate, it is often difficult to ascertain how far it affects plant growth. This difficulty is partly due to the fact that wind may cause damage by a direct mechanical action which is superposed on its influence on the state of turbulence of the air near the ground. LORCH [1959] comparing banana trees in a sheltered area and in the open, arrived at the conclusion that the direct damage of the banana leaves in the open unsheltered area was responsible for the observed lower yield. If the leaves of the sheltered trees were torn to a same degree as those of the unsheltered trees, equal yields were obtained. The reason for the beneficial effect of low hedges on beetroots, bulbs and other plants is probably also a prevention of direct damage by mechanical action. The soil blown away by the wind may cause abrasion of the parts of the plants above the soil and in addition the root system becomes exposed.

An attempt to calculate the change of the diurnal temperature variation behind a shelterbelt was made by VAN WIJK and HIDDING [1955]. The decrease of wind velocity was assumed to cause a decrease of the turbulent exchange coefficient. In a strip of a width equal to approximately 10 times the height of the trees, an effect on plant growth might be expected. This is in agreement with some experimental results.

An increased turbulent exchange coefficient was, however, observed by Romanova. These experiments and many other interesting facts on shelterbelts are discussed by Vitvichkii (article in DZERZEEVSKII [1957]). One of the beneficial effects of shelterbelts in the Russian steppes is conservation of water. Owing to them the snow which falls in the winter is not blown away over large distances. This results in a higher moisture content of the soil between the shelterbelts than in the open steppe. This is obviously a most important factor in a dry year. Experiments in the Kamennaia steppe however showed that the shelterbelts have an additional beneficial effect which is most pronounced in years with frequent hot dry winds (suchovei). Wind screens consisting of stems of sunflowers were compared with shelterbelts formed by strips of wood and with the open steppe. Though soil moisture in the two first mentioned cases was approximately the same, the fields protected by shelterbelts gave a higher yield than those protected by the stems of sunflowers. Both yields were superior to those in the open steppe.

Thus many effects are superposed. A theoretical quantitative treatment would be highly desirable.

8.11. Sinusoidal temperature variation

Writing the apparent conductivity as $\lambda = b(z + z_0)$ one obtains the exchange coefficient for heat transfer

$$K_{\mathrm{he}} = \lambda/C = (b/C)(z + z_0) \tag{8.33}$$

in which b is a constant depending on the roughness of the surface and the wind velocity, whose value can be expressed in τ_0 according to (8.28) if equality of K_{mo} and K_{he} is assumed. At the present state of knowledge of turbulence in air, it seems, however, advisable to consider b as an empirical quantity.

The equation of heat conduction, ignoring advective heat, now becomes

$$\frac{\partial \vartheta}{\partial t} = \frac{\partial}{\partial z}\left(K\frac{\partial \vartheta}{\partial z}\right) = \frac{b}{C}(z + z_0)\frac{\partial^2 \vartheta}{\partial z^2} + \frac{b}{C}\frac{\partial \vartheta}{\partial z}. \tag{8.34}$$

The condition that ϑ varies sinusoidally with the time can be written as $\vartheta = {}^A\vartheta(z) \exp(i\omega t)$ in which ${}^A\vartheta(z)$ is a complex function of z only. One obtains an equation of the Bessel type for the factor ${}^A\vartheta$. Or

$$i\omega\,{}^A\vartheta = \frac{b}{C}(z + z_0)\frac{d^2\,{}^A\vartheta}{dz^2} + \frac{b}{C}\frac{d\,{}^A\vartheta}{dz}. \tag{8.35}$$

This equation admits solutions which are a linear combination of two conveniently chosen general Bessel functions of zero order.

Introducing the auxiliary variable

$$r = 2\sqrt{\left(\frac{\omega\,C(z + z_0)}{b}\right)} \tag{8.36}$$

we have the following solutions of equation (8.35)

$$\vartheta_{\mathrm{I}} = H_0^{(2)}\,[r\sqrt{(-i)}]\,\exp i\omega t \tag{8.37}$$

and

$$\vartheta_{\mathrm{II}} = J_0\,[r\sqrt{(-i)}]\,\exp i\omega t. \tag{8.38}$$

$H_0^{(2)}$ is the second Hankel function of zero order, which approaches zero for large positive values of r and becomes infinite for $r = 0$. J_0 is the first Bessel function of zero order. This function remains finite for finite r but becomes infinite for infinite r. The notation is that of Jahnke-Emde in which the most important properties of the functions H and J are given. It is left to the reader to verify that they are actually solutions of equation (8.35).

In problems concerning an infinite air layer in which ϑ must remain finite for infinite r (or z), only the function $H_0^{(2)}$ can be used, but both functions appear in solutions pertaining to a layer of finite height.

The functions H and J are complex; they may be written

$$H_0^{(2)}\,[r\sqrt{(-i)}] = h_0(r)\exp\left[-\tfrac{1}{2}\pi i\eta_0(r)\right] \tag{8.39}$$

$$J_0\,[r\sqrt{(-i)}] = b_0(r)\exp\left[-\tfrac{1}{2}\pi i\beta_0(r)\right]. \tag{8.40}$$

The functions in the right hand side of these equations are represented in Fig. 8.3. They are tabulated in Jahnke-Emde.

For small values of r, h_0 and η_0 are approximated by the following expressions

$$h_0(r) = -\frac{2}{\pi}\ln\left(\tfrac{1}{2}\gamma r\right) \tag{8.41}$$

and

$$\eta_0(r) = \frac{2}{\pi}\operatorname{arctg}\left[\frac{4}{\pi}\ln\left(\tfrac{1}{2}\gamma r\right)\right] \tag{8.42}$$

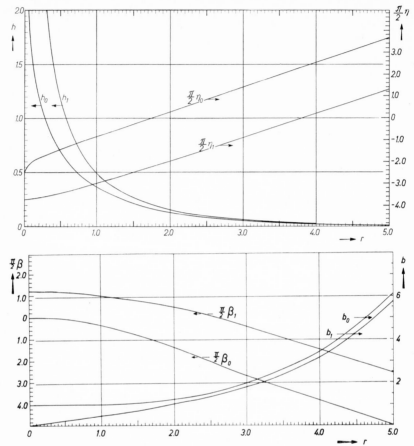

Fig. 8.3. Graphical representation of Hankel and Bessel functions of zero and first order.

in which γ is Euler's constant ($\gamma = 1.781$ and $\ln \gamma = 0.5772$). Equations (8.41) and (8.42) are correct within 5 per cent for $r < 0.1$.

The sinusoidal temperature wave in a semi-infinite air mass in which $\lambda = b(z + z_0)$ and which reduces to $^A\vartheta \sin(\omega t)$ for $z = 0$, is thus

$$\vartheta(z, t) = {}^A\vartheta \frac{h_0(r)}{h_0(r_0)} \sin\{\omega t - \tfrac{1}{2}\pi [\eta_0(r) - \eta_0(r_0)]\}. \tag{8.43}$$

It follows from (8.43) that the amplitude decreases steeply with z near the surface if r_0 is small, since the logarithm tends to infinity (in the negative sense) for r approaching zero.

For large r, $h_0(r)$ becomes asymptotically equal to $\sqrt{(2/\pi r)} \exp(-r\sqrt{2})$. Thus the amplitude decreases more slowly than with a constant diffusivity since r is proportional to $\sqrt{z}$ for large z. As can be seen from Fig. 8.3, η_0 is a linear function of r for large r.

If one defines the damping depth D as the distance corresponding to a reduction of the amplitude by a factor e^{-1}, D turns out to a be function of r. Furthermore D does not in general correspond to an increase of the phase lag by one rad. These conclusions result directly from the graphical representations of h_0 and η_0.

8.12. The heat wave

The heat flux density follows from the temperature and the relation $H = -\lambda(\partial\vartheta/\partial z)$. A characteristic property of the Bessel functions is that they satisfy the relation

$$\frac{d}{dy} Z_0(y) = -Z_1(y) \tag{8.44}$$

in which Z denotes a Bessel function. Thus the functions of the first order $H_1^{(2)}$ and J_1 appear in problems of heat transfer in air. They can be written

$$H_1^{(2)}[r\sqrt{(-i)}] = h_1(r) \exp\left[-\tfrac{1}{2}\pi i \eta_1(r)\right] \tag{8.45}$$

and

$$J_1[r\sqrt{(-i)}] = b_1(r) \exp\left[-\tfrac{1}{2}\pi i \beta_1(r)\right]. \tag{8.46}$$

The functions in the right hand sides are also represented in Fig. 8.3.

Carrying out the differentiation of $H_0^{(2)}$ and J_0 with respect to z, one obtains

$$\frac{dH_0^{(2)}}{dz} = \frac{dH_0^{(2)}}{d[r\sqrt{(-i)}]}\frac{d[r\sqrt{(-i)}]}{dz} = H_1^{(2)}[r\sqrt{(-i)}]\sqrt{\frac{(-i\omega C)}{[b(z+z_0)]}} \tag{8.47}$$

or, since $\sqrt{(-i)} = \exp(-\tfrac{1}{4}\pi i)$,

$$\frac{dH_0^{(2)}}{dz} = -\left(\frac{\omega C}{b(z+z_0)}\right)^{\tfrac{1}{2}} h_1(r) \exp\left[\{-\tfrac{1}{4}\pi - \tfrac{1}{2}\pi\eta_1(r)\}i\right]. \tag{8.48}$$

Thus the heat flux density in a semi-infinite air mass in which the temperature varies as (8.37) is

$$H = {}^{\mathsf{A}}\vartheta\left[\omega Cb(z+z_0)\right]^{\tfrac{1}{2}}\frac{h_1(r)}{h_0(r_0)} \sin\left[\omega t - \tfrac{1}{2}\pi\{\eta_1(r) - \eta_0(r_0)\} - \tfrac{1}{4}\pi\right]. \tag{8.49a}$$

The heat flux density corresponding to $J_0[r\sqrt{(-i)}]$ is simply obtained by substituting the functions $b(r)$ and $\beta(r)$ for $h(r)$ and $\eta(r)$.

Near the ground $h_1(r)$ can be approximated by $2/(\pi r)$, which is correct within 5 per cent when $r < 0.5$. Introducing the approximation (8.41) of

$h_0(r_0)$, (accuracy 5 per cent for $r_0 < 0.1$), one obtains a simple expression for the amplitude of H from (8.49)

$$H = -{}^A\vartheta \left(\frac{b}{2 \ln (\tfrac{1}{2}\gamma r_0)} \right) \sin [\omega t - \tfrac{1}{2}\pi \{\eta_1(r) - \eta_0(r_0)\} - \tfrac{1}{4}\pi]. \qquad (8.49b)$$

The amplitude of H is obviously independent of z in this approximation. To illustrate: Assuming $b = 6 \times 10^{-3}$ cal cm^{-2} sec^{-1} °C^{-1} and assuming $z_0 = 1.0$ cm, one calculates $r = 0.5$ for the diurnal variation at $z = 180$ m. The amplitude of the heat flux density has not decreased by more than 5 per cent over that height.

The phase shift of H with respect to the temperature wave is $\varphi_{he} = -[\tfrac{1}{2}\{\eta_1(r) - \eta_0(r_0)\} + \tfrac{1}{4}]\pi$. If $r = r_0 = 0$, $\varphi_{he} = 0$. Thus heat wave and temperature wave at the surface are nearly in phase if z_0 is small. The phase shift approaches $\tfrac{1}{4}\pi$ for large values of r since $\tfrac{1}{2}\pi[\eta_1(r) - \eta_0(r_0)]$ approaches $-\tfrac{3}{4}\pi$. This infers that the heat wave is advanced by $\tfrac{1}{4}\pi$ rad with respect to the temperature wave for large z, which is exactly equal to the phase shift in case of a constant thermal diffusivity.

As the heat flux density at the surface is proportional to the constant b, the latter is an important quantity in the heat balance. The diurnal variation is unsuitable for a determination of $\lambda = b(z + z_0)$. If (8.43) is used to calculate the amplitude of the temperature at $z = 200$ cm and $z = 10$ cm respectively, assuming different values of b, one obtains only 60 per cent variation in the ratio ${}^A\vartheta(200)/{}^A\vartheta(10)$ for a variation of b from 1.0 to 0.0001 (STERK [1956]). A value $z_0 = 1.0$ cm was assumed in these calculations. Besides, there remains the variation of b owing to a changing air stability in the course of a day and night.

An important factor in the heat balance is the ratio H_{so}/H_{ai} of the heat flux densities to soil and air respectively. This ratio appeared in the comparison of the thermal regimes of different soil types as discussed in Chapter 4. One has at the surface

$$\frac{{}^A H_{so}}{{}^A H_{ai}} = \frac{\pi}{b} (\lambda_{so} C_{so} \omega)^{\tfrac{1}{2}} h_0(r_0) \qquad (8.50a)$$

since $h_1(r_0) = 2/(\pi r_0)$ is always a permissible approximation. The constants λ_{so} and C_{so} pertain to the soil. Introducing the approximate expression of (8.41) gives the result

$$\frac{{}^A H_{so}}{{}^A H_{ai}} = -\frac{2}{b} (\lambda_{so} C_{so} \omega)^{\tfrac{1}{2}} \ln (\tfrac{1}{2}\gamma r_0) \qquad (8.50b)$$

which has been used in Chapter 4. The ratio is proportional to the contact coefficient of the soil $(\lambda_{so} C_{so})^{\frac{1}{2}}$. The contact coefficient of natural surfaces varies from 0.001 cal cm^{-2} °C^{-1} sec$^{-\frac{1}{2}}$ for dry humus to approximately 10 for ocean water.

8.13. General temperature variation

Duhamel's theorem (Chapter 5) also applies to the equation of heat conduction if λ is a function of z. The theorem will be used here to calculate $\vartheta(z,t)$ from the temperature record at a lower height, assuming $\lambda = b(z + z_0)$. No further assumption need be made. In particular the temperature may be an arbitrary function of the time.

Introducing the new variable $u = (z + z_0)^{\frac{1}{2}}$ into (8.34) one obtains

$$\frac{\partial \vartheta}{\partial t} = \frac{b}{4C} \frac{1}{u} \frac{\partial \vartheta}{\partial u} + \frac{b}{4C} \frac{\partial^2 \vartheta}{\partial u^2}. \tag{8.51}$$

This equation is discussed in textbooks of physics or heat conduction to which reference is made for the derivation of the formulas that are used in the following. (See e.g. CARSLAW-JAEGER [1950].) It is the differential equation of radial heat conduction in an infinite circular cylinder of uniform thermal diffusivity. The variable u is the radius vector in the cylindrical problem. It should be noted that the dimension of radial distance is cm$^{\frac{1}{2}}$ in this case.

Duhamel's theorem states

$$\vartheta(u,t) = \int_0^t \vartheta(u,\eta) \frac{\partial \, {}^1\vartheta(u, u_1, t - \eta)}{\partial t} \, d\eta \tag{8.52}$$

where $u_1 = (z + z_0)^{\frac{1}{2}}$ and $\vartheta(u_1, \eta)$ is the recorded temperature at z_1; z_1 must be smaller than z. The temperature ${}^1\vartheta(u, u_1, t)$ would occur at u if the circle with radius u_1 were kept at unit temperature $\vartheta(u_1, t) = 1$ from $t = 0$ on and if the initial temperature $\vartheta(u_1, 0)$ were zero everywhere in the cylinder. One has

$${}^1\vartheta(u, u_1, t) =$$
$$= 1 + \frac{2}{\pi} \int_0^\infty \left[\exp\left(-\frac{b\xi^2 t}{4C} \right) \right] \left[\frac{J_0(\xi u) N_0(\xi u_1) - J_0(\xi u_1) N_0(\xi u)}{\xi \{ J_0^2(\xi u_1) + N_0^2(\xi u_1) \}} \right] \, d\xi \tag{8.53}$$

J_0 and N_0 are the first and second Bessel functions of zero order, respectively. Carrying out the differentiation of ${}^1\vartheta$, equation (8.53) becomes

$$\vartheta(u,t) = \frac{2b}{4\pi C} \int_0^t \vartheta(u_1, \eta) I(u, u_1, t - \eta) \, d\eta \tag{8.54}$$

in which

$$I(u, u_1, t - \eta)$$
$$= - \int_0^\infty \left\{ \exp \left[\frac{- b\xi^2(t - \eta)}{4C} \right] \right\} \left\{ \frac{J_0(\xi u) N_0(\xi u_1) - J_0(\xi u_1) N_0(\xi u)}{J_0^2(\xi u_1) + N_0^2(\xi u_1)} \right\} d\xi.$$
$$(8.55)$$

The function $I(u, u_1, t - \eta)$ must first be calculated for a number of values of $t - \eta$ by numerical integration and then a second numerical integration (8.54) gives $\vartheta(u, t)$. Since the procedure has to be repeated for several values of t if $\vartheta(u, t)$ is sought as a function of the time, a considerable number of

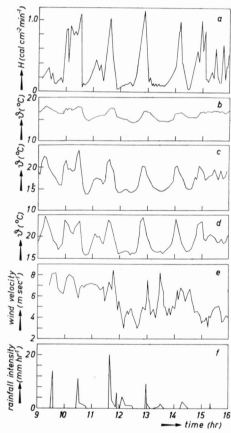

Fig. 8.4. Meteorological records Wageningen July 22, 1958. Record of total global radiation (a), air temperatures at 200 cm (b), 10 cm (c) and 3 cm (d), wind velocity at 21 m (e) and rainfall intensity (f).

numerical calculations must be performed. The method has been applied to the propagation of the temperature variation due to a heat impulse caused by a period of sunshine during a cloudy day.

The meteorological data recorded at Wageningen, July 22, 1958 above a grass field are given in Fig. 8.4 (VAN WIJK et al. [1959]). The temperature at $z = 10$ cm was taken from the record and the temperature at 200 cm calculated from it. As the grass cover became very dense at 1.5 cm, no turbulence could have occurred below that level. A value $z_0 = -1.5$ cm was inserted

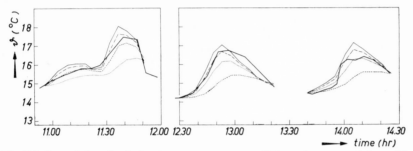

Fig. 8.5. Recorded and calculated temperature at $z = 200$ cm for $z_0 = -1.5$ cm. The temperature at 10 cm was used to calculate the temperature at 200 cm.

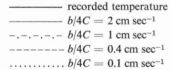

——————— recorded temperature
——————— $b/4C = 2$ cm sec^{-1}
—.—.—.—.— $b/4C = 1$ cm sec^{-1}
————————— $b/4C = 0.4$ cm sec^{-1}
.... $b/4C = 0.1$ cm sec^{-1}

in u_1. The results of the calculations are shown in Fig. 8.5 for three heat impulses. Fair agreement between calculated and recorded temperature can be obtained for a suitable choice of $b/4C$. The best value of this parameter was approximately 0.7.

8.14. Laplace transforms

In many problems of transfer of heat or of matter instantaneous values are of little importance, but averages over a certain interval of time are the interesting quantities. It is then not necessary to obtain the temperature as a function of time, but mean values of b and of $d\vartheta/dz$ are sufficient to determine the average sensible heat flux density. Any function from which these quantities can be calculated will serve the purpose.

The Laplace transform has proved very useful in this respect. Assuming a law of variation of λ, for instance $\lambda = b(z + z_0)$, the heat flux density can be calculated at an arbitrary height from the temperature gradient if b and z_0 are known. The quantity b can be obtained by a procedure similar to that used in Chapter 5 for soil, by comparing the Laplace transforms of the temperature at two heights; z_0 is of little influence at a height which is substantially greater than z_0 itself.

If the law of variation of λ with z is not known or is a complicated function, this law can be determined from the Laplace transforms of the temperature applying the theory of a layered medium.

A very important feature is that the method can be applied to a temperature which is an arbitrary function of the time.

8.15. Laplace transform for $\lambda = b(z + z_0)$

Recalling the properties of the Laplace transform $\mathscr{L}\{\vartheta(z,t) = \int_0^\infty \{\vartheta(z,t) \exp(-pt)\}dt$, in the following abbreviated as $\mathscr{L}$, one obtains a differential equation of the Bessel type for $\mathscr{L}$ as a function of the independent variable $u = (z+z_0)^{\frac{1}{2}}$

$$p\mathscr{L} = \frac{b}{4C}\frac{1}{u}\frac{d\mathscr{L}}{du} + \frac{b}{4C}\frac{d^2\mathscr{L}}{du^2}. \tag{8.56}$$

It has been assumed that the air is initially ($t = 0$) at a constant temperature, which is taken as zero point of the temperature scale. As has been shown in Chapter 5 an extra term $\vartheta(z,0)$ has to be substracted from the right hand side if the initial temperature varies with depth.

Equation (8.56) contains only real terms and now $i H_0^{(1)} [i\{p(z+z_0)4C/b\}^{\frac{1}{2}}]$ is the only solution which is real and approaches zero for (positive) infinite values of z. This function is tabulated in Jahnke-Emde. Thus

$$\mathscr{L}\{\vartheta(z,t)\} = \mathscr{L}\{\vartheta(z_1,t)\}\frac{H_0^{(1)}[i\{(z+z_0)4\,Cp/b\}^{\frac{1}{2}}]}{H_0^{(1)}[i\{(z_1+z_0)4\,Cp/b\}^{\frac{1}{2}}]} \tag{8.57}$$

is the solution which takes the value $\mathscr{L}\{\vartheta(z_1,t)\}$ at $z = z_1$ and vanishes at infinity. An arbitrary value of p can in principle be chosen. However, to obtain the best result, it should not be so large that $\exp(-pt)$ is practically zero except for a small interval of t values near $t = 0$. On the other hand $\vartheta(z,t)\exp(-pt)$ must be so small at the end of the interval in which b is determined, that the contribution of that product to the Laplace interval may be neglected for greater t.

The Laplace transform is obtained by numerical integration. By way of example, some data used in the calculation of b for the heat impulse commencing at 12 hr 30 (Fig. 8.3) are given in Table 8.4.

TABLE 8.4

Calculation of b for the heat impulse 12 hr 30, 22 July 1958 (Fig. 8.3) from $\mathscr{L}\{\vartheta(10,t)\}$ and $\mathscr{L}\{\vartheta(200,t)\}$. $z_0 \approx 0$, $t = 0$ at 12 hr 30, $p = 0.002$ sec^{-1}. ($\vartheta(10,0) = 14.3\,°$C, $\vartheta(200,0) = 14.3\,°$C)

time	$\exp(-0.002\,t)$	$\vartheta(10,t)$	$\{\vartheta(10,t)\}\{\exp(-0.002\,t)\}\varDelta t$
12.30	1	0	0
12.32′24″	0.7498	0.2	32.394*
12.37′12″	0.4215	0.9	109.253
12.42′00″	0.2369	3.4	231.972
12.46′48″	0.13319	5.6	214.808
12.51′36″	0.07487	5.4	116.438
. . .	. . .	. . .	. . .
. . .	. . .	. . .	. . .
$\Sigma\,\{\vartheta(10,t)\}\{\exp(-0.002\,t)\}\varDelta t$			$= 774.723$

* As the trapezoidal rule has been applied, and the first ordinate occurs after an incomplete period ($\frac{1}{2}$) a correction factor $\frac{3}{4}$ is used here.

The sum is taken to be equal to $\mathscr{L}\{\vartheta(10,t)\}$, and a correction is made for the first incomplete trapezium. In a similar way one obtains $\mathscr{L}\{\vartheta(200,t)\}$. According to (8.57) one has:

$$\frac{\mathscr{L}\{\vartheta(200,t)\}}{\mathscr{L}\{\vartheta(10,t)\}} = \frac{H_0^{(1)}[i\{200(4\,Cp/b)\}^{\frac{1}{2}}]}{H_0^{(1)}[i\{10(4\,Cp/b)\}^{\frac{1}{2}}]} = \frac{256}{775} = 0.33 \qquad (8.58)$$

and from the tables of $iH_0^{(1)}$ one calculates $b/(4C) = 0.80$ cm^2 sec^{-1}.

8.16. An instantaneous change of heat flux density

A qualitative understanding of the observed rise of the temperature at different heights owing to a heat impulse can be gained by comparing the actual heat impulse with the limiting case in which heat production changes discontinuously at a certain instant. Three standard cases will be discussed. The associated temperature changes can be expressed in terms of a tabulated function.

First an instantaneous heat source is treated which liberates a finite quantity of heat at $t = 0$. Secondly a jump of the heat flux density from a lower to a higher value at which it stays for an indefinite period of time will be considered and thirdly a jump of H_{ai}, followed by a jump back to the original value, after some time. The heat flux density remains constant in between.

The appropriate solutions of the equation of vertical heat conduction, equation (8.51), in which the variable u has been substituted for $(z + z_0)^{\frac{1}{2}}$, will now be discussed. Reference is made to textbooks of mathematical physics for the derivation of these solutions.

The temperature associated with the instantaneous heat source is given by the function

$$\vartheta = \frac{Q}{bt} \exp\left(-\frac{uC}{bt}\right). \tag{8.59}$$

In this expression Q denotes the total quantity of heat per unit of horizontal area released by the instantaneous heat source at $t = 0$. The source is located at $z = -z_0$, thus $u = 0$. Zero initial temperature is assumed for all values of u.

Equation (8.59) holds for positive values of t; for negative values $\vartheta = 0$. The function ϑ of (8.59) possesses indeed the properties characteristic for a sudden release of heat. For small values of t, it is significantly different from zero only near the plane $z = -z_0$. This means that practically all the heat is concentrated near that plane, as $C\vartheta dz$ is the quantity of heat per unit of horizontal area present between the planes z and $z + dz$. If t is infinite, ϑ has again returned to zero for all values of u. This should be expected as the finite quantity of heat Q is then distributed over a semi-infinite air column of unit horizontal area. The law of conservation of heat is also satisfied. One has $\int_0^\infty 2\,C\vartheta u\,du = Q$, irrespective of the time.

A negative value of Q corresponds to an instantaneous heat sink. A heat sink is an approximation of an abrupt termination of a period of sunshine. The discussion of (8.59) is very similar to the one given in Chapter 5 for one-dimensional heat conduction. Heat transfer by radiation has been ignored. It will also be ignored in the following discussion.

A constant heat source which becomes effective at $t = 0$ causes a rise of the temperature which is obtained from (8.59) by an integration with respect to the time. This again is similar to the procedure explained in Chapter 5. The result of the integration is

$$\vartheta = -\frac{^0H}{b} \operatorname{Ei}\left(-\frac{u^2C}{bt}\right) = -\frac{^0H}{b} \operatorname{Ei}\left(-\frac{(z+z_0)C}{bt}\right). \tag{8.60}$$

The symbol Ei denotes the exponential integral defined as

$$-\operatorname{Ei}(-x) = \int_0^\infty \frac{\exp(-u)}{u}\,du \tag{8.61}$$

which is tabulated in Jahnke-Emde and ^0H is the constant heat flux density of the source at $z = -z_0$.

The temperature variation caused by a heat source of finite duration is calculated as the superposition of a source of infinite duration and of a heat sink of infinite duration. The heat source causes a momentaneous increase of the heat flux density from zero to a positive value ^0H at $t = 0$. The heat sink becomes effective at $t = t_0$. It reduces H_{ai} to zero again.

The rise of the temperature is given by (8.60) in the interval $0 \leqslant t \leqslant t_0$. After $t = t_0$

$$\vartheta = \frac{^0H}{b}\left[- \text{Ei}\left(-\frac{u^2C}{bt}\right) + \text{Ei}\left(-\frac{u^2C}{b(t - t_0)}\right)\right]. \qquad (8.62)$$

The temperature starts to increase at $t = 0$ and continues to do so for some time even after t_0, but decreases again and returns asymptotically to zero. The instant at which the maximum temperature occurs, depends on the value of u and of the ratio b/C. It is interesting at this stage to compare the theory with the data of Fig. 8.4. The record of the solar radiation shows a sharp rise at 9 hr 50 followed by a sharp decrease at 10 hr 23. Though the irradiancy was not constant in the intermediate period it will be approximated by a constant value. The transfer coefficient of the air will be estimated by applying (8.60) to the records of the temperature at 10 cm and at 200 cm height. In the other period of strong variation of solar radiant energy the rise was immediately followed by a decrease of radiant energy. This makes a comparison with the theory more difficult.

Taking the middle of the interval of time during which the sharp rise of the temperature occurred, 9 hr 53, as the instant $t = 0$ at which the heat source became active, one reads a temperature 18.5 °C at 10 cm and 15.0 °C at 200 cm after 1620 sec. This interval of time ends at 10 hr 20 when a new increase of the temperature at 10 cm took place. The initial temperature was, however, not homogeneous in the air and consequently it is not possible to use the same temperature as zero point for all heights. Yet (8.60) can be applied to the rise of the temperature as a result from the increased irradiation. The zero point of the temperature scale is now the interpolated course which the temperature would have taken in the absence of the heat impulse. This follows from the fact that the total temperature can be considered as a superposition of the latter one and the temperature rise due to the impulse. The rise of the temperature at the two heights and the instant mentioned was 4.5 °C and 1.9 °C respectively. Thus denoting 10 $C/(bt)$ by x, one has $\text{Ei}\,(-x)/\text{Ei}\,(-20x) = 4.5/1.9 = 2.37$. The value of x can now be determined by calculating the ratio of the Ei functions with the argument $-x$ and $-20\,x$ respectively, for a series of values of x. For instance, taking successively $x = 0.001, 0.005, 0.010, 0.020$ a ratio $\text{Ei}\,(-x)/\text{Ei}\,(-20\,x) = 1.9, 2.58, 3.28, 4.76$, respectively is calculated. The value of x following from the recorded temperatures is 0.004. Inserting $t = 1620$ sec the value $b/C = 1.54$

cm sec^{-1} is obtained. As the instantaneous heat source is only a crude approximation of the actual phenomenon, the order of magnitude rather than an exact value of b/C is calculated by this method.

8.17. Some references to microclimate

A systematic discussion of the application of the principles set forth in the preceeding text to plant environment would largely surpass the scope of this book. As an example the application of the theory to the climate of a glasshouse is given in the next chapter. Here and in the following sections microclimate and water requirements of plants are briefly discussed. Reference to the literature must, however, be made for a more detailed treatment of the subjects.

The living conditions of plants are greatly influenced by the proximity of the earth's surface, by its shape and structure, by a lake, a hill, a forest, the presence of other plants and by other factors of a typical local nature. Air and soil temperature, air and soil humidity, radiation and wind are strongly influenced by such local factors. This makes it necessary to distinguish between "microclimate" and "macroclimate". The latter is based upon meteorological measurements at screen height at stations which are located such that specific local influences on the meteorological elements are reduced as far as possible. Considerable differences which are highly important for plant life may occur between the meteorological elements in the macro- and in the microclimate. Examples of such differences are the air and soil temperatures below screen height discussed in the foregoing text.

The microclimate of a plant community is largely determined by the heat balance in a horizontal plane at different heights in and above the plant community. In case of scattered plants, the heat balance naturally shows large variations in a horizontal plane. The meteorological elements depend largely on the heat balance at different heights and the heat balance in its turn depends on the state of the atmosphere, the radiant energy received and emitted by the plant community, and the structure of the latter.

Actually a rational definition of microclimate takes recourse to the physical basis itself as for instance: "Microclimate is a complex of quantities, mostly of a physical nature, which together are characteristic of the state of an environment, if they are strongly dependent on local conditions".

For further information on microclimate reference is made to GEIGER [1960], SUTTON [1953], BUDYKO [1956, 1958], DZERDZEEVSKII [1957], ALISSOV et al.

[1956], VAN WIJK and DE WILDE [1960], LAICHTMAN and CHUDNOVSKII [1949], BROOKS [1957, 1959].

The water requirements of plants are strongly dependent on the microclimate in which the plants are growing. The importance of this subject for plant life has given rise to an extensive literature. The recent developments in research as well as in practical applications justify a treatment of the subject separate from general microclimatology. The basic facts and the principles of the most important calculation methods are discussed in the following two sections.

The effect of windscreens and shelterbelts on air temperature and air moisture has been briefly mentioned before.

Important articles on this subject are given in "Suchovei", a collective work on dry winds (DZERDZEEVSKII [1957]). Though some contributions to a theoretical explanation of the empirical knowledge have been made, much remains to be done in this respect. The same conclusion holds for the influence of a mulch on soil and air temperature and on humidity. Again an extensive literature exists giving observations, but very few articles deal with the theoretical background. The subject appears to be amenable for a theoretical treatment which will probably provide a solid basis for practical application. Literature on mulching is given by JACKS, BRIND and SMITH [1955] and in some of the books referred to under general microclimatology.

8.18. Water requirements of crops, transpiration

The water requirements of the common agricultural crops are mainly determined by the amount of water transpired during the growing season. With a crop of potatoes, for instance, a production of total matter amounting to approximately 50 metric tons ha^{-1} is regularly obtained in the Netherlands under favorable conditions. This matter contains 35 to 45 tons ha^{-1} of water (70 to 90 per cent of the total matter production). However, the quantity of water which is transpired during the growing season is of the order of hundred times this value. In the year 1948 in the Netherlands, about 4300 tons ha^{-1} of water, or even more, were transpired during the period March 9 until August 30 by crops giving good yields. Poor yields resulted if only half that quantity of water was available.

From the figures given, it is evident that the quantity of water required by an agricultural crop is practically equal to the amount transpired and consequently, runs parallel to the energy required to evaporate that quantity of water.

Experience has shown that a considerable fraction of the heat generated at the surface of a well-developed, actively growing, crop is used in transpiration if water is amply available*. In that case the heat balance permits calculation of the water needs of plants with satisfactory accuracy. Considerable difficulties arise, however, in case of a crop which is short of water. The total fraction of the energy used for transpiration is now obviously smaller.

Besides this fact, which in itself lowers the accuracy, terms corresponding to advective energy must be taken into account, since in most case plants are no longer growing closely together so as to form a closed vegetative cover.
A third complication may arise from a physiological response to drought conditions which affects transpiration by closing of the stomata or wilting.

The direct calculation of the turbulent transfer of water vapor meets with difficulties. It is difficult to make a reliable estimate of the coefficient of turbulent transfer in and closely above a vegetation and it is also difficult to calculate leaf temperatures with a sufficient degree of accuracy for the purpose in mind. These temperatures determine the saturation vapor pressure in the stomata.

A graph schematically showing the relation between dry matter production and available water is given in Fig. 8.6. Production increases first with

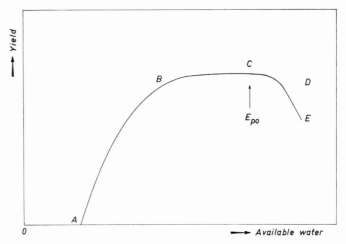

Fig. 8.6. Dry matter production as a function of available water. Point C indicates potential evapotranspiration.

---

* Here, we consider an actively growing crop or single plant as a crop or plant not limited in its growth by lack of soil fertility, by water, CO_2 or light deficiency, by the occurrence of diseases or by damage of some other nature (e.g. frost).

available water (AB), it then becomes more or less independent of it, which results in a flattening of the curve (BD) and finally one expects a decrease owing to superfluous water which interferes with aeration of the roots (DE).

In drawing this curve it is assumed that other circumstances, particularly light intensity, are nonlimiting. The curve is, for that reason, directly applicable to crop response to irrigation water in an arid or a semiarid climate. In a wet climate, when rainfall during the growing season is an important source of available water supply, light intensity is often negatively correlated with available water. This means that a decrease of the latter might to some extent be compensated by a relatively higher rate of photosynthesis. Conversely, with increasing water supply photosynthesis may decrease owing to the occurrence of dense clouds. Such effects have actually been observed. Yet a curve which in its general appearance is similar to that in Fig. 8.6 was obtained for potatoes in the Netherlands (VAN DUIN and SCHOLTE UBING [1955]). This curve is represented in Fig. 8.7. The maximum quantity of water which could be transpired in each growing season was calculated using the heat balance, assuming no shortage of water and a

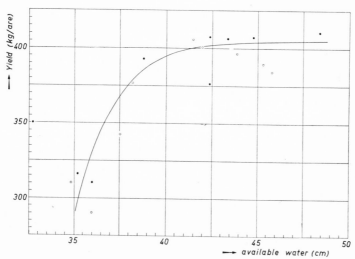

Fig. 8.7. Yield of potatoes as a function of available water on experimental plots in the Netherlands (1940–1952). The maximum quantity of water which could be transpired in each growing season was calculated using the heat balance assuming no shortage of water and a level actively growing crop, completely shading the ground and of large extension (potential evapotranspiration). PENMAN's method [1948, 1956] was used for the calculation of the terms occurring in the heat balance.

level actively growing crop, completely shading the ground and of large extension (potential evapotranspiration). PENMAN's method [1948, 1956] was used for the calculation of the terms occurring in the heat balance. The point C in the curve of Fig. 8.6 corresponds to the situation that a maximum fraction of the heat absorbed at the surface of a low level crop actively growing, not short of water, completely shading the ground, and of large extension, is converted into latent heat of vaporization. The transpiration under these conditions depends largely on the weather. It is called *potential evapotranspiration*. If more water is supplied the surplus is not transpired by a crop. It is removed by drainage in the ground or by surface runoff.

An important feature of the curve is that maximum dry matter production is already obtained at a lower rate of evapotranspiration. The yield shows a definite drop if available water is approximately $0.75 \, E_{po}$. This may be partly ascribed to incomplete shading of the ground by the crop since evaporation of a soil is small when a dry upper layer has been formed. It is expected that for crops shading the ground during the whole growing season, as for instance, grass, and alfalfa, maximum yields will only be obtained with a water supply of 100 per cent E_{po}. By way of example, the yields of some agricultural crops at different water supplies are given in Table 8.5. The data were taken from the literature as indicated and E_{po} was calculated for each site in the year in which the experiments were made.

8.19. Evapotranspiration and potential evapotranspiration

The definition of potential evapotranspiration E_{po}, given in the preceding section, was adopted at the informal meeting of physics in agriculture held at Wageningen in 1955 [Neth. Journal of Agr. Sci., 1956]. It is the maximum transpiration which can occur in a given weather situation with a low growing, level crop satisfying the conditions stated before. If the crop is not level and plants protrude from the surface, or if the crop is high such that air may pass across the upper layer of it, transpiration can be higher. Also for the single plants in a vegetation which is not closed, a considerably higher transpiration rate has been observed. The evapotranspiration is then calculated for the area shaded by the plant. In this case, as also with a high crop, the area of the foliage from which transpiration can take place is greater than in the case of a single plant in a low and level crop which completely shades the ground. Thus morphological factors must also be taken into account in the calculation of evapotranspiration of a well watered crop.

DE WIT [1958], reviewing literature data from all parts of the world, arrived at a conclusion pertaining to the part AB of the curve expressing yield vs. available water in Fig. 8.6. In the arid regions located in the belt of approximately 20 to 40 degrees of geographic latitude, the production of total matter Y of plants grown in containers was found to be proportional to the ratio of actual evapotranspiration over potential evapotranspiration,

$$Y = mE_{ac}/E_{po}. \qquad (8.63)$$

The coefficient m depends on the type of plant but does not depend on the climate, i.e., the same value applies to the entire arid zone. It is also largely independent of the level of fertility of the soil. This may be explained by the fact that water and not fertility is limiting the yield. Soil fertility will only play a rôle if it is extremely low. Equation (8.63) does not apply to humid regions such as the Netherlands and Germany. A proportionality of total dry matter production with E_{ac} was found in that case for plants grown in containers,

$$Y = nE_{ac}. \qquad (8.64)$$

The constant n depends on the type of plant. This different character of the yield-transpiration relations is ascribed to the fact that light intensity is not correlated with actual evapotranspiration in the arid zone where the percentage of bright sunshine is always high during the growing season but that a negative correlation exists in the humid climates at higher latitudes. According to de Wit, the formulas would also apply to a vegetative cover of large horizontal extension and to plants scattered in the field.

The fact that transpiration of plants is largely determined by prevailing weather conditions if water is not limiting, was already proved by BRIGGS and SHANTZ [1916, 1917] and others. These authors correlated evapotranspiration of plants in containers with the solar radiant intensity intercepted by the plants as calculated from the shaded area. They further took advective energy into account by correlating increased evaporation with increasing wind velocity.

8.20. Calculation of potential evapotranspiration

The fact that the total amount of available energy largely controls evapotranspiration of an actively growing crop which is well supplied with water, proves that physiological control is of minor importance in that case. The plant's surface apparently behaves as a wet surface whose reflection coeffi-

TABLE 8.5

Evapotranspiration and yields of agricultural crops

Location	Crop	Yield*	Period	Actual transpiration (E_{ac})* (cm)	Potential transpiration (E_{po})* (cm)	E_{ac}/E_{po}
The Netherlands	Wheat	m	5/1 -8/1 '47	23.9	35.5	0.69
	Grass	m	5/23-8/28'47	22.0	39.3	0.56
	Barley + Alfalfa	m } p }	5/10-9/1 '47	23.7	44.6	0.53
	Sugar beets roots	p	4/28-9/2 '47	25.4	48.5	0.53
	Sugar beets roots	m	4/28-9/2 '47	30.4	48.5	0.63
	Grass	m	4/28-9/2 '47	32.8	48.5	0.68
	Grass	p	4/28-9/2 '47	23.6	48.5	0.49
	Grass	g	4/28-9/2 '47	34.3	48.5	0.71
	Various crops	g	3/9 -8/30'48	47.0	49.2	0.95
	Various crops	g	3/9 -8/30'48	38.3	49.2	0.78
	Various crops	g	3/9 -9/13'48	43.0	53.9	0.80
	Various crops	g	3/11-9/2 '49	49.0	51.4	0.95
	Various crops	g	3/15-9/30'49	41.8	56.0	0.75
Mesa, Arizona	Cotton	g	4/1 -10/31'35	79.0	117.0	0.68
	Grain sorghums	g	7/1 -10/31'35	54.0	63.0	0.86
	Grape fruit orchard	g	3/1 -10/31'35	102.0	125.0	0.82
	Oranges orchard	g	3/1 -10/31'35	82.0	125.0	0.66
	Soy beans	g	6/1 -10/31'35	57.0	81.0	0.70
Scottsbluff, Nebraska	Alfalfa	g	5/14- 9/27'35	66.0	66.0	1.00
	Small grains	g	4/20- 7/25'35	37.0	55.0	0.71
	Sugar beets	g	4/20-10/15'35	61.0	81.0	0.75
	Potatoes	g	6/20- 9/30'35	39.0	51.0	0.76

* g = good; m = moderate; p = poor. Actual transpiration data (E_{ac}) and yields for the crops in the Netherlands are taken from VER-HOEVEN [1953], the figures for Mesa, Arizona and Scottsbluff, Nebraska are "Consumptive Use" data from BLANEY and CRIDDLE [1950]. According to the definition, consumptive use is smaller than E_{po} and it is probably close to actual evapotranspiration. The values of E_{po} were calculated according to PENMAN [1949] and pertain in the U.S. to Phoenix, Arizona and Cheyenne, Wyoming. For further explanation we

cients, shape and evaporating area are the same as those of the mass of leaves from which water is evaporated. The wet surface that may be substituted as a model for the actual vegetative cover with respect to potential evapotranspiration is a horizontal plane. Thus one is led to consider primarily evapotranspiration from a plane horizontal water surface in calculations of potential evapotranspiration.

According to Dalton evaporation from a water surface is given by the equation

$$E_w = f(u)(p_w{}^s - p_w) = H_{ev}/0.1\,L. \tag{8.65}$$

Here, E_w is the rate of evaporation in mm min^{-1}, $p_w{}^s$ the saturation pressure at the water surface and p_w the vapor pressure of water in the air at the height where the wind velocity is u, above a laminar layer in contact with the water surface. The latent heat flux density H_{ev} is equal to E_w times the latent heat necessary to evaporate E_w mm of water per cm^2 and per min. The factor 0.1 results from the fact that the latent heat L refers to 1 g of water. The function $f(u)$ is called "wind function". Empirical as well as theoretical expressions of $f(u)$ are used in evaporation calculations.

The occurrence of the saturation vapor pressure in Dalton's formula requires that the temperature of the water surface should be known. If the formula is applied to lake evaporation, the surface temperature can be measured without difficulty, but it is difficult to obtain a reliable estimate of the effective temperature of a surface consisting of leaves, under natural conditions. This difficulty renders (8.65) less suitable for transpiration calculations.

It should here be emphasized that the model of a water surface corresponding to a crop cover, is not the surface of a lake but a thin layer of water which has a low heat capacity. Evaporation from a lake is, of course, also determined by the weather but the heat capacity of the underlying body of water and the relatively thick upper layer in which the incident solar radiation is absorbed, exert a strong influence on the surface temperature (WARTENA [1959]). Considerable differences exist in respect to instantaneous evaporation under identical weather conditions between a lake, an evaporation pan (WARTENA and BORGHORST [1961]) and the thin layer of water which is used as a model for crop transpiration. These differences are also reflected in the expressions for the wind function applicable to lake evaporation and to the thin water layer, respectively.

MARCIANO and HARBECK [1952, 1958] have tested a number of expressions for $f(u)$ on lake evaporation. In experiments on Lake Hefner (Oklahoma) they found good agreement with the experimental data for SVERDRUP'S [1937] expression,

$$f(u) = \frac{0.623\,\varrho k u^*}{p_{ai}\left[\ln\left(\dfrac{z+z_0}{\delta+z_0}\right) + \dfrac{k\delta u^*}{D}\right]}. \tag{8.66}$$

In this equation ϱ (density of air) $= 0.0012$ g cm^{-3}; $k = 0.40$, von Karman's constant; $p_{ai} =$ atmospheric pressure in mb; $\delta = 30\ v/u^*$ the thickness of the laminar layer; $v = 0.15$ cm^2 sec^{-1}; $z_0 = 0.6$ cm. D is the molecular diffusion constant of water in air: $D = 0.25$ cm^2 sec^{-1}. The formula has been derived assuming a logarithmic wind profile

$$u = \frac{u^*}{k}\ln\left(\frac{z+z_0}{z_0}\right) \tag{8.67}$$

in which u^* is a constant.

It should be noted that the wind function approaches zero if u^* approaches zero; thus according (8.67) evaporation stops if there is no wind. In later experiments on Lake Mead (Nevada), however, Sverdrup's expression gave not the best results.

An empirical expression for the wind function based on measurements with evaporation pans, and on crop transpiration under natural conditions, in particular under irradiation, has been given by PENMAN [1956],

$$f(u) = 0.35\,(0.5 + 0.53\,u_{200}). \tag{8.68}$$

The wind velocity at screen height, 200 cm, is expressed in m sec^{-1} and the vapor pressures in Dalton's formula now in mm Hg.

The function $f(u)$ in (8.68) does not approach zero for zero wind velocity. The heating of the surface of a thin body of water apparently causes an instability in the adjacent air and water vapor is carried away by the resulting convection.

As potential evapotranspiration refers to a crop of very large horizontal extension, it can be calculated from a heat balance in which advective heat is ignored. All terms except the latent heat flux density must be measured or calculated. One has

$$(1 - \varrho_{sh})\,H_{sh} + H_{lo}^{net} + H_{so} + H_{ai} + H_{ev} = 0. \tag{8.69}$$

The energy flux densities are counted positive if they are directed towards the crop surface and negative if they are in the inverse direction. Empirical formulas for H_{sh} and H_{lo}^{net} have been given in Chapter 3, where also some measuring methods are indicated. The heat flux density to the soil is mostly of minor importance if periods of a week or more are considered which is sufficient for many applications. This term has been discussed in Chapters 4, 5 and 6. The term H_{ai} depends on crop surface temperature and on the turbulent transfer coefficient. It has been calculated in the preceding sections of this chapter assuming a linear variation of K with height. Its calculation in a given weather situation presents considerable difficulties.

Penman has given a practical formula, based on the heat balance, by eliminating the surface temperature and using the assumption of equality of the turbulent exchange coefficients of heat and of vapor transfer, thus using Bowen's ratio (PENMAN [1948, 1956]). The surface temperature was eliminated by assuming a linear dependence of saturation pressure on temperature in the range of temperatures involved, thus $\Delta = dp_w^s/d\vartheta$ is considered as a constant. As an approximation of the exact relationship Penman's formula has proved its value in many applications. Evaporation from a thin water layer is given by the expression

$$E_0 = \frac{\Delta H_0 + \gamma E_a}{\Delta + \gamma}. \tag{8.70}$$

Penman's notation H_0 is used to denote the total net radiant energy absorbed during the period considered. Zero reflection for long wave radiation is assumed and H_0 is expressed in the height in mm of water per cm which can be evaporated by this absorbed radiant energy. E_a is the auxiliary quantity: $E_a = 0.35 (0.5 + 0.53 u_{200}) (p_w^s - p_w)$ mm with u_{200} the wind velocity at 200 cm height in m sec^{-1}, p_w^s and p_w the saturation pressure at air temperature at screen height and the partial water vapor pressure respectively, both in mm Hg. γ is the psychrometer constant. Potential evapotranspiration can be calculated from E_0 by multiplication with an empirical reduction factor of approx. 0.8, which was first determined with short grass for monthly or longer periods, but which has proved to apply also to other short crops. This factor accounts mainly for the higher reflection coefficient of leaves in respect to short-wave radiation, for daylength and for the effect that the effective leaf area may be somewhat less than a horizontal plane since the stomata are the most important source of water. There is considerable evidence that the reduction factor also depends on the short-wave radiant intensity.

Several attempts have been made to simplify the calculation. The total net radiation is often the most important source of energy for potential evapotranspiration in a humid climate. This fact suggests the use of formulas correlating E_{po} or E_0 with H^{net} or with other radiation terms closely correlated with the net radiation. For instance MAKKINK [1947] found for grass in the central part of the Netherlands,

$$E_{po} = 0.61 \frac{\Delta}{\Delta + \gamma} H_{su} - 0.12 \quad \text{and} \quad E_0 = 1.01 \frac{\Delta}{\Delta + \gamma} H_{su} - 0.5 \quad (8.71)$$

in which H_{su} is the short-wave radiation from sun and sky. The notation is the same as in (8.70) and the potential evapotranspiration is in mm day^{-1} averaged over a period of a month.

Recently SCHOLTE UBING [1959] has shown that determination of E_{po} is possible over periods of a day or 24 hr if accurate radiation measurements are carried out instead of using the correlation formulas.

In arid regions the advective term in the heat balance becomes very important owing to the dry desert wind (DZERDZEEVSKII [1957]).

Empirical formulas correlating potential evapotranspiration and temperature are in wide use (BLANEY and CRIDDLE [1959], THORNTHWAITE [1948] and others).

Air temperature is strongly influenced by the heat balance but it is in itself not a measure of available energy (VAN WIJK and DE VRIES [1954], SUOMI and TANNER [1958], TANNER [1960]). Particularly in a climate with a strong seasonal variation, temperature lags behind the total net energy flux. The result of this is that if potential evapotranspiration is plotted as a function of air temperature, a loop is obtained instead of a one-valued curve, since the equal air temperatures in the spring and in the fall occur at different values of available energy, and, therefore, at different E_{po}. In the Netherlands for instance, mean monthly temperature is about 5.0 °C in March and about 5.4 °C in November, but E_{po} in March amounted to about 4 times that in November.

CHAPTER 9

THE GLASSHOUSE (GREENHOUSE) CLIMATE

J. A. BUSINGER

Institute of Horticultural Engineering Wageningen,
The Netherlands

9.1. Introduction

Remarkably little glasshouse climate research has been reported during the many years of their use. This is surprising because first, the glasshouse culture is of considerable economical importance in horticulture so that obtaining the best construction with respect to the climate is worth while, and second, the effect of glasshouses on the climate is certainly conspicuous and therefore should challenge scientists to search for a complete explanation.

Until World War II, the research was limited to a single, although fundamental, experiment carried out by Wood in 1909 and collections of data at several places (WOOD [1909]). During the last few years the situation has improved. Several investigations concerning details of the glasshouse climate are published in Great Britain as well as in Germany.

The first theory on the influence of the glass of glasshouses is the so-called mousetrap theory (usually referred to as "greenhouse-effect") which probably originated in the second half of the 19th century. According to this theory the high temperatures in a glasshouse must be ascribed to the fact that the short-wave solar radiation is transmitted whereas the long wave radiation from the glasshouse floor is absorbed by the glass. Thus the solar energy is able to enter the glasshouse, but is unable to leave it again. This theory is still fairly general accepted. The British physicist Wood, however, had his doubts about this theory. In 1909 he carried out an experiment with two frames, one covered with glass and the other with rocksalt, which also is transparent for the long wave radiation. The two frames were placed in the sunlight and the temperature inside was measured. Almost no temperature difference was observed and this should have been the end of the mousetrap theory. In 1910 van Gulik repeated the experiment of Wood, with the purpose to investigate the effect of glass against the nocturnal radiation (VAN GULIK [1910]). The observations of van Gulik show that the frame with the rocksalt had only slightly quicker temperature decrease than the frame with glass. However, since the experiment was carried out in a room where the net long wave radiation was of little importance, the conclusions that there was no difference between glass and rocksalt, were invalid.

Wood concluded that the high temperatures in the glasshouse must be ascribed to the stagnant air. In comparison with the outside air there is practically no air movement in the glasshouse, and the slow air replacement permits the high temperatures. This conclusion is right so far as it explains the main part of the temperature rise. However, the mousetrap mechanism, although of minor importance, plays a certain rôle. As far as the author knows, no further basic research has been done on this point. The next sections try to give an outline of the proportion of both effects under various circumstances.

To do so it is necessary to make an analysis of the mutual interaction of the various climate factors. Starting with the energy budget of the glasshouse, these mutual relations become evident (see section 9.2), and it appears possible to obtain a quantitative relation between temperature and radiation, ventilation, evaporation, etc.

In addition to the climate itself, it is necessary to keep in mind the most favorable conditions of growth for the crop, insofar as they are known (VAN DEN MUIJZENBERG [1951]). Comparison of the real with the desired climate often will indicate desirable modifications of construction, heating, artificial radiation, etc. Deciding which steps are economically justified is a task which depends upon an adequate knowledge of the theoretical foundations.

9.2. The energy budget of the glasshouse

Before discussing the various climate factors which participate in the glasshouse climate, the energy budget will be considered. This approach will enable us to understand the physical behavior of a glasshouse so that the various climate factors will appear in a logical connection.

In order to avoid unnecessary complexity in the treatment, some simplifying assumptions are introduced:

(a) with respect to radiation the glasshouse represents a horizontal surface equal to its ground surface A_{so},

(b) the convective heat transfer from the air to the glasshouse wall is proportional to the wall surface A_w, to the mean temperature differences between inside air ϑ_{in} and outside air ϑ_{ou},

(c) the net radiation in the glasshouse is entirely absorbed at the ground surface,

(d) horizontal radiative transfer can be neglected.

The energy budget of a glasshouse can now be expressed in a set of equations. The equation for the soil surface of the glasshouse is

$$_{gl}H_{net} = {}_{gl}H_{so} + {}_{gl}H_{ai} + {}_{gl}H_{ev}, \tag{9.1}$$

were $_{gl}H_{so}$ is the heat flux density into the soil, $_{gl}H_{net}$ is the net irradiation in the glasshouse, $_{gl}H_{ai}$ is the sensible heat flux density and $_{gl}H_{ev}$ is the latent heat flux density or evaporation. A similar expression for the wall of the glasshouse is

$$(H_{net} - {}_{gl}H_{net})A_{so} = ({}_{gl}H_{con} + {}_wH_{ai} + {}_wH_{ev})A_w, \tag{9.2}$$

where H_{net} is the net irradiation outside the glasshouse, $_{gl}H_{con}$ is the heat transmitted from the glasshouse air to the wall (convection and condensation), $_wH_{ai}$ is sensible heat flux density from glasshouse wall to the outside air. $_wH_{ev}$ is evaporation from glasshouse wall (usually negligible). This equation should include a term considering the heat capacity of the construction. This term is omitted because only nearly stationary conditions are considered which makes this term, regarding the already small heat capacity, very small. And finally an equation which considers that the heat released at the surface must also pass the glasshouse wall

$$A_{so}\,{}_{gl}H_{ai} = ({}_{gl}H_{ven} - {}_{gl}H_{con})A_w, \tag{9.3}$$

where $_{gl}H_{ven}$ is the heat flux due to ventilation of the glasshouse and expressed for convenience per unit area of the glasshouse wall as a flux density. Here again a term considering the temperature change of the air inside the glasshouse is omitted because of the stationary conditions.

9.3. The glasshouse temperature

It is of some practical interest to have an equation expressing the temperature difference inside and outside the glasshouse ($\vartheta_{in} - \vartheta_{ou}$) in terms of the various energy fluxes because this temperature difference is the climate factor to which most growing conditions are related.

First the sensible heat fluxes and the heat flux due to ventilation must be expressed in temperature differences. According to assumption (b) in section 9.2 and neglecting condensation at the glasshouse walls, the heat flux densities $_{gl}H_{ai}$ and $_wH_{ai}$ can be written

$$_{gl}H_{ai} = h_{so}(\vartheta_{so} - \vartheta_{in}), \tag{9.4a}$$

$$_wH_{ai} = h_{ou}(\vartheta_w - \vartheta_{ou}), \tag{9.4b}$$

where h_{so} is the so-called coefficient of convective heat transfer at the soil surface, h_{ou} the coefficient of heat transfer outside the glasshouse, ϑ_{so} the soil surface temperature, ϑ_{in} the air temperature, ϑ_w the wall temperature and ϑ_{ou} the ambient temperature outside the glasshouse. A similar expression can be given for $_{gl}H_{con}$

$$_{gl}H_{con} = h_w(\vartheta_w - \vartheta_{in}), \tag{9.5}$$

where h_w is the coefficient of heat transfer at the wall. Also the ventilation, $_{gl}H_{ven}$, can be written in a similar expression

$$_{gl}H_{ven} = h_{ven}(\vartheta_{in} - \vartheta_{ou}), \tag{9.6}$$

where h_{ven} is a coefficient of sensible heat transfer for ventilation. This coefficient is proportional to the amount of air drainage, which will be discussed in section 9.5.

Equations (9.4), (9.5) and (9.6) combined with (9.3), give

$$h_w(\vartheta_{in} - \vartheta_w) + h_{ven}(\vartheta_{in} - \vartheta_{ou}) = h_{so}\frac{A_{so}}{A_w}(\vartheta_{so} - \vartheta_{in}). \tag{9.7}$$

It is reasonable to assume that $h_w = h_{ven} = h_{in}$, because the air motion inside the glasshouse will be more or less homogeneous (see section 9.9). Combining (9.1), (9.2), (9.4), (9.5) and (9.7) leads to the following result

$$(\vartheta_{in} - \vartheta_{ou}) = \frac{1}{B}\frac{A_{so}}{A_w}[h_{ou}\,_{gl}H_{net} + h_{in}H_{net} - (h_{in} + h_{ou})(_{gl}H_{so} + _{gl}H_{ev})] \tag{9.8}$$

where

$$B = h_{in}h_{ou} + h_{in}h_{ven} + h_{ou}h_{ven}.$$

As soon as the evaporation is considerable, causing condensation on the glasshouse wall, it is necessary to modify (9.8). Without going into detail it is indicated that a possible approach is to lump the sensible and latent heat fluxes together, assuming that heat transfer and moisture transfer are similar processes. It is possible then to write for (9.4a) (see further sections 9.9 and 9.26)

$$_{gl}H_{ai} + _{gl}H_{ev} = h'_{so}(\vartheta_{so} - \vartheta_{in}) \quad \text{and} \quad h'_{so} = h_{so}\frac{1 + b_h}{b_h}, \tag{9.9}$$

where h'_{so} now is a larger quantity than h_{so}, which is a function of temperature and of soil moisture content, and b_h is Bowen's ratio (see section 9.4). In a similar way h'_w and h'_{ven} can be defined (see (9.19) and (9.20)).

The final result is that instead of (9.8) we find

$$(\vartheta_{in} - \vartheta_{ou}) = \frac{1}{B'} \frac{A_{so}}{A_w} [h_{ou} {}_{gl}H_{net} + h'_w H_{net} - (h'_w + h_{ou}) {}_{gl}H_{so}], \qquad (9.10)$$

where

$$B' = h'_w h_{ou} + h'_w h'_{ven} + h_{ou} h'_{ven}.$$

The equations (9.8) and (9.10) indicate the relation between the temperature difference $\vartheta_{in} - \vartheta_{ou}$ and the other climate factors. The derivation of these equations is an approximate one, therefore it is necessary to be careful in drawing conclusions. In cases of rapid changes in time, various neglected heat capacities enter in the picture, especially if the soil has a large heat capacity and causes considerable lag in the phenomena.

9.4. The evaporation

Besides the interrelation with the other terms of the heat budget, the evaporation depends on the soil moisture, the soil structure, the humidity and the motion of the air above the surface.

In the previous section it is already indicated that heat transfer and moisture transfer can be treated as similar processes. This consideration led to the tentative equations (9.9) and (9.10). When we combine (9.4a) and (9.9) we can write for the ratio of the sensible heat flux over the latent heat flux $b_h = {}_{gl}H_{ai}/{}_{gl}H_{ev} = h_{so}/h'_{so} - h_{so}$, where b_h is called the Bowen ratio. Another relation for the Bowen ratio can be found by considering that the latent heat flux will be proportional to the difference in vapor pressure at the surface and in the air

$$_{gl}H_{ev} = h(p_0 - p), \qquad (9.11)$$

where h is the constant of proportionality. When the Bowen ratio is expressed with (9.4a) and (9.11), we find

$$\frac{{}_{gl}H_{ai}}{{}_{gl}H_{ev}} = \frac{h_{so}}{h} \frac{\vartheta_{so} - \vartheta_{in}}{p_0 - p_{in}}.$$

Since heat and moisture transport are similar functions of air movement in the glasshouse, the ratio $h_{so}/h = \gamma$ appears to be the psychrometer constant so

$$b_h = \frac{{}_{gl}H_{ai}}{{}_{gl}H_{ev}} = \gamma \frac{\vartheta_{so} - \vartheta_{in}}{p_0 - p_{in}}. \qquad (9.12)$$

When it is possible to evaluate the Bowen ratio and to neglect the term $_{gl}H_{so}$

from the heat budget, the latent heat flux can be expressed as

$$_{gl}H_{ev} = \frac{_{gl}H_{net}}{1 + b_h},$$ (9.13)

where only the net radiation has to be measured, besides b_h. This approach is used by PENMAN [1948]. An application of Penman's method is given in section 9.26.

Another way to obtain the evaporation of the glasshouse is by comparing a glasshouse with evaporation with a dry glasshouse.

Rewriting (9.8) combined with (9.1) for the dry and the wet glasshouse in the following form respectively

$$B \frac{A_w}{A_{so}} (_{dry}\vartheta_{in} - \vartheta_{ou}) = h_{ou}\, _{gl}H_{net} + h_{in}\, H_{net} - (h_{in} + h_{ou})\, _{gl}H_{so},$$

and

$$B \frac{A_w}{A_{so}} (\vartheta_{in} - \vartheta_{ou}) = h_{ou}\, _{gl}H_{net} + h_{in}\, H_{net} - (h_{in} + h_{ou})(_{gl}H_{so} + _{gl}H_{ev}).$$

Subtracting these two equations from each other and solving for $_{gl}H_{ev}$ gives

$$_{gl}H_{ev} = B \frac{A_w}{A_{so}} \frac{(_{dry}\vartheta_{in} - \vartheta_{in})}{(h_{in} + h_{ou})}.$$ (9.14)

The assumption which is made in this derivation is that $_{gl}H_{net}$ and $_{gl}H_{so}$ are the same in the dry and wet glasshouse and that there is no condensation on the glass. Equation (9.14) indicates that when we have some means of knowing what the temperature of the glasshouse would be if there were no evaporation, then the evaporation can be found by multiplying the difference between this maximum possible temperature and the actual glasshouse temperature with

$$\frac{B}{h_{in} + h_{ou}} \frac{A_w}{A_{so}} = \frac{h_{in} h_{ou}}{h_{in} + h_{ou}} + h_{ven} \frac{A_w}{A_{so}}.$$ (9.15)

In this case, the difficulty of finding the $_{dry}\vartheta_{in}$ replaces the difficulty of determining the evaporation. For experimental purposes it is conceivable to have a dry glasshouse as check. Furthermore, some experience may be obtained in general about dry glasshouse temperatures and net radiation, so that $_{dry}\vartheta_{in}$ can be correlated with $_{gl}H_{net}$.

9.5. Ventilation

In the previous sections the natural ventilation is briefly mentioned insofar

as it represents a heat loss. Now we want to have a closer look at this phenomenon.

The natural ventilation is a function of the wind velocity, the wind
direction, the temperature difference and the size and number of the air leaks
in the wall. It is usually expressed in the number of times the glasshouse
volume is replaced by fresh air per hour, S. In most cases the magnitude of
S varies between 0.5 and 4 (according to measurements by Whittle at John
Innes Horticultural Institute). Both the wind u and the temperature difference
$\vartheta_{in} - \vartheta_{ou}$ will cause a pressure difference over the glasshouse wall. This
pressure difference is actually the cause of the ventilation. To express the
wind and temperature influence quantitatively an equation of the following
form may be suggested

$$S = au^2 + b(\vartheta_{in} - \vartheta_{ou}),$$

where a and b are empirical constants, which are determined by the construction of the glasshouse.

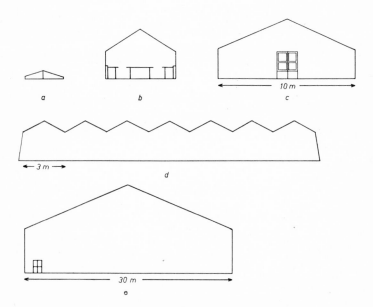

Fig. 9.1. Front view of various types of glasshouses
    a) Dutch light
    b) Nursery greenhouse
    c) Hothouse
    d) Glasshouse complex
    e) Large and tall glasshouse.

When S is known, it is relatively easy to estimate the heat loss due to ventilation $_{gl}H_{ven}$,

$$_{gl}H_{ven} = C_{ai} \frac{V}{A_w} S(\vartheta_{in} - \vartheta_{ou}), \qquad (9.16)$$

where C_{ai} is the volumetric heat capacity of the air and V the volume of the glasshouse. Comparing (9.16) with (9.6) we find

$$h_{ven} = C_{ai} \frac{V}{A_w} S, \qquad (9.17)$$

which means that the coefficient of heat transfer is proportional to S, as is obvious, and depends on the dimensions of the glasshouse. In Table 9.1 the value of $C_{ai} V/A_w$ is given for various glasshouse types (see Fig. 9.1) and also the ratio A_{so}/A_w. Equation (9.16) expresses only the sensible heat loss due to ventilation. There is also a latent heat loss as soon as the specific humidity inside is larger than outside the glasshouse. Instead of (9.16) we then have

$$_{gl}H_{ven} = C_{ai} \frac{V}{A_w} S(\vartheta_{in} - \vartheta_{ou}) + L \frac{V}{A_w} S(q_{in} - q_{ou}), \qquad (9.18)$$

where L is the heat of vaporization (cal cm^{-3}) and q is the specific humidity. From this equation we see that the h'_{ven}, used in (9.10), can be expressed as

$$h'_{ven} = C_{ai} \frac{V}{A_w} S\left(1 + \frac{L}{C_{ai}} \frac{q_{in} - q_{ou}}{\vartheta_{in} - \vartheta_{ou}}\right). \qquad (9.19)$$

The term

$$\frac{C_{ai}}{L} \frac{\vartheta_{in} - \vartheta_{ou}}{q_{in} - q_{ou}} = \beta'$$

is comparable to the Bowen ratio b_h from (9.12), so we can write (9.19), using (9.17)

$$h'_{ven} = h_{ven} \frac{1 + \beta'}{\beta'}. \qquad (9.20)$$

TABLE 9.1

Some characteristics of various types of glasshouses

Glasshouse type	A_{so} (m²)	A_{so}/A_w	$C_{ai} V/A_w$ (cal cm^{-2} °C^{-1})
Dutch light	3 × 10	1 –0.9	0.012–0.015
Nursery greenhouse	6 × 12	0.5	0.03
Hothouse	10 × 40	0.6	0.04 –0.05
Greenhouse complex	50 × 100	0.8–0.9	0.05 –0.06
Large and tall glasshouses	50 × 100	0.6	0.1 –0.15

9.6. The net radiation

There is usually a considerable difference between the net radiation inside and outside the glasshouse. In order to discuss this difference, it is most convenient to consider the net short-wave radiation H_{sh}^{net}, and the net long wave radiation H_{lo}^{net}, separately.

The net short-wave radiation inside the glasshouse is considerably smaller than outside, due to reflection by the glass and interception of radiation by the glasshouse structure. In general we can write

$$_{gl}H_{sh}^{net} = fH_{sh}^{net} \frac{1 - {}_{so}\varrho_{sh}}{1 - f_{so}\varrho_{sh} - {}_{gl}\varrho_{sh}},$$

where f is the so-called daylight coefficient (see section 9.7), ${}_{so}\varrho_{sh}$ is the albedo of the soil surface, and ${}_{gl}\varrho_{sh}$ is the reflectivity of the glasshouse surface.

The net long wave radiation H_{lo}^{net} is usually quite different in and outside the glasshouse, because the glass is opaque for these wave lengths. Consequently ${}_{gl}H_{lo}^{net}$ is determined by the temperature difference between the soil surface and the glasshouse surface. This difference is usually not very large ($< 50\,°C$) and therefore we can write for ${}_{gl}H_{lo}^{net}$

$$_{gl}H_{lo}^{net} = h_{ra}(\vartheta_w - \vartheta_{so}), \tag{9.21}$$

where h_{ra} is the coefficient of heat transfer for radiation (of the order of $4\ kcal\ m^{-2}h^{-1}°C^{-1} = 0.67 \times 10^{-2}\ cal\ cm^{-2}\ min^{-1}°C^{-1}$). The net long wave radiation outside the glasshouse is determined by the glass temperature and the back radiation of the atmosphere. This may have a considerable value ($0.15 - 0.20\ cal\ cm^{-2}\ min^{-1}$).

When combining the net short- and long wave energies the result is that in most cases the net radiation inside the greenhouse still is smaller than outside. In this respect reference is made to observations by SCHOLTE UBING [1959, 1961]. The so-called "greenhouse-effect" therefore does not exist or is very small. The possible contribution of this effect under exceptionally favorable conditions is discussed in section 9.10.

For the net radiation in the glasshouse can be written

$$_{gl}H_{net} = fH_{sh}^{net} \frac{1 - {}_{so}\varrho_{sh}}{1 - f_{so}\varrho_{sh} - {}_{gl}\varrho_{sh}} + h_{so}(\vartheta_w - \vartheta_{so}), \tag{9.22}$$

and the net radiation outside

$$H_{net} = H_{sh}^{net} - H_{lo}^{net}. \tag{9.23}$$

When the albedo or the reflectivity inside the glasshouse is the same, then equation (9.22) reduces to

$$_{\text{gl}}H_{\text{net}} = f H_{\text{sh}}^{\text{net}} + h_{\text{so}}(\vartheta_{\text{w}} - \vartheta_{\text{so}}). \qquad (9.24)$$

Usually the reflectivities are not very well known and probably not very different, therefore (9.24) is of more practical value than (9.22).

9.7. The daylight coefficient f

An extensive analysis of the daylight coefficient f was made in Germany (SCHULZE [1955]). In this section the analysis will be summarized. The daylight coefficient (Schulze used "Lichtkennzahl") is introduced, as the word indicates, to express the ratio of the visible light flux on a horizontal surface inside and outside the glasshouse.

The light flux ϕ on a horizontal surface is composed of diffuse light flux ϕ_{diff}, and beam or parallel light flux ϕ_{dir}. A comparison between these fluxes in and outside the glasshouse can be written as

$$_{\text{in}}\phi_{\text{dir}} = a_1 s_1 \,_{\text{ou}}\phi_{\text{dir}}, \qquad (9.25)$$

$$_{\text{in}}\phi_{\text{diff}} = a_2 s_2 \,_{\text{ou}}\phi_{\text{diff}}, \qquad (9.26)$$

where the indices "in" and "ou" refer to inside and outside the glasshouse respectively; a_1 and a_2 reflect the influence of the glass on the parallel and diffuse light respectively and s_1 and s_2 reflect the influence of the construction on both kinds of light. The constants a_2 and s_2 are characteristic of the glasshouse, and a_1 and s_1 are also characteristic of the glasshouse but vary with the position of the sun. In order to obtain useful values of these quantities with regard to available meteorological data the total amount of light ϕ_{tot} per day is considered.

$$\phi_{\text{tot}} = \int_0^{1\,\text{day}} \phi \, dt. \qquad (9.27)$$

The daylight coefficient then can be expressed as

$$f = \frac{\displaystyle\int_0^{1\,\text{day}} a_1 s_1 \,_{\text{ou}}\phi_{\text{dir}} \, dt + \int_0^{1\,\text{day}} a_2 s_2 \,_{\text{ou}}\phi_{\text{diff}} \, dt}{\displaystyle\int_0^{1\,\text{day}} {}_{\text{ou}}\phi_{\text{dir}} \, dt + \int_0^{1\,\text{day}} {}_{\text{ou}}\phi_{\text{diff}} \, dt}. \qquad (9.28)$$

When we introduce,

$$l = \frac{\int\limits_{0}^{1\,\text{day}} {}_{\text{ou}}\phi_{\text{dir}}\,dt}{\int\limits_{0}^{1\,\text{day}} ({}_{\text{ou}}\phi_{\text{dir}} + {}_{\text{ou}}\phi_{\text{diff}})\,dt}$$

and

$$\overline{a_1 s_1} = \frac{\int\limits_{0}^{1\,\text{day}} a_1 s_1\,{}_{\text{ou}}\phi_{\text{dir}}\,dt}{\int\limits_{0}^{1\,\text{day}} {}_{\text{ou}}\phi_{\text{dir}}\,dt}$$

then equation (9.28) becomes

$$f = a_2 s_2 + b(\overline{a_1 s_1} - a_2 s_2). \tag{9.29}$$

When only the influence of the glass is considered then $s_1 = s_2 = l$ and when only the influence of the construction is considered then $a_1 = a_2 = l$. When there is only diffuse light, $l = 0$ and when there is only parallel light, $l = 1$. The quantity l is a meteorological parameter and can be derived from appropriate measurements of the short-wave radiation components. The quantities a_1, a_2, s_1, and s_2 are related to the glasshouse. They reflect the influence of the construction, the orientation and the location of the glass-house on the daylight factor.

This analysis enabled Schulze to process the data obtained from extensive model investigations on glasshouses. For more detailed information on this subject, reference is made to SCHARRINGA [1956].

TABLE 9.2

Typical daylight coefficient for a number of glasshouses

Glasshouse type	Daylight coefficient determined with spherical light meter in per cent	
	Diffuse light	Direct sunlight
Glasshouse complex with Dutch light units	50–55	55–60
Glasshouse glass pane 60 cm wide	55–60	60–70
Glasshouse glass pane 72 cm wide	60–65	65–75
Dutch lights	50–70	55–80

Table 9.2 gives some information about the daylight coefficient for various types of glasshouses in use. These glasshouses usually had a wooden construction (see further section 9.14).

9.8. The heat flux into the soil

In order to obtain the heat flux density into the soil $_{gl}H_{so}$ of a glasshouse, various methods can be applied. The quantity $_{gl}H_{so}$ is a function of the soil type, the moisture and temperature distribution of the soil and the components of the heat budget. The soil type and the moisture distribution determine the heat conductivity and the heat capacity of the soil. De Vries has shown that the heat conductivity can be computed with reasonable accuracy when the composition and the structure of the soil are known (DE VRIES [1952]).

When averaged over a long time interval (e.g., 10 days) the value of $_{gl}H_{so}$ becomes small in comparison to the other terms in the energy budget, but may not disappear entirely for very long periods as in the case for H_{so} outside the glasshouse. The average temperature inside the glasshouse is higher than outside, therefore an average horizontal temperature gradient exists in the soil under the glasshouse walls. The result is that part of the heat in the glasshouse leaks out through the soil. This average $_{gl}H_{so}$ term is of the order of 5 to 10 per cent of the mean value of $_{gl}H_{ai} + {}_{gl}H_{ev}$, the sensible and latent heat fluxes. Also if the water table is comparatively high (i.e., $1 - 2$ m below the surface), the water will maintain the mean bare soil temperature and some extra heat will be carried away with the water flow.

9.9. The coefficients of convective heat transfer h_{in} and h_{ou}

In section 9.3 the coefficients h_{in}, h_{ou}, and h_w are introduced with the equations (9.4a), (9.4b), and (9.5) respectively. Furthermore, it is assumed that $h_w = h_{so} = h_{in}$, i.e., the coefficient of convective heat transfer is equal from the soil to the air and from the air to the glasshouse wall.

In the field of heating and cooling engineering the coefficient of convective heat transfer have proved to be extremely useful. Extensive studies concerning the magnitude of these coefficients have been made. For more detail, reference is made to MCADAMS [1951]. The coefficient inside the glasshouse, h_{in}, may be expected to be fairly constant. In general h_{in} will vary between 1 and 4 kcal m^{-2} hr^{-1} °C^{-1} or 1.7×10^{-3} cal cm^{-2} min^{-1} °C^{-1}, depending on the size of the glasshouse and the amount of ventilation. For computations of the heat loss of a glasshouse usually $h_{in} = 4$ kcal m^{-2} hr^{-1} °C^{-1} is used.

It is not so evident that h_{ou} is as useful as h_{in}, because the outside conditions vary widely. The wind is the major influence in these variations. Furthermore, the ambient temperature outside the glasshouse, ϑ_{ou}, which is used in (9.4b) is not easy to define, which gives an uncertainty in h_{ou}. However, when the surface of the earth is homogeneous over an extended area, then it is possible to derive a simple relationship between the coefficient of heat transfer and the wind velocity, when the temperature difference is taken between the surface, ϑ_{so}, and a height of 2 m. When the convective heat flux $_{gl}H_{ai}$ is expressed by

$$_{gl}H_{ai} = h_{so}(\vartheta_{so} - \vartheta_{200}),$$

then it can be shown (BUSINGER [1954b]) that under adiabatic conditions and with a roughness parameter $z_0 = 1$ cm, the following relation between h_{ou} and u_{200} holds

$$h_{ou} = 3u_{200},$$

where h_{ou} is expressed in kcal m^{-2} hr^{-1} °C^{-1} and u_{200} in m sec^{-1} at 2 m height. The value of h_{ou} will be somewhat larger under unstable conditions and smaller under stable conditions of the surface layer of the atmosphere.

A value of $h_{ou} = 10$ kcal m^{-2} hr^{-1} °C^{-1} is probably a good average value for the outside coefficient of heat transfer.

In deriving (9.8) it is assumed that h_{in} and h_{ou} are constant over the entire glasshouse surface and over the soil surface. However, in reality there will be large differences in these coefficients going from one place to another.

9.10. Discussion of the greenhouse-effect

In order to estimate the magnitude of the greenhouse-effect it is necessary to make a few imaginary experiments. First we assume a glasshouse with normal net radiation, but with unlimited ventilation. This means that h_{ven} attains large values e.g. 100 kcal m^{-2} hr^{-1} °C^{-1}. The result is that $\vartheta_{in} - \vartheta_{ou}$ becomes very small. Suppose, in a normal closed glasshouse, $\vartheta_{in} - \vartheta_{ou} = 30$ °C and $h_{ven} = 1$, then for $h_{ven} = 100$, the corresponding $\vartheta_{in} - \vartheta_{ou} < 2$ °C. The temperature difference inside and outside the glasshouse becomes almost negligible. This illustrates the fact that with an unrestricted ventilation the increase of net radiation in the glasshouse has only a small effect on the temperature.

The second imaginary experiment is the comparison of an ordinary glasshouse to a glasshouse which is transparent for both short- and long wave radiation. Since the net radiation for the transparent house is equal inside and outside, equation (9.2) reduces to

$$_{gl}H_{con} = - \,_{w}H_{al},\qquad\qquad(9.2a)$$

and consequently instead of (9.8) we find

$$\vartheta_{in} - \vartheta_{ou} = \frac{h_{in} + h_{ou}}{B}\frac{A_{so}}{A_{w}}\,(_{gl}H_{net} - \,_{gl}H_{so} - \,_{gl}H_{ev}).\qquad(9.8a)$$

Comparing (9.8) and (9.8a) by assuming reasonable values for the various parameters will illustrate the greenhouse-effect: $_{gl}H_{net} = 200$ is the net radiation in the imaginary glasshouse and outside, further $B = 54$; $h_{in} = 4$; $h_{ou} = 10$; $h_{ven} = 1$; $A_{so}/A_{w} = 0.6$ and $_{gl}H_{so} + \,_{gl}H_{ev} = 100$. The fluxes are in kcal m^{-2}hr^{-1} and transfer coefficients in kcal m^{-2} hr$^{-1}\,°$C^{-1}. With these values (9.8) gives

$$\vartheta_{in} - \vartheta_{ou} = 19.8\,°\text{C}$$

and (9.8a) gives

$$\vartheta_{in} - \vartheta_{ou} = 15.4\,°\text{C}.$$

The greenhouse-effect therefore amounts to 4.4 °C in this case or about 22 per cent of the total temperature increase in the glasshouse. The other 78 per cent must be ascribed to the fact that the glasshouse is a closed unit. Actually the temperature difference between the two glasshouses will be somewhat smaller because $_{gl}H_{ev} - \,_{gl}H_{so}$ in the regular glasshouse will be larger than in the imaginary glasshouse.

9.11. The natural glasshouse climate

When no control measures are taken in a glasshouse, then we may say that its natural climate will develop. Considerations of the natural climate will have no direct practical applications, but may serve to deepen the insight in the physical phenomena.

The natural climate of a glasshouse can best be compared with a desert climate. No precipitation will occur and consequently there will be nothing to evaporate. The temperature fluctuates between extremely high maxima and quite low minima. No vegetation can develop under these circumstances.

9.12. The temperature

A number of observations of the temperature recorded in a closed and empty glasshouse in June 1951 gives an impression of the range and the level (Fig. 9.2). The soil was completely dry to a depth of about 5 cm, so evaporation was negligible. Although the soil was dry, the heat flux $_{gl}H_{so}$ into the soil may nevertheless assume considerable values during the period of maximum irradiation.

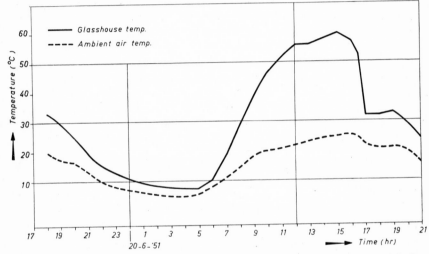

Fig. 9.2. Comparison between glasshouse temperature and ambient air temperature during a period of clear summer weather. The glasshouse was kept closed, so the natural ventilation was small. Height of thermometers ± 1.50 m.

The maximum temperature difference $\vartheta_{in} - \vartheta_{ou}$ observed in Fig. 9.2 is about 35 °C. When we make some rough estimates of the quantities appearing in (9.8) we find about the same value for this quantity: Assuming a temperature gradient of 10 °C cm^{-1} and a thermal conductivity of 0.03 cal cm^{-1} min^{-1} °C^{-1} (0.18 kcal m^{-1} hr^{-1} °C^{-1}) gives a heat flux into the soil $_{gl}H_{so} = 0.3$ cal cm^{-2} min^{-1}. Assuming further, that $H_{net} = {}_{gl}H_{net} = 0.65$ cal cm^{-2} min^{-1}; $_{gl}H_{ev} = 0$; $h_{in} = 0.006$ cal cm^{-2} min^{-1} °C^{-1}; $h_{ven} = 0.001$ cal cm^{-2} min^{-1} °C^{-1}; $h_{ou} = 0.015$ cal cm^{-2} min^{-1} °C^{-1}, then equation (9.8) gives $\vartheta_{in} - \vartheta_{ou} = 40$ °C. All the assumed values are quite plausible for the given situation and give a result which is close to the observed temperature difference. Above estimation must be regarded as an example rather than a proof of (9.8).

Observations in Dutch lights showed maximum temperatures of 80 °C and a value of $\vartheta_{in} - \vartheta_{ou} = 55$ °C. The fact that these values are larger than for the glasshouse can be attributed to the smaller air circulation and ventilation and consequently smaller values of h_{in} and h_{ven} for the Dutch lights.

Generally it will be observed that with the same daylight coefficient and the same amount of air leaks per unit area of glasshouse wall, the highest temperatures occur in the lowest glasshouses. The increase in wind speed and the decrease of the ratio A_{so}/A_w with height both tend to increase h_{ven} and h_{ou} and to a lesser extent h_{in}. The coefficient of heat transmission by ventilation h_{ven} should not be confused with the ventilation coefficient S, which decreases with a higher construction (compare (9.16) and Table 9.1).

9.13. Air circulation

The air in a glasshouse is usually moving slowly. This is caused by local heating and cooling of the air (convection) and by the wind pressure distribution over the glasshouse surface in combination with air leaks. The latter effect is predominant under most circumstances in common types of glasshouses. The air leaks in the house pass the wind pressure distribution somewhat on to the inside air, which causes an air flow. The resulting air flow pattern is schematically represented in Fig. 9.3. The main characteristic of this picture (i.e., the flow in the wind direction aloft and a flow opposite to the wind direction near the gound) is generally valid independent of the orientation of the glasshouse with respect to the wind direction.

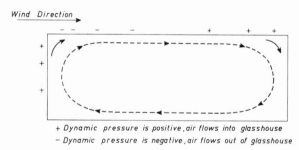

+ Dynamic pressure is positive, air flows into glasshouse
− Dynamic pressure is negative, air flows out of glasshouse

Fig. 9.3. Schematic representation of the air circulation in a closed glasshouse due to the outside wind.

As a consequence of this flow the temperature and the humidity show a specific distribution. The heat absorbed by the ground is partly transferred to the adjacent air and carried away to the weather side of the glasshouse.

Consequently the temperature and the humidity are considerably higher at the weather side than at the lee side. Observations of the temperature and humidity distribution during favorable conditions of this phenomenon are represented in Fig. 9.4. The humidity distribution indicates that evaporation took place during these observations and therefore that we were not strictly dealing with the natural glasshouse climate. The phenomenon itself, however, is a characteristic of the natural climate.

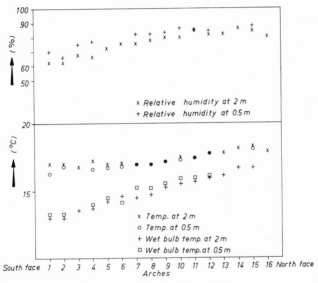

Fig. 9.4. Temperature and humidity distribution in a glasshouse as a consequence of the air circulation (see Fig. 9.3). The wind is from the north.

The circulation due to convection is usually quite small, because the air close to the ground is heated rather uniformly and the air close to the glass-house wall is cooled rather uniformly. So there is no strong preference for upward and downward flows and consequently a whimsical flow pattern develops. The resultant flow usually is weakly ascending at the center and descending at the wall.

9.14. Climate control in the glasshouse, the glasshouse construction

Throughout our discussion of the general characteristics of the glasshouse climate the glasshouse, itself, has been treated generally as an enclosure bordered by walls which transmit most of the solar light. In the following sections we will discuss more specifically the glasshouse construction in its relation to the climate and to some control measures which may be taken in order to create favorable growth conditions for the plants.

The type of glasshouse and its construction will depend on the purpose one has in mind. In this connection the historical surveys by van den Muyzenberg are of interest (VAN DEN MUYZENBERG [1943, 1948]).

During the winter season there will be a shortage of light and heat, thus in this period it will be important to have as high a daylight coefficient as possible and to have little heat loss at the same time. During the spring usually enough light is available for most crops. Then the daylight coefficient is no longer critical and it becomes more important to have a good mechanism for the ventilation in order to be able to remove the excess of heat during clear days. Special provisions in summer are required for light shielding and heat removal.

Economically, the heated glasshouses or hothouses used during the winter are the most important. In this case the requirements for the construction are: (a) maximum daylight coefficient, and (b) minimum natural ventilation.

Several design measures which favor better light conditions in the glasshouse during the period of low natural light intensities are possible.

(i) The construction has to be light and still strong enough to meet various weather conditions. The loss in light, due to the construction, amounts to 60–70 per cent of the total light losses in the glasshouse. The use of strong materials makes it possible to reduce the sizes of the opaque construction parts and to increase the daylight coefficient. A compromise of economy and strength determines which materials are best suited for the construction of the glasshouse. A survey of the daylight coefficient for various glasshouse types is given in Table 9.2 (section 9.7). Specially designed light constructions with large size glass panes may have up to 10 per cent better daylight coefficients.

(ii) The light loss caused by reflection and absorption of the glass must be considered inevitable. It is already indicated that a large size of the glass pane is favorable for a high value of the daylight coefficient. According to LAWRENCE [1948], the optimum width of the glass is between 60 and 72 cm. In the Netherlands several types of glasshouses are developed with the glass pane size of the Dutch lights (72 cm). In Germany, a glass pane size of 60 × 200 cm is receiving considerable use.

A further light loss is in many cases due to pollution (dirt film) of the glass. Both VAN GINSEL [1943] and SEEMAN [1952] have carried out investigations of the light loss by pollution and were able to establish that the main sources of pollution were highways, railroads and factories in the neighborhood. It is especially worthwhile to keep the glass clean in early spring.

(iii) The orientation of the glasshouse and the slope of the roof is of particular interest with respect to direct sunlight. Studies with respect to this subject were reported by LAWRENCE [1948], SEEMAN [1952] and SCHULZE [1955].

According to Lawrence the most favorable orientation of the glasshouse is E 15° N – W 15° S during the winter season. The direction is not perfectly E – W because of the fact that on the average there is more sunshine in the morning than in the afternoon. Furthermore he advises an asymmetrical roof with a steep slope facing N. Several experiments were carried out to find out whether there is any difference in plant growth between asymmetrical and symmetrical glasshouses. Nor Plant Protection at Fernhurst (England), neither the Institute of Horticultural Engineering at Wageningen, the Netherlands [1954], have found any difference between the two. However, a marked difference was found between the N – S and E – W orientation of the glasshouse. The E – W orientation gives better results, especially during winter and early spring.

SCHULZE [1955] has determined (with a special model setup) the daylight coefficient of several glasshouse types. He used exclusively symmetrical models and found that high glasshouses (i.e. with steep roof slopes) provide best results with a N – S orientation. Also, SEEMAN [1952] came to this conclusion. The explanation of this phenomenon lays in the fact that a considerable amount of radiation reflected from the inside walls and roof reaches the ground with low sun angles. Schulze found this effect even with diffuse light. So also in this case reflection plays a significant role.

(iv) The color of the construction plays a considerable rôle in the daylight coefficient. Measurements of Schulze show that a white painted construction gives 5 to 10 per cent more light in the glasshouse than a black painted construction.

(v) It is conceivable that plastics will replace the glass of greenhouses in the future. Construction of greenhouses with plastics will be lighter in weight than with glass and consequently will be cheaper. However, plastics have some great disadvantages with respect to glass: (a) large light losses (scattering), (b) short life, (c) liability for rapid pollution. These disadvantages are not compensated for by the advantages of low cost, light weight and infrangibility. To date plastics have not proven economical expect for a few special cases (GERMING [1956]).

(vi) Several experiments were carried out comparing regular flat glass with frosted glass (SCHULZE [1955]; Institute for Horticultural Engineering [1953]).

The result of these experiments was that both types of glass transmit about the same amount of light but the distribution of light under frosted glass because of scattering, is more even. Under frosted glass the maximum light intensity is lower and the minimum light intensity higher than under regular glass. This characteristic has a specially favorable effect on the plants because: (a) under frosted glass shielding is not necessary as early in the spring, and (b) the assimilation will be increased when it is limited by light in the shade and saturated in direct light.

The natural ventilation is mainly due, as we have seen in section 9.5 to the glasshouse construction during the winter season. In the ordinary types of glasshouses the ventilation may cause 10 to 30 per cent of the total heat losses. This can be saved by making the glasshouse construction airtight. A special airtight glasshouse together with a special ventilation system was developed in Germany with apparently satisfying results.

The objections against airtight glasshouses are:

(i) If there is no proper drainage for the water condensed on the glass, the water may fall on the crop and damage it.

(ii) The ventilation may become so small, that the supply of CO_2 for crop assimilation is inadequate.

(iii) The construction is more expensive.

With regard to these objections it may be noted that:

(i) It is possible to drain the condensate with relatively simple provisions.

(ii) With controlled ventilation the CO_2 supply can be maintained. This will be discussed in section 9.23.

TABLE 9.3

Temperature observations during a cold spell in a number of glasshouses indicating the effect of orientation and construction

Date	Outside temp.		Glasshouse orientation E–W		Glasshouse orientation N–S		Glasshouse complex	
	min (°C)	max (°C)	min (°C)	max (°C)	min (°C)	max (°C)	min (°C)	max (°C)
2/14	−15	−2	−6	5	− 5	4	−6	0
2/17	−18	−6	−7	4	− 8	2	−8	−1
2/18	−14	−5	−6	8	− 6	3	−7	−1
2/23	−18	−7	−7	11	−10	5	−9	−2
2/25	−15	−2	−8	18	− 9	8	−8	0
Average over period 2–13 through 2–27:								
	−13.0	−4.1	−5.7	9.1	−6.2	4.6	−6.2	0.2

The choice of an airtight glasshouse with controlled ventilation vs. an ordinary glasshouse with sufficient air leaks depends mainly on the glasshouse economy. Fuel costs and construction expenses are deciding factors.

As an illustration some temperature observations are given in two glasshouses with large glass panes (size of Dutch lights) and a glasshouse complex with Dutch light units. The observations, see Table 9.3, were made in February 1956 during a period of severe frost.

The snow thawed from the glasshouses but remained on the complex.

These observations taken under extreme conditions clearly show the effect of orientation and construction on the climate. The glasshouse with E – W orientation maintained an average temperature above zero throughout the period, so almost every day the ground was defrosted.

9.15. Heating of glasshouses

The purpose of heating is to increase the temperature to a level where special crops will grow. A complete treatment of the heating technique would be a chapter in itself. Therefore, only an outline will be given of the requirements for heating installations, the principle of heating and a discussion of the effect of some installations in use on the climate.

The general requirements for a good heating system are: (a) the capacity of the installation must be sufficient to maintain the desired temperature in the glasshouse under the occurring weather conditions; and (b) the installation must be economically justified as far as investment, fuel consumption, maintenance and labor are concerned.

Special requirements concerning the glasshouse climate may be formulated: (i) The temperature must be evenly distributed in the horizontal as well as in the vertical.

(ii) The installation must be controllable with a high adaptability.

(iii) The light loss due to the heating installation must be minimum.

(iv) The installation should not hinder cultivation of the ground.

To provide a certain object with a desired amount of heat it is necessary to generate this amount of heat first in a source and then to transport it to the object. The problem is to design a heat source with the correct capacity and to find the most efficient way to transport the heat. There are three basic mechanisms for the heat transportation or the heat transfer, i.e., radiation, convection, and conduction. Radiation is the most direct form of heat transfer. In this case the heat source may transfer the heat directly to the crop. Convective heat transfer needs the air to bring the heat where desired. The air is heated by the heat source and the hot air in turn heats the crop. Heat conduction through the air usually is negligible. However, when the soil is heated it may be the most important means of heat transfer.

The most common heating of glasshouse is with hot water pipes as heat source. Therefore it is of interest to discuss the heating characteristics of pipes. Many investigators have studied this subject exhaustively (see MCADAMS [1951]).

The heat transmission of a pipe is proportional to the temperature difference between pipe, ϑ_p, and ambient air, ϑ_{ai}. The constant of proportionality is called the coefficient of heat transfer h, which is composed of a part due to radiation h_{ra} and a part due to convection h_{con}. The heat transmission H per m² of pipe surface is then

$$H = (h_{ra} + h_{con})(\vartheta_p - \vartheta_{ai}).$$

The coefficient of heat transfer is not entirely a constant. The radiation coefficient h_{ra} is a function of the pipe temperature ϑ_p and the temperature difference, $\vartheta_p - \vartheta_{ai}$, whereas h_{con} is a function of the temperature difference and the diameter of the pipe. These relations are given in Fig. 9.5.

Because heat transfer by radiation is direct, whereas convective heat

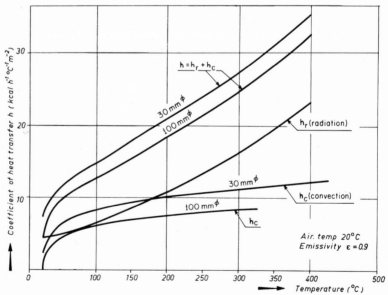

Fig. 9.5. Relation between the coefficients of heat transfer and the temperature for pipe diameters of 30 and 100 mm.

transfer is indirect and consequently of less quality, it is desirable to keep these two types of heat transfer separated in the consideration of various techniques. In Fig. 9.6 the ratio of the radiative transfer over the total transfer is presented as a function of the temperature difference between pipe and ambient air. It is not completely correct to take the radiative transfer

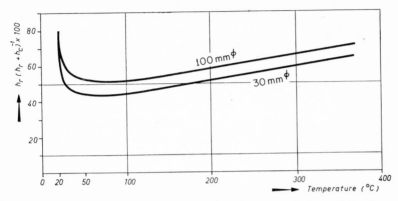

Fig. 9.6. Relation between the radiative part of the heat transmission and the pipe temperature.

with respect to the air temperature. It is more precise to take the temperature of the objects which receive the radiation. This temperature is in general somewhat lower than the air temperature because it is determined mainly by the temperature of the glasshouse surface. The error can be corrected by introducing a correction factor as done by HOARE and MORRIS [1956]. However, the uncertainty which exists in the h_{ra} in the first place because the absorption coefficients of the surfaces are not well known, is much greater than the error introduced by taking the air temperature. It is noted that Hoare and Morris apply the same correction factor to the convective part of the transfer, introducing a new error. Unless very careful observations are undertaken, the above correction factor can be neglected.

In Fig. 9.7 the temperature of a leaf is given for various percentages of the radiative transfer, under otherwise fixed circumstances. Assuming that the leaf temperature defines the required amount of heating, the air temperature may be considerably lower with a large than with a small percentage of radiative transfer, and consequently with less heat losses through the glasshouse wall.

Besides pipes, convective heaters have been used recently for glasshouse heating. The heat transfer in this case is almost entirely convective. The large

amounts of air which are stirred into motion by this heating system will
increase the coefficient of heat transfer between the air and the crop and
consequently decrease the temperature difference between air and crop, so
Fig. 9.7 does not apply in this case. The true situation is not so bad as this
figure implies.

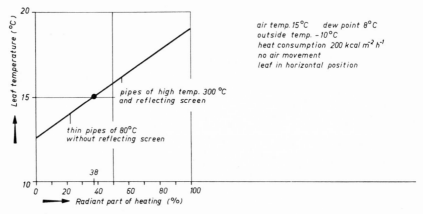

Fig. 9.7. Relation between leaf temperature and radiative part of the heating.

9.16. Heating systems

In the following sections only those aspects of the various heating systems
will be discussed, which are of direct influence on the glasshouse climate.
This means that we will discuss the location and the characteristic properties
of the transfer units and not the technical details of the installation as steam
or hot water heating, forced or free circulation, etc. Following the principles
developed it is logical to classify the various heating systems according to
the percentage of radiative transfer.

9.17. Air heating

As indicated in section 9.15 the radiative part of the air heating systems
can be neglected. The use of hot air stoves and also of convective heaters is
attractive in connection with the small investment and the fact that requirements (ii), (iii) and (iv) (see section 9.15) are satisfied.

The main difficulty is to obtain a homogeneous temperature. Considering
the forces acting on a jet of hot air it is possible to find a criterion for the
penetration distance of the air (BUSINGER [1956a]). The relative low density

exerts an upward force on the hot air. The momentum of the forward moving air creates an inertial force. The ratio of these two forces determines the penetration of the air. This ratio defines a dimensionless parameter G of the form

$$G = \frac{g(\vartheta_{\text{hot}} - \vartheta_{\text{cold}})d}{u^2 \theta_{\text{ai}}},$$ (9.30)

where g = acceleration due to gravity,
      d = diameter of the hot air jet,
      u = velocity of the hot air,
      θ_{ai} = mean absolute temperature of ambient air,
      ϑ_{hot} = temperature of hot air,
      ϑ_{cold} = temperature of surrounding air.

From the distribution of the air flow as a function of the distance to the air duct, x, it can be deduced that a reasonable approximation of G is given by

$$G = G_0 \frac{(d_0 + cx)^3}{d_0},$$ (9.31)

where the index 0 indicates the air flow when entering the glasshouse and c is a constant of proportionality ($c \approx 0.5$).

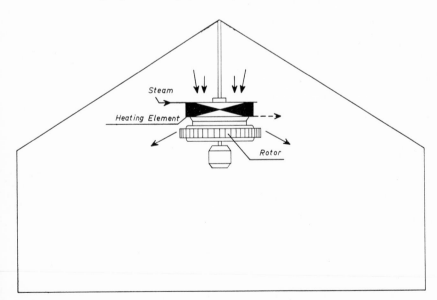

Air-heating system

Fig. 9.8. A simple air heating system.

There is a critical value of G which determines the penetration of the hot air. This critical value of G will be of the order of one. When $G > 1$ the air will mainly rise and for $G < 1$, horizontal flow will predominate. Because G rapidly increases with the distance x, it will eventually pass the critical value. Consequently all air heating systems are limited with respect to the homogeneity of the temperature distribution. The temperature in the top of the glasshouse is always higher than at the bottom.

To comply as well as possible with the requirement of an even temperature distribution it is suggested that 1000 m³ injected hot air should not carry more than 10000 kcal. This means that the temperature at the nozzle is maximal 35 °C warmer than the glasshouse temperature. A consequence of this compromise is that, as SPOELSTRA [1954] has indicated, air heating is only suitable for so-called "light heating". For heavy heating too much air movement would be required, which has unfavorable secondary consequences. Furthermore, it is important with respect to the homogeneity of the temperature that the air is injected at many places as may be deduced from (9.31).

An economical air heating unit which comes close to the requirements and which has a favorable ratio of heat transfer over air resistance consists of a heater combined with rotor as illustrated in Fig. 9.8. In this unit a large volume of air is displaced with little power consumption.

9.18. Thin pipe heating

The usual heating with thin pipes (3/4″ to 5/4″ diameter) with hot water under forced circulation or low pressure steam, has a low percentage radiative heating reaching the ground (about 25 per cent) (see Fig. 9.7). With a good distribution of the pipes, the convective part of the heat is released evenly over the glasshouse and is carried upward. The difficulty with this system, as with air heating, is to obtain a favorable vertical temperature distribution. The solution for this problem is sought in two directions:

(i) Mounting the pipes close to the ground gives a reasonable temperature distribution. The objection is that the handling of the soil is hampered by the low mounting of the pipes. By making a flexible mounting it is possible to overcome this objection to some extent.

(ii) By adding ceiling fans to high mounted pipes, the vertical temperature distribution is improved by air mixing leaving the ground free for handling.

Heating with thin narrow pipes is attractive because of the ready control and quick adjustment of the heating and because the investment is relatively low. This system is widely used at present.

9.19. Heating with large pipes (4″)

Fig. 9.6 indicates that the radiative part of the transfer increases with increasing pipe diameter. This increased amount of radiation causes a reasonable temperature distribution. Another advantage of this system is its reliability. The large pipes allow natural circulation through the system and the large heat capacity of the circulating water will prevent crop damage in the event of power failure. However, the large heat capacity makes this system difficult to control. A minor disadvantage of this system is the light loss because of the high mounted pipes.

The effective radiative part of the pipes can be increased somewhat by covering the glass-facing side of the pipes with aluminum paint, leaving the other half in normal radiating paint.

This system is extensively used in horticulture because of its simplicity and reliability.

9.20. Systems with large radiative part

A large radiative part in heating can be obtained either by reducing the convective transfer or by increasing the radiative transfer. The convective transfer can be reduced by using heating elements with large dimensions (compare large pipes with thin pipes). The most feasible means to increase radiative transfer is to increase the temperature of the heating element

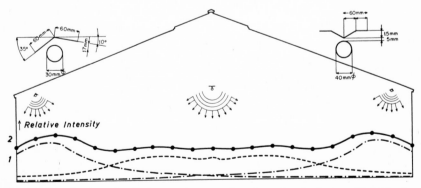

Fig. 9.9. Distribution of radiation on the ground surface of a glasshouse with high pipe temperatures and reflectors.

———————————— total radiation

— — — — — — — contribution from the center pipe

–.–.–.–.–.–.– contribution from the wall pipes

(BUSINGER [1956b]). Increasing the temperature of pipes increases the heat transfer for two reasons. First, the temperature difference between pipe and ambient air is increased, and second, the coefficients of heat transfer, in particular h_{so}, are increased (see Fig. 9.5).

The radiative part of the heat transfer at 300 °C is about 60 per cent (see Fig. 9.6). Half the radiation is directed upward and therefore is not useful for the heating. Because of the intensity of the heat transfer at this temperature only 1/8 of the pipe surface, which is used with hot water heating, is required. This makes it possible to apply reflectors to the pipes which may increase the downward directed radiation to about 80 per cent of the total radiation. Specially designed reflectors can be used to obtain an even distribution of the radiation on the ground. Fig. 9.9 shows the distribution of the radiation in a glasshouse obtained with an experimental heating system using pipe temperatures up to 300 °C.

Although a very good temperature distribution and satisfactory heating control is obtained, the technical difficulties are too large and cost of the installation is too high for practical application of this system.

Another possibility to obtain a large radiative component in the heating is with propane gas radiators. The propane is burnt in a ceramic material, which in turn radiates intensively. It is possible to obtain 80 per cent of the total heat transfer in radiation. This system has to be worked out yet. A definite disadvantage is the high price of the fuel.

9.21. Some remarks concerning the influence of the heating system on the climate

Besides a rise in temperature, most heating systems have characteristic influences on other climate factors. These influences can be studied best, when weather influences are small e.g. in case of an overcast sky and no wind.

Under these circumstances, it appears that the evaporation is mainly dependent of the type of heating system. Evaporation increases with the air movement. It is remarkable that the house with the 300 °C pipe temperature heating system showed the smallest evaporation regardless of the fairly intensive radiation. The homogeneity of the radiation apparently does not initiate convective air motion near the ground. The relative humidity within the crop obtains high values and the evaporation remains small. Other systems use convection as an essential part of the heating and have, therefore, a certain amount of air motion. It appears that the evaporation is mainly determined by the amount of air motion.

Another important difference between the heating systems can be observed in the temperature difference between soil and air. Fig. 9.10 illustrates that a radiative heating system (glasshouse II) develops a higher soil temperature than a predominantly convective heating system (glasshouse I). The soil temperature increases with respect to the air temperature with an increasing radiative part of the heating. This relation is similar to the relation given in Fig. 9.7 showing the leaf temperature as a function of the radiative transfer.

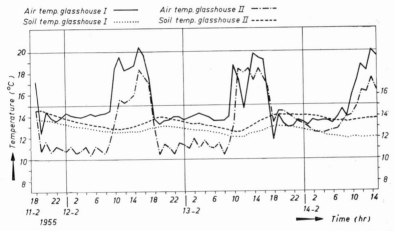

Fig. 9.10. Comparison of air and soil temperatures between a glasshouse with a low radiative part (I) and a glasshouse with a high radiative part of the heating (II).

As we have seen, systems with predominantly convective heating easily develop large vertical temperature differences. This effect will be most pronounced when the natural radiation is small. The bottom air layer including the crop, will have the lowest temperature. Above this layer the temperature increases rapidly with height. As soon as the natural radiation becomes significant, the cold bottom layer will increase rapidly in temperature because in this layer the radiation will be absorbed. The consequence is that, with a constant heating keeping the average air temperature constant, the temperature of the crop will be a function of the natural radiation, i.e. the light intensity. This relation appears to be favorable for the plant growth, because usually the plant needs a high temperature with high light intensity in order to have maximum assimilation. Consequently, we may conclude that the vertical temperature gradient development with convective heating systems is not so serious as is generally believed. The disadvantage of the vertical temperature gradient remains, however, during the night. The cold air in the bottom layer is stagnant and has a high relative humidity, which may be an unfavorable situation in connection with plant diseases.

In contrast to the unheated glasshouse, the convective air motion is significant in glasshouses with normal pipe heating. The convective flow above pipes, especially when the pipes are placed vertically above each other can be considerable. When the horizontal distribution leaves relative large openings a pattern of descending cooled air in between the pipes may develop and create the so-called "cold spots" in the glasshouse. It is observed (GRAY [1947]) that the cold spots move under the influence of the outside wind. This can be understood when we consider that the air circulation due to the wind is superposed on the convective motion.

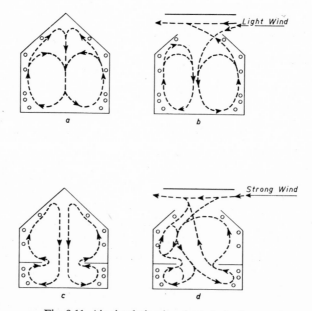

Fig. 9.11. Air circulation in a heated glasshouse.

More information on the convective flow was obtained by Renard at Hannover (Germany). He used glasshouse models and applied the so-called "schlieren" method. In Fig. 9.11 several flow patterns are illustrated, which were obtained by this method. This will be further discussed in section 9.23.

9.22. Plant radiation

As mentioned in section 9.14, during the winter months the amount of daylight available is the limiting factor for plant growth, provided the temperature is controlled. An obvious measure under these circumstances is to irradiate the plants with artificial light sources. In order to be able to apply the correct radiation it is necessary to know the reaction of the crop to the various types and intensities of radiation. Several characteristic influences of the radiation on the plant growth are known. These influences appear to be related to the wave length of the radiation. This has led the committee on plant radiation of the "Nederlandse Stichting voor Verlichtingskunde" to divide the spectrum in the following ranges:

(i) All radiation with wave lengths larger than $1.0\,\mu$ does not show a specific influence on plants. It is assumed therefore, that when this radiation is absorbed by the plant it does not influence biochemical processes, except through its conversion into heat.

(ii) The radiation with wave lengths between $1.0\,\mu$ and $0.7\,\mu$ has a specific stretching effect on many plants. Although the spectral range does not precisely coincide with the limits where stretching is observed, it may be assumed that the amount of radiation from a source falling in this range is a measure of the stretching effect this source will have.

(iii) The radiation with wave lengths between $0.7\,\mu$ and $0.61\,\mu$ include the range where strong red absorption by chlorophyl and strong photosynthetic activity takes place. In many cases also a strong day length effect is observed.

(iv) Radiation with wave lengths between $0.61\,\mu$ and $0.51\,\mu$ include the spectral range with weak photosynthetic activity in the green and a weak formative effect.

(v) Radiation with wave lengths between $0.51\,\mu$ and $0.4\,\mu$ are in the range of strong chlorophyl absorption and photosynthetic activity in the blue violet although not so strong as in the red. The radiation in this range is also absorbed by yellow pigments and has a strong formative effect.

The knowledge in the field of plant radiation is still very limited. Much research will yet be required in order to obtain a better insight in the phenomena. It seems likely, however, that important practical applications of artificial plant radiation will be found in the future.

The choice of a source of radiation depends on the effect one tries to obtain with the radiation. There are no special lamps developed for plant radiation. Therefore, existing lamp types have to be tested on their usefulness

for plant radiation. ROODENBURG [1948, 1949] has carried out extensive investigations in this field. In selecting radiation sources he considered the following characteristics of the source:
(a) the spectral distribution,
(b) the required power for operation,
(c) the efficiency,
(d) the cost.
Besides considering the characteristics of the radiation source, it is necessary also to develop economic and effective mountings for the lamps in order to obtain an even distribution on a horizontal surface.

The commercially available light sources are developed to give favorable light distributions and are compared with the sensitivity curve of the eye. The units of lumen and lux used for light flux and illuminations are not suitable for the plant radiation because spectral sensitivity of the various reactions in the plant are entirely different from the sensitivity curve of the eye. It is better, therefore, as suggested by the committee on plant radiation, to use radiation flux expressed in mW instead of light flux expressed in lumen and to use radiation flux density expressed in mWm^{-2} instead of illumination (1 mWm^{-2} = 1 erg cm^{-2} sec^{-1}).

In Table 9.4 data are collected from a number of light sources from which the characteristic properties with respect to plant radiation can be deduced.

TABLE 9.4

The efficiency of various light sources in the spectral ranges as defined in section 9.22

Light source	Gross power (W)	Net power (W)	Percentage of gross power in the spectral ranges				
			1	2	3	4	5
incandescent	500	500	60	13.6	4.3	2.3	0.9
high pressure mercury	475	450	60	0.9	0.3	6.5	3.3
high pressure mercury	83	75	40	2.0	0.7	5.6	4.1
sodium	106	85	30	0.6	0.2	12.6	0.02
fluorescent	49	40	30	0.0	2.9	5.5	5.8

The quality of a light source for plant radiation depends on the purpose for which it is used. The determination of this is very difficult in many cases because too little is known about the spectral sensitivity distribution of the processes. A tentative efficiency comparison with respect to photosynthesis is made by CANHAM [1956]. He compared the spectral distribution of the light sources with the spectral sensitivity curve of Gabrielsen. Also, the initial cost and the power consumption were considered. The result was that the fluorescent tubes and the high pressure mercury lamp combined with fluorescence proved to be most promising. Good results with fluorescent tubes were obtained by GERMING [1956] when nursing tomato seedlings in an otherwise dark room.

Diverse opinions exist with respect to the intensities to be applied for additional radiation. In England usually higher intensities and shorter periods are applied than in the Netherlands. The British method has the advantage that the radiation equipment can be used continuously by replacing the equipment every 12 hours because the plants receive 12 hours of additional radiation. This can be arranged by dividing a glasshouse into two sections A and B, applying radiation to section A from noon till midnight, then replacing the equipment to section B and applying radiation from midnight till noon, etc. In the Netherlands usually 16 hr of additional radiation is applied (say from 7 a.m. to 11 p.m.). In this case the radiation equipment cannot be used continuously.

TABLE 9.5

Examples of usage of light sources in horticulture

Purpose of irradiation	Recommended light source	Required power $(W m^{-2})$	Used for
increase of daylength	incandescent lamp	5–50	various types of bulbs sensitive to photoperiodism
forcing (eventually without daylight)	incandescent lamp	50–100	shrubs
increase of photosynthesis	fluorescent tube or high pressure mercury lamp	80–160 100–200	seedlings seedlings
complete culture in only artificial light	fluorescent tube	160–360	seedlings

A survey of the recommended intensities and the choice of light source for various methods of plant radiation is given in Table 9.5. Use is made of data obtained by ROODENBURG [1949].

9.23. Ventilation

In the discussion of the glasshouse construction (see section 9.14) it is pointed out that with respect to fuel economy, it is desirable to build the glasshouse as tight as possible in order to prevent natural ventilation. However, this introduces the danger that the provision of CO_2 or the removal of moisture may be inadequate. During the summer, a large ventilation is required to reduce the temperature. When the natural ventilation is suppressed it is necessary to have a controlled ventilation in its place and safety measures have to be taken.

The ventilation of a closed glasshouse can be measured best with a CO_2 indicator. It is possible to arrive at the ventilation by releasing an amount of CO_2 in the glasshouse and measuring the CO_2 content as a function of time. If C_{gl} is the concentration of CO_2 in the glasshouse and if C_{ou} is the concentration in the outside air, then the decrease of C will be proportional to $C_{gl} = C_{ou}$ and the constant of proportionality is a measure of the ventilation S (see section 9.5). In equation

$$\frac{dC}{dt} = - S(C_{gl} - C_{ou}). \qquad (9.32)$$

Integrating and solving for S gives

$$S = - \frac{1}{t} \ln \frac{C_{gl} - C_{ou}}{C_0 - C_{ou}}, \qquad (9.33)$$

where C_0 is the initial concentration for $t = 0$. By plotting the logarithm of the concentration versus the time, a linear relation is obtained with a slope equal to S (MORRIS and NEALE [1954]).

A special advantage of using CO_2 is that the required CO_2 indicator also can be used for the determination of the assimilation of the crop. However, other gases such as H_2 or radioactive isotopes can be used according to the same principles, although these methods are more expensive.

In case the glasshouse is ventilated through ventilators, the ventilation will be so large that the CO_2 method becomes inaccurate. A method which can be used in this case is applied by BUSINGER [1954a]. When a constant amount of heat is supplied to the glasshouse the temperature difference inside and outside the glasshouse will be a measure of the ventilation. It is necessary that the applied heat be the only source of energy in the glasshouse. Therefore, in order to obtain good measurements, the natural radiation must be low and the wind speed and direction must be constant. In that case we may assume that the coefficients of heat transfer are constant and that the heat loss due to ventilation is the only variable. The constant amount of heat Q which enters the glasshouse is lost be heating transfer and ventilation,

$$Q = (\vartheta_{in} - \vartheta_{ou})(h_{ra} + h_{con} + h_{ven}) A_w. \tag{9.34}$$

It is assumed that the heat flux into the soil, the evaporation, and the radiation are negligible. The coefficient of heat transfer due to ventilation h_{ven} can be divided in two parts i.e., a part which expresses the heat transfer h_{v0} in the closed glasshouse and a part, h_{v1}, due to opening of the ventilators. By adjusting the heat supply till a temperature difference $\vartheta_{in} - \vartheta_{ou} = 10\,°C$ is obtained for the closed glasshouse, the solution for h_{v1} can be written as

$$h_{v1} = \frac{Q}{A_w} \left(\frac{1}{\vartheta_{in} - \vartheta_{ou}} - \frac{1}{10} \right). \tag{9.35}$$

When Q and $\vartheta_{in} - \vartheta_{ou}$ are measured then h_{v1} can be computed.

A difficulty of this method is that the wind velocity usually varies which makes it necessary to introduce corrections. Table 9.6 shows values of h_{v1} obtained with this method (see section 9.26).

9.24. The ventilation required for conditioning the glasshouse

The CO_2 consumption of the plants is determined by the rate of photosynthesis. The photosynthesis is at a maximum with a high light intensity and an optimum temperature. Each crop has different requirements, which have to be determined separately. MORRIS, POSTLETHWAITE and EDWARDS [1954] have investigated the amount of ventilation required to maintain a maximum CO_2 consumption.

During the summer a S value of $10 \times$ per hour is required under favorable light conditions. During winter and early spring this value is certainly lower.

It is not easy to indicate the ventilation required for reducing the humidity because this depends entirely on the outside conditions and conditions in the crop. Tomato plants often require lowering of the humidity for protection against mildew.

The ventilation required to remove heat can be computed with equations (9.34) and (9.17) when the amount of heat to be removed and $\vartheta_{in} - \vartheta_{ou}$ are known.

This method is successful only when the outside temperature is considerably below the desired glasshouse temperature. HOARE and MORRIS [1956] indicate that a ventilation of 50 to $100 \times$ per hour may be required. This corresponds to a value of $h_{ven} = 25$ to 50 kcal cm^{-2} hr^{-1} °C^{-1} in an average glasshouse. During calm hot weather it is difficult to obtain sufficient ventilation.

9.25. Methods of ventilation

The most usual means of ventilation is to open ventilators in the glasshouse. The effect of this measure depends on several factors such as the size and location of the ventilator and the wind speed and direction. It is not easy to take these factors into account in such a manner that the desired ventilation will be obtained. This is a matter of experience for the grower.

In order to obtain some quantitative insight, experiments were carried out using the second method described in section 9.23. In the experiment, four almost identical glasshouses with an N – S orientation were used. The wind velocity was 7 m sec^{-1} from the West. For several observation periods it was necessary to correct for the wind velocity and direction, assuming that h_{ven} was proportional to the wind velocity. The result of this experiment is given in Table 9.6.

TABLE 9.6

Comparative results of a ventilation experiment

Glasshouse I		Glasshouse II		Glasshouse III		Glasshouse IV		Averaged	
situation	h_{v1}	situation	h_{v1}	situation	h_{v1}	situation	h_{v1}	situation	h_{v1}
4	12.5	7	17.9	5	10.0	7	18.5	7	12.7
5	9.9	12	14.0	7	9.9	4	12.3	5	10.2
12	7.7	5	10.1	4	7.1	5	10.2	4	9.3
13	7.7	11	9.3	2	6.0	3	9.2	12	8.5
11	7.0	6	8.6	12	6.0	2	7.5	11	6.8
2	6.8	10	6.3	13	5.9	12	7.3	2	6.6
7	6.4	2	6.2	11	4.7	11	6.2	3	5.9
6	5.7	3	6.0	3	3.8	6	5.6	6	5.8
3	4.6	4	5.3	10	3.3	10	4.9	13	5.5
10	4.2	13	3.8	6	3.3	13	4.9	10	4.7
8	2.7	1	2.5	15	2.9	1	2.7	8	2.2
1	2.1	8	1.8	8	1.7	8	2.6	1	1.9
14	2.0	15	0.8	14	1.0	14	2.1	15	1.8
15	1.6	9	0.4	1	0.3	15	1.9	14	1.3
9	0.6	14	0.1	9	0.2	9	0.3	9	0.4

The table shows that although the scattering is rather large in the individual observations there are significant differences between the various ventilator positions. Furthermore, it is seen that the highest ventilation obtained is less

Fig. 9.12. Glasshouse with a chimney ventilator. (Photograph P. C. HOUTER.)

than the minimum requirement during warm summer weather ($h_{ven} = 25$).
The relation between the ventilation S and h_{ven} for these glasshouses was

$$S = 2.2\, h_{ven}.$$

Air circulation was considered in addition to the ventilation. In practically
all cases this appeared to be a circulation as sketched in Fig. 9.3. Only the
magnitude of the circulation varied with the ventilator positions.

A new method of ventilation, studied in Germany, introduced chimney
ventilators (Fig. 9.12). The wind generates a low pressure at the top of the
chimney which causes the suction of air out of the glasshouse while fresh air
moves in through inlets in the side walls. This system, though still dependent
on the wind velocity, is not dependent on the wind direction as the conventional system is, and therefore, easier ventilation control may be expected.

A complete ventilation control can only be obtained with fans. The
ventilation which is required in winter time can easily be delivered with ordinary fans without too much power consumption. The maximum S during
the winter is $5 \times$ per hour and would require a fan capacity of $5000\ \mathrm{m^3hr^{-1}}$ for
a glasshouse with a volume of $1000\ \mathrm{m^3}$. The maximum ventilation needed
during the summer may be 10 times as large. This would require special
construction and may require prohibitively high power consumption.
Economic considerations determine whether a complete ventilation control
is desirable or not.

9.26. Evaporation

The estimation of evaporation is necessary to determine the required water
supply. PENMAN [1948] has developed a method to determine the potential
evapotranspiration in the open air (reference is made to a recent survey
given by him). Potential evapotranspiration is the evaporation which takes
place when the crop has sufficient water available. When we assume that
this is the case in the glasshouse, then it is possible to apply Penman's
equation in the glasshouse. Actually, the conditions in the glasshouse are
somewhat simpler. The equation for the potential evaporation, which will be
used here is a modified Penman equation (BUSINGER [1956a]; PENMAN [1948])

$$E_{po} = \frac{\Delta_{gl} H_{net} + \gamma f(p_w{}^s - p_w)}{\Delta + \varepsilon\gamma}, \tag{9.36}$$

where E_{po} = potential evapotranspiration,
       Δ = the slope of the saturation vapor pressure curve,

TABLE 9.7

Comparison of evaporation in identical glasshouses with different heating system

1956 dates	Glasshouse I					Glasshouse II				
	ϑ_{in} (°C)	$p_w{}^s\text{-}p_w$ (mb)	Δ (mb °C⁻¹)	E_{po} (div hr⁻¹)	f (div hr⁻¹)	ϑ_{in} (°C)	$p_w{}^s\text{-}p_w$ (mb)	Δ (mb °C⁻¹)	E_{po} (div hr⁻¹)	(di
24/25–1	8.5	1.9	0.78	0.7	0.80	13.5	5.2	1.02	2.2	1
25/26	14.1	3.3	1.05	1.2	0.93	14.2	5.7	1.05	2.4	1
27/28	13.6	3.5	1.04	1.1	0.80	12.6	4.8	0.96	2.0	1
28/29	13.6	2.8	1.04	1.1	1.00	13.6	5.3	1.03	2.4	1
29/30	13.2	3.6	1.00	1.3	0.90	12.9	6.4	0.99	2.2	0
30/31	11.9	4.9	0.92	1.5	0.72	11.2	5.8	0.89	2.8	1
1/2–2	6.9	3.0	0.70	1.6	1.09	10.0	6.8	0.83	2.9	0
2/3	13.6	4.5	1.04	1.6	0.91	13.7	6.9	1.03	2.8	0
4/5	13.1	4.5	1.00	1.4	0.77	13.7	7.2	1.03	2.8	0
5/6	13.9	4.0	1.05	1.3	0.83	14.4	6.7	1.06	2.6	1
6/7	13.1	3.9	1.00	1.3	0.83	13.6	7.0	1.03	2.8	1
7/8	13.2	4.4	1.00	1.5	0.84	13.1	6.9	0.98	2.5	0
9/10	11.3	4.7	0.89	1.7	0.84	12.0	7.2	0.92	2.7	0
11/12	10.1	2.5	0.83	1.4	1.25	12.2	7.3	0.94	2.8	0
12/13	11.6	4.0	0.91	1.4	0.82	13.0	6.9	0.98	2.9	1
13/14	11.2	3.4	0.89	1.4	0.96	12.0	6.7	0.92	2.6	0
14/15	11.1	2.9	0.88	1.3	0.97	10.3	4.3	0.84	2.1	1
16/17	10.2	4.0	0.84	1.5	0.84	9.4	5.2	0.80	2.5	1
17/18	10.8	3.8	0.87	1.2	0.72	10.8	6.2	0.87	2.5	0
				average	0.88 ± 3.5%				average	1 ± 2

γ = psychrometer constant = 0.65 mb°C⁻¹,

$p_w{}^s$ = saturation vapor pressure,

p_w = vapor pressure,

f = factor depending on wind velocity, surface roughness and stability of the air layer close to the ground,

ε = empirical constant = 0.95.

Measurements of the evaporation were carried out in the four hothouses of the Institute for Horticultural Technique. The surface area of each glasshouse was 10 × 40 m². The following heating systems were used:

Glasshouse I : Thin pipe heating with high temperatures up to 300 °C. The pipes were mounted at 2 m height.

Glasshouse II : Thin pipes heating with forced hot water circulation. The pipes were mounted at 0.3 m height.

TABLE 9.7

omparison of evaporation in identical glasshouses with different heating system

	Glasshouse III				Glasshouse IV				
	$p_w{}^s-p_w$ (mb)	Δ (mb °C^{-1})	E_{po} (div hr^{-1})	f (div hr^{-1})	ϑ_{in} (°C)	$p_w{}^s-p_w$ (mb)	Δ (mb °C^{-1})	E_{po} (div hr^{-1})	f (div hr^{-1})
4	5.6	1.02	2.1	0.95	14.3	5.2	1.06	1.9	0.94
2	4.8	1.05	2.2	1.18	15.0	5.8	1.10	2.1	0.96
7	5.6	1.03	2.1	0.95	13.5	5.2	0.99	1.7	0.81
9	5.6	1.04	2.2	1.00	14.2	5.2	1.05	1.9	0.94
8	5.0	1.04	2.6	1.33	14.0	5.9	1.04	2.2	0.95
2	7.7	1.01	2.9	0.95	12.7	6.1	0.96	2.4	0.96
1	7.3	0.88	3.4	1.08	9.8	6.0	0.82	2.8	1.03
9	6.2	1.04	2.2	0.90	14.2	6.3	1.06	2.2	0.90
4	7.4	1.02	2.4	0.82	14.4	7.4	1.07	2.3	0.81
7	5.9	1.03	2.2	0.95	14.9	7.1	1.09	2.3	0.84
6	7.0	1.03	2.5	0.90	14.3	6.5	1.06	2.4	0.95
7	7.7	1.03	2.3	0.76	14.7	7.7	1.08	2.2	0.75
1	7.8	1.00	2.9	0.94	13.2	7.1	1.01	2.6	0.96
9	7.2	1.04	3.5	1.24	12.7	6.7	0.96	2.4	0.87
7	7.4	1.03	3.0	1.03	14.2	7.3	1.06	2.7	0.96
7	7.4	1.03	3.0	1.03	11.8	5.9	0.91	2.3	0.92
3	6.8	0.93	2.5	0.88	12.1	5.5	0.92	2.0	0.86
0	5.8	0.92	3.0	1.22	10.8	6.9	0.87	2.2	0.73
3	4.5	0.89	2.6	1.34	10.8	6.9	0.87	2.2	0.73
		average		1.02 ± 4%			average		0.89 ± 2.5%

Glasshouse III: Air heating with three heating units according to Fig. 9.8.
Glasshouse IV: Thin pipe heating with forced hot water circulation. Pipes
mounted at 2.20 m. Large fans were mounted just above
the pipes blowing air slowly in downward direction.

The evaporation was measured with piche evaporimeters as designed by
the KNMI (Royal Netherlands Meteorological Institute). By measuring
only during the night, it is possible to neglect the radiation term in (9.29),
so we have left

$$E_{po} = \frac{\gamma f(p_w{}^s - p_w)}{\Delta + \varepsilon\gamma}. \tag{9.37}$$

In this equation the factor f is the only unknown quantity. Because in one
and the same glasshouse the circulation and convection are constant it may

be assumed that f is a constant. On the other hand, if the experiment shows that f is a constant then this is a justification of (9.36) and (9.37).

The potential evaporation measured with the evaporimeters was expressed in divisions per hour i.e. in $0.1\ cm^3\ hr^{-1}$. The surface of the ceramic material which evaporated was 35 cm², so

$$1\ \text{div hr}^{-1} = 0.028\ \text{mm hr}^{-1}. \tag{9.38}$$

Results of observations taken in the period from 24 January till 18 February 1956, are presented in Table 9.7. The numbers represent average values for the period from 5.00 p.m. till 9.00 a.m. the next morning. The table shows that f is approximately a constant. The fluctuations may be due to observational errors. The heating systems have little but a systematic effect on the factor f. The glasshouses I and IV have a 12 per cent lower mean value of f than the glasshouses II and III. A larger value of f was expected in glasshouse III. The heating systems with high mounted pipes (I and IV) appear to have lower evaporation than the other two systems. It is remarkable that the ceiling fans in glasshouse IV have little effect on evaporation. The low evaporation rate in glasshouse I is mainly due to the low average temperature and consequently, high relative humidity.

During the daytime some extra convection has to be taken into account because of the natural radiation. In this case it is advisable to take a value of $f = 0.28$ mm $mb^{-1}\ hr^{-1}$. This value corresponds with a coefficient of heat transfer for the evaporimeters of 27 kcal $m^{-2}\ hr^{-1}\ °C^{-1} = 0.044$ cal cm^{-2} $min^{-1}\ °C^{-1}$, which is higher than the value found by DE VRIES and VENEMA [1954] for a similar evaporimeter.

The data given in Table 9.7 do not present the actual evaporation in the glasshouse, but relate the evaporation of a piche evaporimeter to Penman's formula written in the form of equation (9.37). However, it is reasonable to assume that the evaporation from the crop and ground surface is proportional to the evaporation of the evaporimeter so that the comparison of the heating systems of the glasshouses is justified. In order to translate the evaporimeter reading into actual evaporation, it is necessary to correlate the evaporimeter to lysimeters. Once this "calibration" is done, it is probably possible to use piche evaporimeters for the determination of the water consumption of glasshouses, provided the radiation is taken into account. This may be done by comparing an exposed evaporimeter with a shielded one, when the absorption coefficients of the evaporimeters and the crop are the same.

Measurements of the water use of tomato plants and lettuce were carried out by MORRIS, POSTLETHWAITE, EDWARDS and NEALE [1953]. They show that a distinct correlation exists between the net radiation, $_{gl}H_{net}$, and the evaporation. When the radiation is the only heat source in the glasshouse, then $\vartheta_{in} - \vartheta_{ou}$ is proportional with $_{gl}H_{net}$ and in first approximation also $p_w{}^s - p_w$. Equation (9.36) indicates that then $E_{po} \approx {}_{gl}H_{net}$, which is consistent with the observations by MORRIS *et al.* [1953]. During the winter this correlation is less pronounced because the extra heating causes extra evaporation. VAN DER ENDE [1955] emphasizes the importance for horticulture of a simple, reliable method to determine the evaporation during the winter months.

9.27. Methods of water supply

The water supply of the glasshouse is artificial, unless the water table is so high that the capillarity of the soil is sufficient.

Without discussing technical details the following methods of water supply exist:

  (i) subirrigation with controlled water tables,
 (ii) furrow irrigation,
(iii) sprinkling of water,
(iv) atomizing of water.

The methods (i) and (ii) have only indirect effect on the evaporation i.e. the water will be mainly vaporized through the plants. Also, the effect on the humidity of the air is indirect and very small.

The method (iii) increases both the moisture content of the soil and the air. As a result the temperature decreases in the glasshouse because a large part of the net radiation is used for evaporation and a smaller part for the sensible heat flux. This effect is even stronger with method (iv). With this method it is possible to increase the humidity of the air without increasing the soil moisture noticeably. KREUTZ [1949] shows some striking examples of a drop in temperature because of atomizing water in the glasshouse. It may be noted that by sprinkling with cold water it is possible to decrease the vapor pressure of the air although the relative humidity will rise.

9.28. Supply of CO_2

In section 9.24 the ventilation required for the CO_2 supply is discussed. It is also possible to inject CO_2 directly into the glasshouse and maintain the desired CO_2 concentration, which may be a higher concentration than available in the outside air. In this case a good airtight glasshouse is required.

Growing of horticultural crops in an atmosphere with increased CO_2 is yet entirely experimental. It is expected that the investigations in this field, especially in relation to plant radiation will lead to important practical results.

9.29. Automatic control of climate factors

It is outside the scope of this discussion to treat the technique of automatic control. However, a few remarks should be made.

In hothouses the temperature control is already widely used. Usually a constant temperature during the day and a constant lower temperature during the night is applied.

Automatic ventilation has been introduced recently in some glasshouses to reduce the temperature when necessary in spring and early summer. Also, the humidity can be more or less controlled by this technique.

A method of temperature control which is in a stage of development uses the light intensity to monitor the temperature. SEEMAN [1952] reported a number of experiments in this direction and showed that this technique provides considerable savings in fuel consumption.

The automatic control of water supply, humidity, ventilation and CO_2 concentration is carried out in a few experimental glasshouses. The techniques are in development and still too expensive for practical use.

CHAPTER 10

ATMOSPHERIC POLLUTION

F. H. SCHMIDT

Royal Netherlands Meteorological Institute, De Bilt

10.1. Introduction

Atmospheric air always contains quantities of substances other than those mentioned in Table 2.1. They may be gaseous or solid or they may occur in the form of small water droplets containing high concentrations of salts or acids. Their amount is generally very small, so that it is mostly expressed in p.p.m., parts per million by weight or even in p.p.b., parts per billion (10^9). The component SO_2 for instance, often occurs in towns in quantities up to about 1 p.p.m., i.e. 1,2 mg per m^3 air under normal circumstances. In spite of these small concentrations the occurrence of these substances, summarized as *atmospheric pollution* (or *aerosol*, as far as they are not gaseous), is of great importance for general meteorological theory as well as from an economic, medical and biological point of view (Air Pollution Handbook [1956]).

Generally speaking, one can distinguish between two sorts of air pollution, the *natural one* and the *artificial pollution*. The former originates from natural processes whereas the latter is the result of activities of man. Both may cause damage to vegetation (Fig. 10.1) and it is desirable, therefore, to consider their behavior in some detail.

However, it is especially artificial pollution that has long been recognized as a nuisance or even a hazard for agriculture.

It will be evident that its effect is greatest in the neighborhood of big industries and large cities. Unfortunately horticulture is often concentrated in the neighborhood of the latter.

The problem of air pollution is not a relatively new one. As early as in 1661 a book appeared on the polluted atmosphere of London (I. EVELYN [1661]). Indeed, London is the almost classical example of a city where, especially during the winter months, smog (= smoke + fog) occurs on many days, resulting sometimes in catastrophes like the one during the first week of December, 1952, when 4000 people died due to an accumulation of air pollution, without precedent so far.

Meanwhile, due to growing industrialization and ever intensifying traffic, other cities begin to show similar phenomena.

At the moment Los Angeles even surpasses London as an example of a producer of air pollution. Not only men but also crops suffer severely from the continuous production of great amounts of artificial pollution that are dispersed in the atmosphere. In 1949 the total damage done to agriculture in the environments of the city amounted to $ 480000; in 1953 $ 3000000 (MIDDLETON [1954])!

Since the second world war plants in the parks of Paris show increasing damage done by pollution, probably originating from motor cars.

It would be easy to mention many more examples. However, it may be clear from these few items that the agiculturist cannot any longer ignore the unfavorable effects air pollution may have on his industry.

We start this chapter with a survey of the most important components of natural and artificial pollution and their influence on vegetation. Next some methods for measuring the amount of pollution are mentioned whereas the rest of the chapter will be devoted to the problem of the diffusion of pollution in the atmosphere.

10.2. Natural pollution

Natural pollution consists of several components. As a first example we mention *dust* that may be brought into the atmosphere by moderate or strong winds blowing over dry and barren soils. Well-known are the sand storms in desert countries such as the Haboob in the Sudan. Similar dust-clouds may occur in moderate latitudes, by wind erosion, after long droughts connected with incorrect management of the soil. As an example of a region where this erosion is an important phenomenon we mention the Great Plains in the United States (WARN [1953]). It is clear that dust- and sandstorms, if they are of great intensity (Fig. 10.2), may cause serious damage to crops.

In continental areas ice crystals may come in the place of dust during the winter months, e.g. the blizzard of North America. (The dust storms of the Great Plains are often called "black blizzards").

Vulcanic eruptions or extensive *forest fires* may bring dust or smoke into the atmosphere. It generally accumulates in the higher levels, say between 3 and 10 km, and may remain there even for years, as a consequence of the low falling velocity of the very small particles. Such dust or smoke clouds may diminish the intensity of the solar radiation to a large extent. The

Fig. 10.1. Damage done by air pollution to gladiolus. (Courtesy of F. H. F. G. Spierings.)

Fig. 10.2. Heavy dust storm in United States. (G. F. WARN [1953].)

eruption of Mount Katmai in Alaska reduced radiation in Northern Europe to 60% of its normal value.

Great forest fires in western Canada in 1950 reduced radiation in Washington D.C., at a distance of about 3000 km, by almost 50%, resulting in an estimated decrease of maximum temperatures of about 3 to 4 degrees centigrade. Even in western Europe the smoke caused the sun to get a bluish color (WEXLER [1950]).

A very important form of natural pollution consists of small droplets of highly concentrated sea salt solutions, the so-called *sea salt nuclei*. They are brought into the air in the surf and probably also in open sea due to wind. Recent investigations show how very small droplets may be ejected to relatively large heights when bubbles of air reaching the air-water interface burst (BLANCHARD and WOODCOCK [1957]).

Partial evaporation of the water causes an increase of salt concentration in the droplets and reduces their diameter to about 10^{-4} to 10^{-5} cm so that they are easily transported to great heights and distances by turbulence and air currents. Although their number may vary from place to place it amounts to 10 to 100 per cm^3 at least. As condensation nuclei these sea water droplets play an important rôle in the formation of clouds and fog (MASON [1957]). Therefore, indirectly these nuclei are of great importance for agriculture. But also directly they may be of some importance from an agricultural point of view, especially close to the coast, as they may influence the constitution of the soil.

Results of measurements in the Netherlands show that the occurrence of various substances originating from seawater decreases with increasing distance from the coast (LEEFLANG [1938]).

The following table showing the quantity of Cl in g per m^3 rain water gives an illustration.

TABLE 10.1

Quantity of chlorine as a function of distance from the coast

Distance from coast (km)	0.44	2.28	3.00	5.60	48.0	86.0
Cl content (gm^{-3})	16.2	9.1	7.5	6.5	4.0	3.2

The rapid decrease in the amount of Cl with growing distance from the coast is probably a consequence of the transport of the nuclei to great heights, due to turbulence. Similar results have been found in the United States (JUNGE and GUSTAFSON [1957]).

Moreover, investigations in Sweden showed that the ratio between Na and Cl in rainwater varies significantly with the distance from the coast. Therefore, the problem of the contamination of rain water seems to be a very complicated one (EMANUELSSON et al. [1954]).

Apart from the above mentioned examples of inorganic natural pollution, great amounts of *spores* and *pollens* may be present in the atmosphere during certain periods of the year. Part of them, known as *aero allergens*, are responsible for hay fever and asthma. Their production as well as their dispersion in the atmosphere are closely connected with meteorological circumstances, such as rain, wind and humidity (WENDELL HEWSON [1953]).

The take-off or separation of the spores from the stratum where they were formed is generally initiated by raindrops. The drops first loosen the spores from the sticky material in which they are imbedded. Secondly the smaller droplets splashed upward by the raindrops carry the loosened spores into the atmosphere, the droplets evaporating rapidly and leaving the spores to dry and to be transported by the wind. Sometimes the spores are ejected into the atmosphere when their container is hit by a raindrop. Low-level turbulence and gustiness of the atmosphere play an important rôle in the spreading of the spores.

The distance pollens will travel through the atmosphere depends on many factors. High relative humidity hampering their drying usually reduces the distances covered. Turbulence is an important factor in maintaining the pollens in the air. Pollens of a diameter of about 50 μ occur at breathing level only on windy days.

For spores and smaller pollens originating at a source of relatively small extension, it appears that the dispersion downwind of the source obeys almost the normal distribution law

$$f(x,y) = \frac{1}{\sigma\sqrt{(2\pi)}} \exp\left[-\tfrac{1}{2}(y/\sigma)^2\right], \tag{10.1}$$

with

$$\sigma = Cx^a, \tag{10.2}$$

where the symbols have the following meaning:

x = distance downwind from the source,

y = distance from the x-axis,

$f(x,y)$ = fraction of the total number of spores along a cylinder with unit cross section and x = constant, found per unit volume at y,

C = a constant, playing the rôle of a generalized diffusion coefficient,

a = a constant between 0.5 and 1, depending on the stability of the atmosphere,

σ = standard deviation of the distribution.

At $y = \pm \sigma$ we find the concentration to be 0.6 times the concentration in the x-axis (Fig. 10.3).

Integrating (10.1) from $y = -2\sigma$ to $y = +2\sigma$ we find that 95% of the spores at the relevant value of x are contained between these boundaries.

The most important feature of (10.1) and (10.2) is that, at least approximately, the width of the area covered with spores increases with some power of the distance downwind from the source.

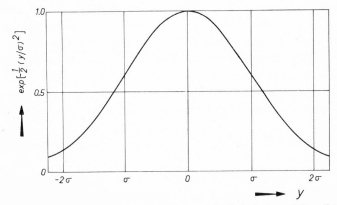

Fig. 10.3. Normal distribution. σ denotes the standard deviation of the distribution.

As a consequence of sedimentation the distance travelled by organic pollution is generally rather short. Under normal atmospheric conditions it seldom surpasses 1 km, whereas 10 km may be an absolute maximum. Some authors mention much larger distances, however (MALONE [1951], article by JACOBS).

Especially in moist, hot countries with abundant vegetation an almost permanent blue haze is observed, which seems to be connected with organic natural pollution.

Recent investigations have shown that gaseous natural pollution occurs as well as the liquid and solid type we mentioned before. Hydrogen sulfide, H_2S, e.g., escapes from the sea surface and from the ground. It is oxidized into SO_2 in the atmosphere and subsequently transformed into small droplets of relatively highly concentrated H_2SO_4. These droplets also act as condensation nuclei. In rural regions the SO_2 content of the air is of the order of 1 γ per m^3 (JUNGE [1958]).

10.3. Artificial pollution

Artificial pollution is by far the most important one from an agricultural point of view, owing to the damage it may cause to plants. It may enter into the atmosphere from chimneys, both industrial and domestic, or it may originate from the combustion of mineral oil by motor cars.

An excellent survey of the causes and the properties of artificial pollution has been given by MEETHAM [1952].

In describing artificial pollution we may distinguish between smoke, ash and gaseous pollution. *Smoke* is the term normally applied to the visible products of imperfect combustion. Smoke trails from chimneys may have different lengths according to circumstances but ultimately smoke becomes invisible as a consequence of mixing with the surrounding air. It remains, however, a potential cause of dirt and damage, even then.

The average diameter of a smoke particle is very small, about 0.075 μ for carbon smoke. Consequently smoke particles behave in many respects similarly to gases and their diffusion by the atmosphere may be treated along the same lines. Smoke particles have recently been photographed with the help of the electron microscope (Fig. 10.4).

Ash is the unburnable solid material that escapes from chimneys by the upward currents. The particles are much larger than smoke particles and so they fall out relatively quickly. They, herefore, are especially a nuisance in the direct environment of chimneys. Although particulate pollution is, generally speaking, less harmful to vegetation than some of the gaseous components to be discussed below, its adverse effects on plants cannot be neglected altogether.

Since the second world war radioactive debris, brought into the atmosphere by test explosions of atomic and thermonuclear bombs, has drawn a good deal of attention from meteorologists and biologists.

It may result in undesirable concentrations of certain radioactive isotopes (90 Sr!) in human food.

In addition the increasing number of nuclear reactors may give rise to new pollution problems which the agriculturist cannot neglect.

A discussion of radioactive pollution lies outside the scope of this survey, however.

The most important components of artificial pollution are *gaseous sub-*

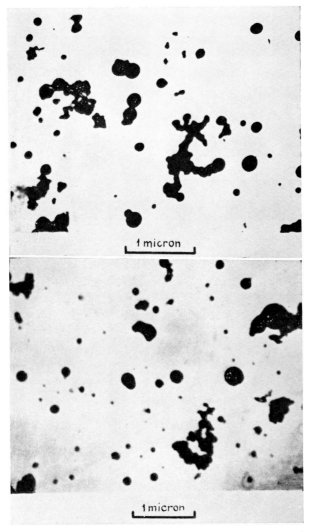

Fig. 10.4. Smoke particles photographed with the help of the electron microscope.
(A. R. Meetham [1950].)

stances. They may or may not give rise to the formation of small droplets due to hygroscopicity. Originally they escape from chimneys or motor cars as gases and as such, although subject to dilution by turbulence, they are easily transported over relatively large distances in the atmosphere.

We mention some of the most common sorts of gaseous pollution. Sulfur dioxide, SO_2, is formed in considerable quantities when coal, coke or certain fuel oils, and to a lesser degree when purified gas or petroleum, are burned, as these products contain sulfur in a quantity of the order of some hundredths of a per cent to some per cents. Although it does not represent the most active part of gaseous pollution, it may do much harm by the comparatively great quantities in which it often is released. It can sometimes be faintly smelt in the open air of industrial towns, where under favorable circumstances its concentration may rise up to several p.p.m. It is especially responsible for the corrosion of metals, a process activated by the oxidation of SO_2 into SO_3. Small drops of concentrated H_2SO_4 solutions may act as artificial condensation nuclei. They are mainly responsible for the high frequency of fog in many industrial areas and cities.

Sulfur may also reach the open air in the form of H_2S. It is very noxious for animals, much less so for plants. It does generally not occur in great amounts, since H_2S readily is transformed into SO_2.

Very noxious for plants as well as for animals are HF and HCl. They also originate in very small quantities from the combustion of coal. Fluorine may escape, however, from superphosphate works as well as from factories manufacturing aluminum and in small amounts from brick factories. The maximum concentration of HF found in cities is about 0.025 p.p.m.

Dangerous oxides of nitrogen are liberated by many chemical processes, e.g. by the combustion of organic matter. Concentrations as high as 0.5 p.p.m. have been found in Los Angeles.

It is clear, that in general chemical works are apt to produce much harmful gaseous pollution. Fortunately most of these gases are themselves chemicals with a certain market value and can easily be removed from the effluent gases.

Only recently a new sort of gaseous pollution that is very noxious for plants has been discovered. Its various components are summed up under the name of "oxidants". These oxidants occur especially during smog situations and then result from the oxidation, by O_3 or nitrogen oxides, of unsaturated hydrocarbons from refined petroleum under the influence of ultraviolet light. It is for this reason that the oxidant level shows a pronounced diurnal variation with a maximum at noon and a decrease to almost zero at 7 p.m.

The concentration of the hydrocarbons, the so-called precursors, not noxious by themselves, may rise in the Los Angeles region during smog situations to about 2 p.p.m.

The smog itself is a very complex mixture of inorganic and organic pollutants of which some 50 have been identified by chemical methods and by the mass spectograph (see for smog composition: Air Pollution Handbook 9, 1956).

A special form of gaseous pollution is CO that occurs in city air in concentrations up to about 55 p.p.m. It is transformed in the atmosphere into CO_2, which occurs in a concentration of about 300 p.p.m. Concentrations may be as high as 600 p.p.m. in industrial areas, however.

Measurements of the CO_2-content of the atmospheric air, made during about 100 years, seem to indicate that the amount of CO_2 has increased during the last half century to an extent that can roughly be explained as due to industry (BRAY [1959]).

10.4. Influence of air pollution on plants

The adverse influence of air pollution on plants has many aspects and it will not be possible to go into detail within the scope of the present chapter. We must distinguish here between particulate and gaseous pollution.

A first obvious result of the presence of particulate pollution is that smoke and other small solid particles in general may do damage by clogging to the stomata.

Probably more important is the effect of particulate pollution on the intensity of solar radiation. A comparison between Boston (Mass.) and the nearby observatory at Blue Hill showed that during the cold season (October through March) the city received in the mean only 82% of the total radiation received at the observatory (HAND [1949]).

Although this percentage will be somewhat higher during the growing season, it may be of great importance due to the selectivity in the reduction of radiation. Especially in the ultraviolet part of the spectrum this reduction is large.

Moreover, large cities or concentrations of factories may cause increased cloudiness which also tends to reduce the insolation at the leeward side of these areas. Fig. 10.5 shows both effects in the London area (VERYARD [1958]).

Soot and ash may cover glasshouses in horticulture districts, again reducing insolation. This effect should be recognized clearly in horticultural districts where artificial heating is applied.

Therefore, although the damage that can be done to plants by particulate pollution can certainly not be ignored, the effects of the gaseous components of air pollution are generally much more serious.

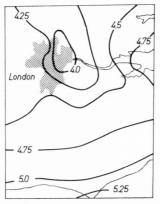

Fig. 10.5. Daily mean of sunshine in the neighborhood of London for the period 1949–1953. (After R. G. VERYARD [1958].)

As to the poisonousness of these components with respect to plants, damage done seems to decrease in the order: HF, HCl, SO_2, NH_3, H_2S. This is a different order than for the animal world as H_2S seems to be the most noxious component for animals and men.

On the other hand different plants show different sensitivity to pollution. Leafy vegetables seem to suffer most, especially from the oxidants of hydro-carbons.

In general the duration of the exposure of the plant to the polluted air seems to be of importance, but a certain maximum concentration may be allowed in many cases for a very long time without any recognizable effects. In order to describe these empirical results in a quantitative way O'GARA [1956] proposed the following law

$$(C - C_0)t = K, \tag{10.3}$$

where C denotes the concentration in p.p.m., t the time in hours and C_0 and K are constants depending on the plant species as well as on the sort of pollution. For example, for alfalfa and SO_2 it has been found by some inves-tigators that $C_0 = 0.33$ and $K = 0.92$ in the case of maximum susceptibility. This equation states that a concentration of 0.33 p.p.m. can be endured indefinitely, whereas on the other hand a concentration of 1.25 p.p.m. causes injury in an hour's time.

O'Gara's law, being rather vague as it remains arbitrary what has to be understood by "injury", has been generalized later so that the time-concentration relationships could be calculated for different degrees of injury. Again for alfalfa and SO_2 the following equations found from experiments are given in Table 10.2.

TABLE 10.2

Time concentration relationships for different degrees of injury

traces of leaf destruction:	$(C - 0.24)$	$t = 0.94$
50% leaf destruction:	$(C - 1.4)$	$t = 2.1$
100% leaf destruction:	$(C - 2.6)$	$t = 3.2$

Obviously O'Gara's constants refer to traces of injury. On the other hand the complexity of the phenomenon is shown by the fact that exposure to 0.10 to 0.20 p.p.m. SO_2 during 25 days had no negative effect or appeared to be even favorable for the development of the plants.

Similar formulas might be obtained for other plants and other pollutants.

It is often possible to connect the extent of leaf destruction due to pollution, with economic crop damage by means of a linear relation

$$y = a - bx, \qquad (10.4)$$

where y is the yield in per cents, a approximates 100% (theoretically it should be 100% exactly), b is a constant and x the extent of leaf destruction, also expressed in per cents.

The Air Pollution Handbook [1956] gives amongst others the following examples of the relation in the case of SO_2, where n is the number of experiments and r the correlation coefficient, a measure for the reliability of the formula in use.

Alfalfa: triple fumigation, subsequently at early, medium and late stages in the growth of the crop:

$$y = 96.6 - 0.75x; \quad n = 12; \quad r = 0.98.$$

Barley; fumigations after heading out began:

$$y = 98 - 0.40x; \quad n = 60; \quad r = 0.74.$$

Wheat; single fumigation:

$$y = 100 - 0.59x; \quad n = 142; \quad r = 0.93.$$

Some other experiments lead to much smaller correlations. As a matter of fact, in applying simple equations like the ones mentioned above, one should never forget that they be assumed to describe exactly the relations between such complicated phenomena like leaf damage and yield.

In all experiments that have been performed in order to find the influence of pollution on the behavior of plants, meteorological circumstances appeared to be of great importance as the gas adsorption by the leaves is controlled by the degree of opening of the stomata. Damage was reduced to a great deal by low temperatures. The same effect was observed when plants rooted in dry soil or were exposed to full sunshine. High relative humidities seem to increase sensitivity. Table 10.3 shows the effect of relative humidity on the sensitivity of various plants to SO_2 as found by O'GARA [1956a].

But also other than meteorological conditions play a rôle. Young plants often show greater resistance than old ones. Experiments with about 0.05 p.p.m. hydrofluoric acid gas showed that young as well as old leaves were more resistant to damage than middle-aged leaves.

A solution of HF in water gave rise to damage at values of 0.01 p.p.m. Wetting of the leaves did not result in more damage done.

The few foregoing examples may show that the effect of air pollution on plants is a very complicated one. It is almost impossible, therefore, to give any quantitative rule for the relative susceptibility of different plants for pollutants.

From various investigations it seems as if alfalfa, barley, endive and cotton are most sensitive for SO_2, gladiolus, azalea, prune and tulip for HF, whereas leafy vegetables, such as endive and spinach, may suffer great damage from smog.

TABLE 10.3

Effect of relative humidity on sensitivity to SO_2

Relative humidity	Relative sensitivity
100	1.00
80	0.89
60	0.77
40	0.54
20	0.18
0	0.10

It can be stated, however, that much research in the field as well as by means of fumigation chambers will still be needed before we will have a sufficient insight into the problem.

10.5. Measuring methods for particulate pollution

Measuring pollution in the atmosphere is a very complicated procedure. Distinction has to be made between the measurement of particulate and gaseous pollution.

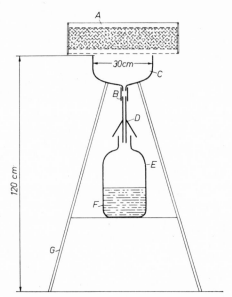

Fig. 10.6. Deposit gauge. (From L. McCabe [1952].)
A = Bird shield.
B = Rubber tubing.
C = Glass collecting bowl.
D = Inverted funnel.
E = Collecting bottle, 10 litres.
F = Rain water with solids in solution and suspension.
G = Stand.

One of the best known procedures to measure particulate pollution is by means of the so-called *deposit gauge* (Fig. 10.6). It has been developed in Great Britain but is now in use in many countries. It consists of a glass collecting bowl about 30 cm in diameter. The material deposited into the bowl, including rain, is collected in a bottle of 10 litres capacity.

The material collected (usually during a month) is divided into water, dissolved material and undissolved matter. The volume of the water is measured and its *p*H determined. Undissolved matter is separated by decanting and filtration, dried, weighed and further analyzed as far as possible.

Although the instrument shows limitations—it only measures the particles that are subject to fall-out or wash-out by precipitation—it seems to permit to a satisfactory degree the measurement of particulate pollution in a simple way.

Other instruments equally simple to handle, such as the so-called *Liegean sphere*, a sphere covered with vaseline on which particulate pollution sticks, seem to give less satisfactory results. For example the amount of matter caught depends strongly on the wind. However, using a number of such spheres, a comparison between various places may be possible.

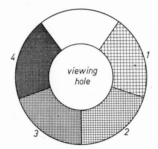

Fig. 10.7. Ringelmann chart for estimating the greyness of smoke.

Measurement of the thickness of smoke can be made by the so-called *Ringelmann chart* (Fig. 10.7). It may consists of five more or less shaded areas representing gradations: 0 is completely white, and the intervening ones increase in greyness by about 25 per cent, so that 4 is completely black.

As the blackness of smoke depends on its carbon content and on its steam content, as well as on wind and turbulence and the type of background, its measurement by comparing it with the *Ringelmann chart* gives only a superficial idea of the amount of particulate pollution leaving a stack.

Owens' dust counter is an example of a small instrument that can be used for incidental measurements. It consists in principle of a small hand pump by means of which air is forced through a filter. The intensity of the stain formed on the filter by pollution is visually compared with a calibrated scale of shades. The instrument may be automatized in such a way that periodically a smoke stain is formed on a circular sheet of filter paper, turning a few degrees or at a tape moving a small distance at regular intervals. The disk or tape is examined by transmitted or reflected light after exposure. Instruments of this kind are very suitable to investigate the diurnal variation of the dust content of urban atmospheres.

Other methods involve sampling by *thermal* and by *electrostatic* precipitation. The first method is based on the fact that dust particles are repulsed from a hot surface, so that they can be collected on the opposite cold surface. Thermal precipitators have very high collection efficiencies, especially for particles less than 1μ in size. As a consequence of the necessarily small dimensions of the sampling room they sample at a small rate which may be a disadvantage (Air Pollution Handbook [1956], section 10.1.3.).

One can distinguish between alternating and direct current electrostatic precipitators. In both instruments the polluted air is blown through a cylindrical electrode in the axis of which a wire is acting as second electrode. A voltage of about 10^4 then forces particulate pollution to be collected on both or in the case of direct current on one of the electrodes. Modern instruments use a 110 V alternating current or a 6 V direct current. Electrostatic dust collectors may obtain efficiencies of 100% (BARNES [1956]). They have the disadvantage, however, that sparking may occur and therefore they should not be used in explosive atmospheres.

Other relatively simple instruments, called *impactors*, are based on the fact that when rapidly flowing air is forced to change its direction of flow, particles contained in the air will try to continue to move in the original direction (Air Pollution Handbook [1956], section 10.1.3).

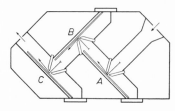

Fig. 10.8. Scheme of the Sonkin impactor. Particulate matter is deposited in A, B and C.

Figure 10.8, representing a sketch of the so-called *Sonkin* impactor, shows the principle clearly. Particles are collected on glass plates in the points A, B and C. Impactors of this kind are very easy to handle but they are not particularly efficient in collecting particles under $1\ \mu$ in diameter. By giving the jets different speeds, particles can be classified according to size.

Sampling of dust should always be *isokinetic*, at least as far as possible. Isokinetic sampling occurs when the suspension enters the orifice of the sampling device without any disturbance or acceleration. When the air is sucked into the instrument orifice with a greater velocity than exists in the ambient air, streamlines will converge towards the instrument, the air taking with it the smaller particles whereas the larger ones will not or only partly follow. It is clear that this will lead to an underestimation of the dust content of the air.

10.6. Measuring methods for gaseous pollution

The measurement of gaseous pollution is even more complicated in general (MEETHAM [1952]). We restrict ourselves to some examples.

Of great importance is the measurement of sulfur dioxide in the atmosphere. By chemical analysis of the dust collected in a deposit gauge a rough impression of the amount of SO_2 can be gained, but this method is not sufficiently accurate.

Other measuring devices of SO_2 relate to two different aspects of damage done by this gas:

(i) the rate at which the gas will attack sheltered surfaces including internal walls of buildings and

(ii) the concentration of SO_2 in the air breathed by men, animals and plants.

To get an impression of the first effect, the atmospheric SO_2 has to be absorbed by a solid surface in much the same way as it is absorbed by building stone. Usually the surface used for this measurement is composed of lead peroxide, reacting with SO_2 according to the equation

$$PbO_2 + SO_2 = PbSO_4.$$

The amount of $PbSO_4$ produced during the time of exposure can be determined by chemical analysis.

Although many difficulties due to the effect of humidity (rain), temperature, wind direction, etc. must be overcome in carrying out the measurement, the method finds wide application and seems to be the one most in use at the moment.

Of much more importance for the agriculturist is the measurement of the concentration of SO_2 in the air. This is generally done by a bubbler method by which a known quantity of air is drawn through a bubbler containing a dilute solution of hydrogen peroxide. All the sulfur dioxide is effectively removed from the air bubbles according to the reaction

$$H_2O_2 + SO_2 \rightleftharpoons H_2SO_4.$$

The amount of H_2SO_4 is measured by comparing the pH of the solution before and after the exposure to the air. In order to make reliable measurements possible, small amounts of alkali are added to the solution of H_2O_2.

Usually the bubbler is preceded by a smoke filter which absorbs SO_2 only to a negligible extent.

In general the errors of the volumetric sulfur dioxide method are very small. The standard deviation has been estimated to be about 3 per cent of the average concentration of SO_2.

Recording instruments based on similar principles have been developed and are commercially available.

Similar instruments are in use for measuring other contaminants of the air.

The most sensitive analytical methods to determine the concentration of *fluorides* are based on color reactions caused by the fluoride.

A relatively simple method to determine differences in the fluoride content of the air, at least qualitatively, is employed in the Netherlands.

Filter paper impregnated by $Ca(OH)_2$ is placed in screens in order to protect it against the influence of sun and rain.

HF in the air reacts with $CA(CH)_2$ according to

$$Ca(OH)_2 + 2HF \rightleftharpoons CaF_2 + 2H_2O.$$

After exposure, normally during a month, the paper is dried and ashed. Then by adding H_2SO_4 and SiO_2, SiF_4 is obtained after which the fluoride content is measured by a normal colorimetric method.

10.7. Diffusion of pollution in the atmosphere

It will be clear from the foregoing sections that it is worth while for the agriculturist to try to estimate the ground concentrations that are to be expected as a consequence of the presence of sources of pollution in the environment.

These ground concentrations will depend on a number of parameters, the exact influence of most of which is generally difficult to estimate.

We mention the following ones:

(i) Strength of the source; dilution of the waste material in the chimney.

(ii) Height and dimensions of the source (e.g. diameter of the orifice, many stacks close together acting simultaneously as one big source).

(iii) The properties of the waste material (e.g. fall velocity of particulate pollution, disintegration of radioactive material, excess temperature of waste gases).

(iv) The diffusion of the waste material in the atmosphere, depending on wind structure and stability of the relevant air layers.

(v) The influence of the earth's surface on the air motion.

Most theories take these parameters into account only to a very limited extent.

As to (i) it is customary to treat the problem as if the pollution escaped from a point source. With regard to (ii), only the height H of the source is taken into account in most cases. Next, with respect to (iii) it is assumed in general that the waste gases have the same density as the environmental air. Fall velocities of particles are in some cases introduced by adding a correction term. Some results have been obtained recently by introducing the influence of the temperature of the waste gases on ground concentrations. (iv) The influence of the atmosphere is included by allowing variations in certain constants, occurring in the usual formulas describing the diffusion. Finally, (v), the effect of the earth's surface is mostly introduced in a more or less qualitative way.

We now give an elementary introduction to the diffusion theories mostly in use. For a thorough physical treatment see F. PASQUILL [1962].

Assume a point source in $x = 0$, $y = 0$, $z = 0$, continuously emitting pollution drifting away horizontally in the x-direction with the mean wind, U, supposed to be constant with time. Due to atmospheric turbulence the plume will spread irregularly, but by sampling over a sufficiently large time interval a more or less constant distribution of the contaminant may be obtained (Fig. 10.9).

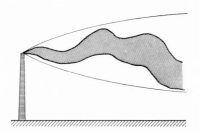

Fig. 10.9. Momentary position of smoke plume compared with average distribution of the contaminant.

Assume further that this constant distribution is similar in all cross sections perpendicular to the mean wind direction for $x > 0$.

Assume that this distribution can formally be written as

$$\chi(x,y,z) = f(x)\, g(x,y)\, h(x,z), \qquad (10.5)$$

where $\chi(x,y,z)$ is the concentration of the pollution in the point x,y,z, expressed e.g. in mg m^{-3} or in p.p.m., $f(x)$ is a function describing the variation of χ

along the axis of the plume as a function of x, and $g(x,y)$ and $h(x,z)$ describe the distributions in the y- and z-directions respectively. The fact that x is included in the functions g and h indicates that certain parameters, contained in the distribution laws, may depend on the distance from the source.

From the definition of $f(x)$ it follows that $g(x,y)$ and $h(x,z)$ must be unity for $y = 0$ and $z = 0$ respectively. On the other hand concentrations will be zero for $y = \pm \infty$ and $z = +\infty$.

Two different assumptions for $g(x,y)$ and $h(x,z)$ have been introduced in order to solve the problem of giving an adequate description of the behavior of a plume in the atmosphere over a sufficiently long period.

BOSANQUET and PEARSON [1936] as early as 1930 proposed

$$\chi_{\mathrm{BP}}(x,y,z) = f(x) \exp\left[-\frac{y^2}{R_y{}^2}\right] \exp\left[-\frac{|z|}{R_z}\right], \qquad (10.6a)$$

where R_y and R_z are functions of x, whereas SUTTON [1947] introduced normal distributions in both the y- and z-directions

$$\chi_{\mathrm{S}}(x,y,z) = f(x) \exp\left[-\frac{y^2}{R_y{}^2}\right] \exp\left[-\frac{z^2}{R_z{}^2}\right], \qquad (10.6b)$$

R_y and R_z again being functions of the distance from the source.

The principle difference between the two solutions lies in the assumption

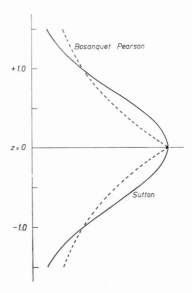

Fig. 10.10. Vertical distribution of pollution in a smoke plume according to Sutton and to Bosanquet and Pearson (z is expressed in R_z as unit).

with respect to the distribution of pollution in the vertical direction. It seems that Sutton's approach, assuming normal distributions in both directions, is to be preferred (see Fig. 10.10).

It is obvious that $f(x)$ is connected with $g(x,y)$ and $h(x,z)$. The total flux of pollution through any plane x = constant must of necessity equal the production by the source per unit time Q. Or

$$Q = U \int_{-\infty}^{+\infty} \int_{-\infty}^{+\infty} \chi(x,y,z)\, dy\, dz = U \int_{-\infty}^{+\infty} \int_{-\infty}^{+\infty} f(x)\, g(x,y)\, h(x,z)\, dy\, dz. \qquad (10.7)$$

Performing the integration, we find for Bosanquet's and Pearson's solution and for Sutton's

$$\chi_{BP}(x,y,z) = \frac{Q}{2(\sqrt{\pi})\, R_y R_z U} \exp\left[-\frac{y^2}{R_y{}^2}\right] \exp\left[-\frac{|z|}{R_z}\right], \qquad (10.8a)$$

$$\chi_{S}(x,y,z) = \frac{Q}{\pi\, R_y R_z U} \exp\left[-\frac{y^2}{R_y{}^2}\right] \exp\left(-\frac{z^2}{R_z{}^2}\right). \qquad (10.8b)$$

A second difference between both solutions lies in the assumed relation between the parameters R_y and R_z and the distance x downwind.

According to Bosanquet and Pearson, $R_y = (q\sqrt{2})\, x$ and $R_z = px$, p and q being constants depending on atmospheric conditions, e.g. stability.

According to Sutton, $R_y = C_y x^{1-\frac{1}{2}n}$, and $R_z = C_z x^{1-\frac{1}{2}n}$, C_y, C_z and n again being constants connected with atmospheric conditions.

Introducing the relevant expressions for R_y and R_z in (10.8a) and (10.8b) we find

$$\chi_{BP}(x,y,z) = \frac{Q}{2(\sqrt{\pi})\, pqx^2\, U} \exp\left[-\frac{y^2}{2(qx)^2} - \frac{|z|}{px}\right], \qquad (10.9a)$$

according to Bosanquet and Pearson and

$$\chi_{S}(x,y,z) = \frac{Q}{\pi C_y C_z\, x^{2-n}\, U} \exp\left[-\frac{1}{x^{2-n}}\left(\frac{y^2}{C_y{}^2} + \frac{z^2}{C_z{}^2}\right)\right], \qquad (10.9b)$$

according to Sutton.

In (10.9a) and (10.9b) no account has been taken of the earth's surface. This can be done qualitatively by the method of images. It consists of adding a virtual source at the height $-H$, with H the height of the real source above the ground (Fig. 10.11).

The increase of concentrations in the air due to the (assumed) impermeability of the earth's surface is then obtained by addition of the concentrations caused by both sources. The method is not exact as the influence of the surface on the wind velocity U is not taken into account. It may be of interest to observe that the neglect of the vertical windshear in the final equations (although considered by Sutton in a certain stage of his theory) is the weak point of all these heuristic diffusion theories (SMITH [1957]).

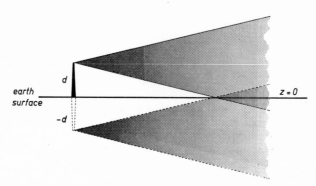

Fig. 10.11. Illustration of mirror principle. The earth's surface is supposed to reflect all pollution.

Applying the procedure described above and taking $z = 0$ at earth's surface, we get

$$\chi_{BP}(x,y,z) = \frac{Q \exp\left[-y^2/2(qx)^2\right]}{2(\sqrt{2\pi})\,pqx^2\,U} \exp\left[-\frac{|z-H|}{px} - \frac{|z+H|}{px}\right], \quad (10.10a)$$

and

$$\chi_{S}(x,y,z) = \frac{Q \exp\left[-y^2/C_y^2 x^{2-n}\right]}{\pi\,C_y\,C_z\,x^{2-n}\,U} \exp\left[-\frac{(z-H)^2 + (z+H)^2}{C_z^2\,x^{2-n}}\right]. \quad (10.10b)$$

For $z = 0$ we find the ground concentrations

$$\chi_{BP}(x,y,z) = \frac{Q \exp\left[-y^2/2(qx)^2\right]}{(\sqrt{2\pi})\,pqx^2\,U} \exp\left[-\frac{H}{px}\right], \quad (10.11a)$$

and

$$\chi_{S}(x,y,0) = \frac{2Q \exp\left[-y^2/C_y^2 x^{2-n}\right]}{\pi\,C_y\,C_z\,x^{2-n}\,U} \exp\left[-\frac{H^2}{C_z^2\,x^{2-n}}\right]. \quad (10.11b)$$

These are the relations that are generally used to compute, or more precisely to estimate concentrations that may occur at ground level due to the presence of a continuous point source at an elevation H.

Both relations show the same general characteristics. In the first place, the largest ground concentrations are found in the downwind direction, $\exp\left[-y^2/2(qx)^2\right]$ and $\exp\left[-y^2/C_y^2 x^{2-n}\right]$ being unity along the x-axis.

Second, ground concentrations along the x-axis are zero for $x = 0$ as well as for $x = \infty$ so that there must exist a maximum value at some distance x_{max} from the source. This distance can easily be found from $\partial\chi(x,0,0)/\partial x = 0$ and amounts to $H/2p$ for Bosanquet and Pearson's and to $(H^2/C_z^2)^{1/(2-n)}$ for Sutton's theory.

Substituting these values for x_{max} into (10.11a) and (10.11b), respectively, we find the maximum ground concentrations according to both theories to be

$$\chi_{max\ BP} = \frac{4Q}{(\sqrt{2\pi})e^2\,UH^2}\frac{P}{q} = 0.215\frac{Q}{UH^2}\frac{P}{q}, \qquad (10.12a)$$

and

$$\chi_{max\ S} = \frac{2Q}{\pi e\,UH^2}\frac{C_z}{C_y} = 0.235\frac{Q}{UH^2}\frac{C_z}{C_y}. \qquad (10.12b)$$

Obviously both theories give comparable maximum ground concentrations, provided that $p/q \approx z/C_y$. From the expressions for x_{max} it is in principle possible to connect p with C_z and n in such a way that the distance from the stack where the maximum occurs is also correctly indicated by both theories. The most striking result found so far is the fact that the maximum concentrations are inversely proportional to the square of the stack height according to both theories.

As Sutton's theory is doubtless the more realistic one of the two, we henceforth restrict ourselves to this one. We therefore omit the index S from now on.

10.8. Some numerical results

Dimensional analysis (SCHMIDT [1957]) shows that the value of n in (10.11b) lies between 0 and 1, the latter value pertaining to extremely stable conditions, the former to extreme instability. According to Sutton $n = 0.25$ must be considered as an acceptable value for normal atmospheric circumstances.

From empirical results the "generalized diffusion coefficients" C_y and C_z are found to be of an order of magnitude of $0.1\ m^{\frac{1}{2}n}$ ($0.13\ ft^{1/8} = 0.11\ m^{1/8}$ at a height of 30 m for $n = 0.25$ according to Sutton).

Fig. 10.12 shows the distribution of ground concentrations expressed in $10^{-6}Q$ for a stack height of 100 m, $n = 0.25$ and $C_y = C_z = 0.1\ m^{1/8}$. U is taken to be 1 m sec^{-1}. Concentrations at other wind velocities can be computed by dividing U according to (10.11b).

It is worth while to discuss Sutton's constants C_y, C_z and n somewhat more in detail.

The constant n was connected by Sutton with the vertical windprofile, written as a power of the height above the ground,

$$U = U_1 \left(\frac{z}{z_1}\right)^{n/(2-n)}, \tag{10.13}$$

U, being the wind velocity at the reference level z_1.

Adopting the value $\frac{1}{7}$ for $n/(2-n)$ as normal we find $n = 0.25$, the value mentioned above. Very large stability would involve a linear increase of wind velocity with height, or $n = 1$, whereas extreme instability would lead to a constant wind velocity or $n = 0$, the same values as found by dimensional reasoning.

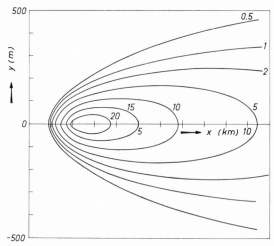

Fig. 10.12. Ground concentrations expressed in $10^{-6} Q$ for a stack height of 100 m; $n = 0.25$; $C_y = C_z = 0.1$ m$^{1/8}$; $U = 1$ m sec^{-1}.

Although recent investigations (BARAD and HAUGEN [1959]) have made it plausible that no simple connection as proposed by Sutton exists between n and the vertical windprofile, this may not influence the maximum and minimum values 1 and 0.

With respect to the so-called generalized diffusion coefficients C_y and C_z, Sutton assumed that they both tend to decrease with increasing height and with increasing stability, both constants having the same value above about 25 m. Apart from the fact that this last assumption does not hold in the case of inversions, the whole concept leads to difficulties when again we consider real stacks.

In order to illustrate this we return to the relations $C_y = R_y x^{\frac{1}{2}n-1}$ and $C_z = R_z x^{\frac{1}{2}n-1}$.

Let us assume that the plume escaping from the orifice bends over immediately and that at a very short distance from the stack $R_y = R_z R_0$ R_0 being of the order of magnitude of the radius of the orifice. This means that a virtual point source must be introduced at a distance $-x_0$ on the windward side of the stack so that $C_y = C_z = C = R_0 x_0^{\frac{1}{2}n-1}$.

From this relation an estimate of C could be made if x_0 could be connected with R_0. Such a connection has only been found for the case of a jet escaping in a vertical direction from a horizontal nozzle, which can be described quantitatively by assuming a vertical point source, at a distance $x_0 \approx 8\ R_0$ below the orifice (SCHMIDT [1957]).

Tentatively we adopt the same relation $x_0 \approx 8\ R_0$ for the case of the horizontal plume, so that we may put $C = 8^{\frac{1}{2}n-1}\ R_0^{\frac{1}{2}n}$.

On the other hand we assume that for a normal stack $H = k R_0$, H being the stack height, where we take $k = 70$.[*] Or, $C \approx (\frac{1}{8})(\frac{1}{9})^{\frac{1}{2}n}\ H^{\frac{1}{2}n}$.

Table 10.4 shows C as a function of H and n according to these assumptions. As a matter of fact the values of C from this table can at best be considered of the right order of magnitude.

TABLE 10.4

The constant C as a function of H and n

n \ H	10	20	30	40	50	100	150
0.0	0.125	0.125	0.125	0.125	0.125	0.125	0.125
0.2	0.126	0.135	0.141	0.145	0.148	0.159	0.166
0.4	0.128	0.147	0.159	0.168	0.176	0.202	0.219
0.6	0.129	0.159	0.179	0.195	0.209	0.257	0.291
0.8	0.130	0.172	0.202	0.227	0.248	0.327	0.385
1.0	0.132	0.186	0.228	0.263	0.295	0.417	0.510

It follows from Table 10.4 that C increases with increasing height and increasing stability, a result opposite to the one obtained by Sutton. The difference is due to the fact that in the present treatment account has been taken of the real dimensions of the stack (at least approximately) so that the point source is situated on the windward side of the real source (a distance

---

[*] Calculated as an average value from 56 industrial stacks in the Netherlands, the standard deviation amounting to 22 m.

of about 17 m in the case of a chimney with a height of 150 m). By the way, apart from the case $n = 0$, the exact value of the proportionality factor R_0/x_0 has only a minor influence on the value of C, so that the present values seem to be relatively reliable.

Table 10.5 shows the maximum concentration χ_{max} of a pollutant, e.g. SO_2, at ground level in 10^{-3} g m^{-3} and the distance x_{max} from the stack where the maximum occurs, both in dependence of H and n and for a wind velocity U of 1 m sec^{-1}.

$C = C_y = C_z$ has been taken in accordance with Table 10.4. Q is assumed to be 1 g sec^{-1}.

For other values of U the maximum concentration is obtained by multiplying the value from the table by $1/U$. x_{max} does not depend on U. Higher values of Q result in proportionally higher values of χ_{max}. In the case of SO_2 multiplication by 0.83 gives the concentration in p.p.m.

TABLE 10.5

Maximum concentration of pollant (10^{-1} g m^{-3}) at ground level as a function of H and n

n \ H		10	20	30	40	50	100	150	units
0	max	2.345	0.588	0.262	0.147	0.094	0.024	0.010	10^{-6} g m^{-3}
	x_{max}	79	158	237	316	394	789	1183	m
0.2	max	2.345	0.588	0.262	0.147	0.094	0.024	0.010	10^{-6} g m^{-3}
	x_{max}	128	255	383	511	637	1276	1913	m
0.4	max	2.345	0.588	0.262	0.147	0.094	0.024	0.010	10^{-6} g m^{-3}
	x_{max}	232	464	696	928	1160	2320	3479	m
0.6	max	2.345	0.588	0.262	0.147	0.094	0.024	0.010	10^{-6} g m^{-3}
	x_{max}	499	999	1497	2003	2494	4991	7486	m
0.8	max	2.345	0.588	0.262	0.147	0.094	0.024	0.010	10^{-6} g m^{-3}
	x_{max}	1383	2768	4152	5534	6917	13158	20748	m
1.0	max	2.345	0.588	0.262	0.147	0.094	0.024	0.010	10^{-6} g m^{-3}
	x_{max}	5756	11524	17280	23040	28799	57580	86387	m

The table gives rise to some remarks. With growing values of n, i.e. growing stability, the distance from the stack where the maximum concentration occurs, increases, the maximum itself remaining the same, depending as it does on the height of the stack only. This result can be understood qualitatively in the following way. Growing stability means that the plume (considered to have definite boundaries for the moment) is reduced to a cone with smaller aperture. It reaches the earth at a greater distance from the stack but with the same radius, notably H! And it is this radius that determines exclusively the concentration at ground level. (It should be borne in mind that Table 10.5 is based on the assumption that turbulence, in spite of stability, remains isotropic!)

Table 10.5 can be used as a preliminary guide for decisions with respect to the possibilities of growing specific plants in the neighborhood of industries. It appears, for example, that no alfalfa ($C_0 = 0.33$ p.p.m., see formula (10.3)) should be grown in the neighborhood of a stack of 25 m high from which 1 g SO_2 escapes per second. By the way, 1 g $\sec^{-1}$ SO_2 is brought into the air by burning about 30 g of ordinary coal per second, i.e. 0.1 ton per hour.

10.9. Modifications of the theory, stack height

Figure 10.13 shows a qualitative picture of damage done by SO_2 and HF during the summer of 1954 in the province of North Holland. The damage was probably due to a steel plant to the west of Amsterdam.

It is seen from the figure that the damage pattern shows the general form predicted by Sutton's theory, the maximum damage occurring in a north-easterly direction, seen from the center of the steelworks. Only the lateral dimensions of the pattern are larger than those in Fig. 10.12 due to the fact that obviously during a whole season the wind direction fluctuates considerably.

Such fluctuations of wind direction will, generally speaking, have a diminishing effect on the maximum concentrations found at ground level. To take account of this effect the following expression for this maximum concentration has been proposed

$$\chi_{\text{max}} = \frac{2Q}{\pi e H^2} \left(\frac{a_m}{U} \right) \tag{10.14}$$

where a_m is the frequency with which the dominant wind direction occurs during periods of ten minutes. Obviously a_m replaces C_z/C_y and must therefore be considered as a measure for stability (LOWRY [1951]).

GIFFORD [1959] made a similar approach by assuming a normal distribution of the wind directions around its mean value. The wind fluctuations result in a stronger lateral diffusion leading to lower maximum concentrations.

Generally speaking, it can be stated that it is the consequence of fluctuations in wind direction that makes a difference whether the sampling period is a short one (e.g., 3 min as in Sutton's experiments) or a longer one.

This difference must be taken into account when adopting values for the constants *C* and *n*.

A second remark can be made with reference to Fig. 10.13. The damage

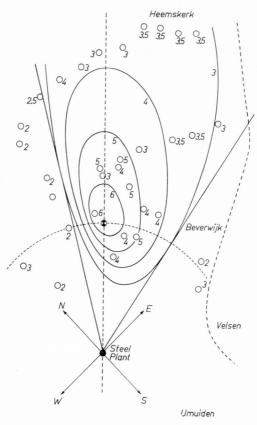

Fig. 10.13. Qualitative picture of damage done by air pollution to vegetation north of a steel plant in the Netherlands. Damage is estimated according to an arbitrary scale, 6 denoting maximum damage.

pattern shows that on the average the maximum concentration at the ground occurred at a distance of some 2200 m from the centre of the steel industry that was held responsible for the damage. The average stack height was about 60 m, so that according to Table 6.5 the mean value of *n* should have been about 0.5. This is an improbably high value for the summer season, especially near the coast as on the average stability will only be small there. The apparent inconsistency can be removed by taking account of the fact that the waste gases escape from the chimneys with a temperature some 300 °C in excess of that of the environmental air. This excess temperature causes stack gases to rise above the level of the stack's orifice due to buoyancy, so that the so-called *effective stack height* (i.e. the height of the plume's axis) may be some tens of meters more than the real stack height.

Assuming an effective stack height of 120 m, which may be of the right order of magnitude, the value of x_{max} can be explained by taking $n = 0.35$, a reasonable value for the wet summer of 1954.

Many attempts have been made to compute the effective stack height as a function of the exit velocity and the excess temperature of the stack gases. It will be clear that the ultimate height reached by a plume will also depend on the wind velocity and the thermal structure of the atmosphere, high wind speeds and thermal stability tending to decrease the effective stack height.

As to the influence of stability it can be stated that a plume will be able to rise in a stable atmosphere only as long as its temperature is higher than that of the environmental air. A large exit velocity of waste gases that have the same temperature as the surrounding air will only result in an increase of plume height when the atmosphere is in indifferent or unstable equilibrium. This being relatively seldom the case except during the afternoon hours, a large exit velocity in itself will generally be of little effect in diminishing the adverse influence of air pollution, as the plume will have a tendency to sink back to the level of the orifice. The only thing that happens when stack gases emerge with large velocities into the atmosphere is a thorough mixing with the air, resulting in a decrease of concentration above the orifice and eventually an artificial decrease of Sutton's constant n. The concentration of noxious pollution can be adequately diminished already in the stack by adding large quantities of clean air. The procedure is a common one at atomic reactors. Of course, the supply of air will result in an increased exit velocity. In that case R_0 (as far as a single value R_0 is adequate in these circumstances) will be substantially larger than the radius of the orifice. Consequently the value of x_0 will be larger and, therefore, as x is measured from the virtual point source, smaller concentrations in the axis of the plume will result according to (10.9b).

Apart from a slight increase in H, the effect on χ_{max} is small, however.

An important increase of the plume height H can only be effected by a high temperature of the waste gases.

It may be clear from the foregoing that the problem of the rise of stack gases in the atmosphere is a rather complicated one. Several investigators introduced models in order to describe the phenomenon mathematically.

However, no absolutely satisfying solution has been found so far (MAGILL, *et al.* [1956]; U.S. Atomic Energy Commission [1955]; SCHMIDT [1957]).

On the other hand, when the pollutant has a higher density than the environmental air the effective stack height may be less than the real height of the orifice above the ground. The most important cases are those when particulate matter escapes from the stack and when stack gases are effectively washed in order to remove as much of the harmful constituents as possible, as is often done with respect to HF. In the latter case the effluent gases may contain large quantities of water droplets which will evaporate when the outer air is relatively dry. The evaporation results in a cooling of the effluent plume (about 2 °C per g water per m³ air) which, therefore, may become cooler and consequently denser than the environmental air sink towards the ground. It follows that washing, which will never lead to a 100 per cent removal of the constituent in question, is not in all cases favorable.

With respect to the downward motion of particulate pollution, CSANADY [1955] modified Sutton's formulas by substituting

$$H^* = H[1 - (f/u)(x/H)] \tag{10.15}$$

for H where f is the velocity of free fall for the particles concerned. Further, he modified the concept of the image stack in order to obtain a dust deposition rate equal to $c_0 f$, c_0 being the concentration of dust particles at ground level.

TABLE 10.6

Fall velocity of spherical particles of density 2.5 under normal atmospheric conditions (After U.S. Atomic Energy Commission [1955])

Radius (μ)	Fall velocity (cm/sec)
20	3
40	12
60	24
80	37
100	52
200	130
400	290
600	440
800	600
1000	700

Table 10.6 shows the fall velocities of spherical particles of density 2.5 under normal atmospheric conditions. Effective stack heights H^* can be easily computed from this table and formula (10.15).

10.10. Modifications of the theory, influence of the atmosphere

Plumes escaping from a stack's orifice into the atmosphere may show quite a different behavior from one day to the next. These differences are for the greater part connected with the thermal structure of the atmosphere (Fig. 10.14).

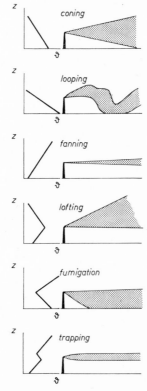

Fig. 10.14. Plume behavior in relation to stability conditions in the lower atmosphere.

Up to now we have assumed that a plume moves as a symmetric cone along the mean wind direction, the aperture of the cone depending on the degree of turbulence in the atmosphere. This case, called *coning*, occurs during situations with moderate vertical temperature lapse rates, say when $\partial T/\partial z$ lies between -0.4 and $-0.8\,°C/100$ m, T being the air temperature and z the height.

The symmetry of the plume is due to the fact that under these circumstances turbulence will be almost isotropic (apart from very close to the earth's surface) resulting in substantially the same broadening of the plume in all directions with increasing distance from the source.

For larger temperature lapse rates, notable for $\Gamma > \Gamma^{\mathrm{ad}}$ (unstable atmosphere) irregular vertical as well as horizontal motions of relatively large air parcels will cause a more or less strong meandering of the plume resulting among others in downward motions of the waste gases now and then (*looping*). This may lead to short-lasting high concentrations at the ground.

It is especially under these circumstances that a high exit velocity of the stack gases is favorable, as due to the atmosphere's instability these gases will continue to move upwards even if their temperature is not higher than that of the environment.

The next possibility is that the atmosphere shows a very stable stratification in the lowest layers but at least high above the stack orifice. This situation occurs during inversions, i.e. when the temperature increases with height.

The vertical turbulent velocity component of the wind will then in general be smaller than the horizontal one. Consequently a plume will flatten gradually with growing distance from the source (*fanning*).

Putting

$$C_y = R_{y1}\left(\frac{1}{x_1}\right)^{1-\frac{1}{2}n} \quad \text{and} \quad C_z = R_{z1}\left(\frac{1}{x_1}\right)^{1-\frac{1}{2}n},$$

x_1 referring to a point at a short distance from the orifice (but where the plume is already substantially horizontal), it is immediately clear that no flattening is possible without introducing two values n_y and n_z instead of the one value n proposed by Sutton.

From

$$R_y = R_{y1}\left(\frac{x}{x_1}\right)^{1-\frac{1}{2}n_y} \quad \text{and} \quad R_z = R_{z1}\left(\frac{x}{x_1}\right)^{1-\frac{1}{2}n_z}$$

respectively, it follows that in the case of fanning, i.e. in a stable atmosphere, n_z must be n_y. The fact that n_y need not equal n_z has been shown experimentally during the Prairie Grass Project (BARAD and HAUGEN [1959]).

Applying the procedure of section 10.7 ($\partial \chi(x,0,0)/\partial x = 0$) we find for the maximum concentration at the earth's surface and for the distance from the source at which this maximum concentration is found, respectively

$$\chi_{max} = \frac{2Q}{\pi R_{y1} R_{z1} U} \left[\frac{R_{z1}^2}{H^2} \alpha \right]^\alpha \exp[-\alpha], \tag{10.16}$$

$$x_{max} = x_1 \left[\frac{H^2}{R_{z1}^2} \frac{1}{\alpha} \right]^{1/(2-n_z)}, \tag{10.17}$$

with $\alpha = [2 - \frac{1}{2}(n_y + n_z)]/(2 - n_z)$.

The result shows that with $n_z > n_y$ the maximum concentration due to a single stack $(R_{z1} \ll H)$ is smaller than that predicted by Sutton with $n_y = n_z = n$. This is in accordance with experimental results (SMITH [1951], SCHMIDT [1960]).

Further interesting situations occur when stable and unstable, neutral or indifferent layers $(\Gamma = \Gamma^{ad})$ are adjacent in the relevant part of the atmosphere.

As a first example we mention *lofting*. It occurs when an inversion between the ground and a level below the stack orifice (ground inversion) hampers the downward diffusion of the waste gases, whereas the diffusion upwards can take place unopposed in the upper layer.

Second, it is possible that an inversion starts just above the stack's orifice, the lower layer being in almost indifferent equilibrium. This case is the opposite of the foregoing one, more pollution than normal being diffused towards the earth's surface (*fumigation*).

Assuming that the inversion above the stack acts as an absolute barrier, we can again apply the method of images by introducing two mirrors now, one in the earth's surface and one in the bottom of the inversion.

The most important result of the relative computations is, that in case of a strong inversion just above the orifice the maximum concentration at the ground is doubled.

Situations with relatively low lying strong inversions occur frequently, especially during the morning hours. They must be considered as highly unfavorable from the agriculturist's point of view.

Finally a normal or indifferent layer almost at stack height may be embedded between two inversions, e.g. the lower one being a ground inversion. Then the waste gases will remain principally enclosed within the layer between the two inversions (*trapping*).

Apart from the fact that the earth's surface acts as a barrier to the waste gases, it also influences the air flow, especially when obstacles are present.

Buildings, for example, induce a certain degree of turbulence on the wind and so do other obstacles like trees, dunes, small hills etc. Consequently, the diffusion of stack gases will be stronger in the neighborhood of such obstacles than it would have been over flat country. This may result, for example, in a decrease of Sutton's parameters C_y and C_z with growing distance from factory buildings (STEWART et al. [1957]).

Special attention should be drawn, therefore, to the geometry of a stack in connection with the structures surrounding it, the latter tending to increase the degree of turbulence, causing eventually downward diffusion of stack gases leading to higher ground concentrations at short distances of the stack.

Apart from increased diffusion unfavorable dimensioning of buildings and stack may cause a general downward motion of the stack gases at the lee side of the buildings, so that the effective stack height becomes smaller than the real stack height.

This downwash is supposed not to take place when the stack is at least $2\frac{1}{2}$ times the height of any structure located within 20 stack lengths of the stack (SHERLOCK and STALKER [1940]).

10.11. Influence of many sources

In the foregoing we restricted ourselves to the effects of single stacks. Some final remarks must be made with respect to the ground concentrations that are to be expected when a large number of stacks is responsible for the pollution. The problem is of importance, e.g. for understanding the behavior of pollution in large cities dependant on meteorological conditions. It is a well known fact, that a single stack does not give rise to large ground concentrations during stable weather conditions (fanning). On the other hand, pollution concentrations are especially large under these circumstances in large cities (London, Los Angeles!).

The difference can be understood with the aid of (10.16). Rewriting it as

$$\chi_{\max} = \frac{2Q}{\pi e U H^2} \left(\frac{R_{z1}}{R_{y1}}\right) \exp\left[1 - \alpha\right]\alpha^\alpha \left[\frac{R_{z1}}{H}\right]^{2(\alpha-1)}, \qquad (10.18)$$

we see that the correction on Sutton's equation (10.12b) is given by the factor $\exp(1 - \alpha)\alpha^\alpha (R_{z1}/H)^{2(\alpha-1)}$. In this correction factor (R_{z1}/H) plays a predominant rôle. For a single stack it is always $\ll 1$, but this need not be so when pollution is created by many stacks distributed over a large area and differing in height. In that case R_z may be larger than the average stack height H and then with $n_y < n_z$, formula (10.18) shows that ground concentrations must be larger than in the case of isotropic turbulence.

The result can easily be appreciated qualitatively. Under stable conditions pollution escaping from a single, slender stack will only very slightly diffuse downwards so that ground concentrations remain small (fanning). Pollution escaping from an extensive relatively low lying source, on the contrary, will be hampered by the stable stratification of the atmosphere in diffusing to higher levels, this leading to high ground concentrations.

The effect of many stacks can also be evaluated by the integration of (10.11b) in which Q is replaced by q, the average emission of pollutant per unit area, each unit area considered as a point source. For a point at ground level at a distance x from the windward edge of a town, for example, we then find

$$\chi(x) = \int_0^x \int_{y_1}^{y_2} \frac{2q \exp\left[-H^2/C_z^2 x^{2-n} - y^2/C_y^2 x^{2-n}\right]}{\pi C_y U x^{2-n}} \, dx \, dy. \qquad (10.19)$$

In case the width of the town represented by y_1 and y_2 is not small compared with x we can replace y_1 and y_2 by $-\infty$ and $+\infty$ and get

$$\chi(x) = \frac{q}{U} \int_0^x \frac{2 \exp\left[-H^2/C_z^2 x^{2-n}\right]}{(\sqrt{\pi}) C_z x^{1-\frac{1}{2}n}} \, dx. \qquad (10.20)$$

The integral I can be evaluated numerically by adopting adequate values for H, n and C_z (LUCAS [1958]).

Fig. 10.15 shows the results of the evaluation based on the figures of Table 10.4 and for $H = 30$ m. Concentrations are found in relevant units by multiplication of I with q/U. For example, from the curves for $n = 0.25$ and $n = 0.75$ it appears that up to 5 km from the windward edge to the pollution emitting area, ground concentrations are smaller for the more stable case. At greater distances from the windward edge, however, ground concentrations in the stable atmosphere are in excess of those encountered during less stable conditions.

It is estimated that the highly industrialized region of Rotterdam in the Netherlands produces 7.5×10^{-6} g SO_2 per sec and per m^2 in the average. This means that under normal conditions ($n = 0.25$, $U = 3$ m sec^{-1}) the ground concentration at a distance of 5 km from the windward edge to the area will be 10^{-4} g m^{-3} SO_2. i.e. 0.08 p.p.m., by weight in the average. Concentrations will be larger during winter months and smaller during summer.

Finally a third approach may be mentioned shortly. If it is assumed that wind velocity may be neglected during periods of large concentrations of air pollution in cities and further that sources are evenly distributed over the area, so that the x- and y-directions do not enter into the problem, the changes in concentration will depend on the production rate and on the vertical transport due to turbulence only.

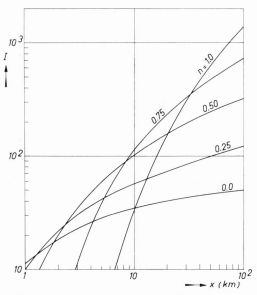

Fig. 10.15. Values of the integral I as a function of stability index n and distance from the windward side of a city x, expressed in km. It appears that for small distances I is larger than for large ones.

The problem can in that case be described by the equation

$$\frac{\partial \chi(z,t)}{\partial t} = K\frac{\partial^2 \chi(z,t)}{\partial z^2} + Q(z), \qquad (10.21)$$

where K is the vertical component of eddy diffusivity, considered independent of z for simplicity reasons and $Q(z)$ is the production of pollution per unit volume in the city.

Assuming further a sudden decrease of K, i.e. a sudden increase of stability of the atmosphere, equation (10.21) can be solved for $\chi(0,t)$, the concentration at the ground. It appears that this concentration increases proportionally with the square root of time (BOUMAN and SCHMIDT [1961]). This result has been confirmed by several observations, e.g. by those made during the great smog in London, December 1952.

Table 10.7 shows the mean daily concentrations of SO_2 on the ground computed from the observations at three points all lying within 2 miles' distance from Charing Cross (WILKINS [1954]).

TABLE 10.7

Mean daily ground concentrations of SO_2 in the center of London during the period 3–10 December 1952

3	4	5	6	7	8	9	10	December
0.22	0.17	0.59	0.84	1.09	1.23	0.83	0.22	p.p.m.

From meteorological observations it can be concluded that stability increased rather abruptly from 4 to 5 December and remained almost constant during the next four days. From 9 December on it decreased again.

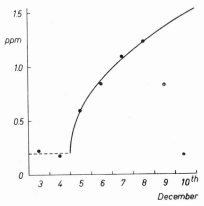

Fig. 10.16. SO_2 ground concentrations $\chi(0,t)$ in p.p.m. in the center of London during the period 3–10 December 1952. The curve represents the function $\chi(0,t) = 0.55\sqrt{t}$, with $t = 0$ at midnight of the 5th of December. The dotted line shows the mean value of SO_2 ground concentration on 3 and 4 December from which the concentration rise is supposed to start.

Figure 10.16 shows the mean daily ground concentration for 3, 4, 5, 6, 7 and 8 December, plotted at midday.

The curve represents a concentration change equal to $0.55\sqrt{t}$ p.p.m., where t is expressed in days, starting in the night from 4 to 5 December. It shows a satisfactory agreement with the measured values.

The advantage of this approach lies in the fact that it makes it possible to discuss variations of ground concentrations with time whereas those mentioned before, refer to equilibrium situations only.

In some cases the heat output of a large industrial area as well as the friction it exerts on the motion of the air may be such that a local circulation is created, which makes the application of the simple models treated before highly questionable.

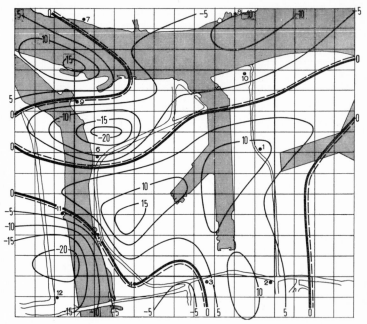

Fig. 10.17. Average vertical velocities in cm sec^{-1} at a height of 100 m over and around a large refinery computed from the divergence of the winds observed in the observation points numbered 1 to 12. The figure shows the mean vertical motion determined from 8 situations during August 1960 with winds between NW and SW. The sides of the heavily drawn square which almost coincides with the refinery area have lengths of 2 km. The largest heat production takes place in the western part of the refinery where also the largest average upward velocities (15 cm sec^{-1}) are found. Vertical velocities in individual plumes may be much larger, of course. Shaded areas indicate water surfaces.

As an example Fig. 10.17 shows the vertical velocities above and around a large oil refinery west of Rotterdam. These velocities have been computed from the divergence of the wind measured around the refinery at a height of 3 m in the 12 indicated observation posts, the refinery occupying almost a square with sides 2 km long.

In constructing the figure it has been assumed that the divergence was constant with height and the numbers give the vertical velocity in the 100 m level in cm sec^{-1} (SCHMIDT and BOER [1963]).

It will be clear that under such circumstances pollution may reach the surface in the immediate neighborhood of the industry involved, due to the created downdrafts. As a matter of fact such a behavior cannot be predicted by the models that have been described in section 10.7.

REFERENCES

ACTINOMETRIC BULLETIN, nr. 28, 1950. Central Met. Obs., Tokyo.

AIR POLLUTION HANDBOOK, 1956. McGraw-Hill, New York.

ALBRECHT, F., 1940
Untersuchungen über den Wärmehaushalt der Erdoberfläche in verschiedenen Klima-gebieten. Reichsamt für Wetterdienst, Wiss. Abh. Berlin *8* (2) (1940).

ALBRECHT, F., 1951
Intensität und Spektralverteilung der Globalstrahlung bei klarem Himmel. Arch. Met. Geophys. Bioklim. *3* (1951), p. 220–243.

ALISSOW, B. P., O. A. DROSDOW and E. S. RUBINSTEIN, 1956
Lehrbuch der Klimatologie (German translation from the Russian (1952)). Deutscher Verlag der Wissenschaften, Berlin.

ALKALI, I. C. I.
(Australia), Pty. Ltd., Records of.

ANDERSON, E. R., 1952
vide Lake Hefner.

ANGOT, A., 1883
Recherches théoriques sur la distribution de la chaleur à la surface du globe. Ann. Bur. Centr. Mét. France, Paris *1* (1883), p. 16–169.

ANGOT, A., 1907
Résumé des observations météorologiques. Ann. Bur. Centr. Mét. France (1907), p. 76.

ÅNGSTRÖM, A., 1915
A study of the radiation of the atmosphere. Smithsonian Inst. Misc. Coll. *65* (1915).

ÅNGSTRÖM, A., 1924
Solar and terrestrial radiation. Q. J. Roy. Met. Soc. *50* (1924), p. 121.

ÅNGSTRÖM, A., 1925
The albedo of various surfaces of ground. Geogr. Annaler *7* (1925), p. 323–342.

ÅNGSTRÖM, A., 1928
Recording solar radiation. Met. Hydr. Inst., Meddelanden *4* (3) (1928), p. 1–36.

ÅNGSTRÖM, A. and O. TRYSELIUS, 1934
Total radiation from sun and sky at Abisko. Geogr. Annaler *16* (1934), p. 53–69.

ANNALES AGRONOMIQUES, Versailles 1936–1952.

ASKLÖF, S., 1920
Über den Zusammenhang zwischen der nächtlichen Wärme-Ausstrahlung der Bewölkung und der Wolkenart. Geogr. Annaler *3* (1920).

BADEN, W., 1952
Festschrift zum 75-jährigen Bestehen der Anstalt. Mitteilungen über die Arbeiten der Moor-Versuchsstation in Bremen. Bremen (1952).

BARAD, M. L. and D. A. HAUGEN, 1959
A preliminary evaluation of Sutton's hypothesis for diffusion from a continuous point source. J. Met. *16* (1959), p. 12.

BARNES, E.C., 1956
Atmospheric sampling by electrostatic precipitation (in L. C. McCabe, 1956).

BAVEL, C. H. M. VAN, N. UNDERWOOD and R. W. SWANSON, 1956
Soil moisture measurement by neutron moderation. Soil Sci. *82* (1956), p. 29–41.

BAVER, L. D., 1956
Soil Physics. John Wiley & Sons, New York.

BELCHER, D. J., T. R. CUYKENDALL and H. S. SACK, 1950
The measurement of soil moisture and density by neutron and gamma ray scattering. Civil Aer. Adm. Tech. Dev. Rep. *127*, Washington, D.C. (1950).

BÉNARD, M., 1901
Les tourbillons cellulaires dans une nappe liquide transportant de la chaleur par convection en régime permanent. Ann. Chim. (Phys.) *23* (1901), p. 62–144.

BENER, P., 1951
Untersuchungen über die Wirkungsweise der Solarigraphen Moll-Gorczynski. Arch. Met. Geophys. Bioklim. *2* (1950), p. 188–249.

BERLIAND, O. S., 1950
An exact theory of the diurnal variation in air temperature considering the diurnal variation in the coefficient of turbulent diffusion of heat. Akad. Nauk, U.S.S.R., Izvestiia, Ser. Geogr. Geofiz. *14* (1) (1950), p. 70–81.

BERNHARDT, F. und H. PHILLIPS, 1958
Die räumliche und zeitliche Verteilung der Einstrahlung, der Ausstrahlung und der Strahlungsbilanz im Meeresniveau. Akademie Verlag, Berlin.

BERRY JR., F. A., E. BOLLAY and N. R. BEERS, 1954
Handbook of Meteorology. McGraw-Hill, New York-London.

BEST, N., R. HAVENS and H. LA GOW, 1947
Pressure and temperature of the atmosphere to 120 km. Physical Review *71*, p. 915–916.

BLACK, J. N., C. W. BONYTHON and J. A. PRESCOTT, 1955
Solar radiation and the duration of sunshine. Q. J. Roy. Met. Soc. *80* (344) (1955), p. 231–235.

BLACK, J. N., 1956
The distribution of solar radiation over the earth's surface. Arch. Met. Geophys., Bioklim. *7* (1956), p. 165–189.

BLANCHARD, D. C. and A. H. WOODCOCK, 1957
Bubble formation and modification in the sea and its meteorological significance. Tellus *9* (1957), p. 145.

BLANEY, H. F. and W. D. CRIDDLE, 1950
Determining water requirements in irrigated areas from climatology and irrigation data. N.S. Soil Cons. Serv. Techn. Pub. *96* (1950), p. 1–48.

BOLTZMANN, L., 1884
Wiedemanns Annalen *22* (1884), p. 291.

BOLZ, H. M. und G. FALCKENBERG, 1949
Neubestimmung der Konstanten der Ångströmischen Strahlungsformel. Z. Met. *3* (4) (1949), p. 97–100.

BOSANQUET, C. H. and J. L. PEARSON, 1936
The spread of smoke and gases from chimneys. Trans. Faraday Soc. *32* (1936), p. 1249.

BOUMAN, D. J. and F. H. SCHMIDT, 1961
On the growth of ground concentrations of atmospheric pollution in cities during stable atmospheric conditions. Beitr. Phys. Atm. *33* (1961), p. 215.

BOUTARIC, A., 1920
Sur l'intensité du rayonnement nocturne aux altitudes élevées. C.R. Acad. Sc. Paris *170* (1920), p. 1195–1196.

BOUYOUCOS, G. J., 1952
Methods for measuring the moisture content of soils under field conditions. Highway Research Board Special Report No. 2 (1952), p. 64.

BOWEN, I. S., 1926
The ratio of heat losses by conduction and by evaporation from any water surface. Physical review *27* (1926), p. 779–787.

BRACHT, J., 1949
Über die Wärmeleitfähigkeit des Erdbodens und des Schnees und den Wärmeumsatz im Erdboden. Veröff. Geophys. Inst. Univ. Leipzig, 2. Ser. *14*, Heft 3 (1949).

BRAY, J. R., 1959
An analysis of the possible recent change in atmospheric carbon dioxide concentration. Tellus *11* (1959), p. 220

BRIGGS, L. J. and H. L. SHANTZ, 1916
Daily transpiration during the normal growth period and its correlation with the weather. J. Agr. Res. *7* (1916), p. 155.

BRIGGS, L. J. and H. L. SHANTZ, 1917
Comparison of the hourly evaporation rate of atmometers and free water surfaces with the transpiration rate of Medicago sativa. J. Agr. Res. *9* (1917), p. 277.

BROCKS, K., 1948
Über den täglichen und jährlichen Gang der Höhenabhängigkeit der Temperatur in den unteren 300 m der Atmosphäre und ihre Zusammenhang mit der Konvektion. Berichte des Deutschen Wetterdienstes in der U.S. Zone No. 5, Bad Kissingen.

BROOKS, F. A., 1957
An introduction to physical microclimatology. Chapters I, II, III. University of California, Davis Campus.

BROOKS, F. A., 1959
An introduction to physical microclimatology. Chapters IV, V, VI, VII. Univ. of California, Davis Campus.

BROUWER, R., 1956
Radiation intensity and transpiration. Neth. J. Agr. Sc. *4* (1956), p. 43–48.

BRUIJN, P. J., 1960
On the solar constant and the energy distribution of the solar radiation. Meded. Landbouwhogeschool, Wageningen 60 (*15*) (1960), p. 1–6.

BRUINENBERG, A., 1946
A numerical method for determining temperature variation by radiation in the free atmosphere. Algemene Landsdrukkerij, 's Gravenhage. (Dutch).

BRUNT, D., 1932
Notes on the radiation in the atmosphere. Q. J. Roy. Met. Soc. *58* (1932), p. 389.

BRUNT, D., 1933
The adiabatic lapse-rate for dry and saturated air. Q. J. Roy. Met. Soc. *59* (1933), p. 351–360.

BRUNT, D., 1944
Physical and dynamical meteorology. London, Cambridge Univ. Press.

BUDYKO, M. I., D. L. LAICHTMAN and M. P. TIMOFEEV, 1953
Determination of the coefficient of turbulent exchange in the layer near the ground. Meteorologiia i Gidrologiia no. 3 (1953).

BUDYKO, M. I., 1956
The heat balance of the earth's surface. U.S. Dept. of Commerce Washington 25, D.C. (1958), 259 pp. (Eng. transl. from the Russian edition (1956)).

BULL. INST. AGR. STAT. RECH., Gembloux 1940–1951.

BURGER, H. C., 1915
Das Leitvermögen verdünnter mischkristallfreier Lösungen. Phys. Zs. 20 (1915), p. 73–76.

BUSINGER, J. A., 1954a
De invloed van raamstanden op de ventilatie van kassen. Meded. Dir. Tuinb. 17 (1954), p. 897.

BUSINGER, J. A., 1954b
Some aspects of the influence of the earth's surface on the atmosphere. Thesis Utrecht. Staatsdrukkerij en Uitgeversbedrijf, 's Gravenhage.

BUSINGER, J. A., 1954b
Some aspects of the influence of the earth's surface on the atmosphere. Meded. Verh. Kon. Ned. Met. Inst., serie B, nr. 61 (1954).

BUSINGER, J. A., 1955
Some remarks on glasshouse heating. Proc. XIV Int. Hort. Congress (1955), p. 1106–1113.

BUSINGER, J. A., 1956a
Some remarks on Penman's equations for the evapotranspiration. Neth. J. Agr. Sc. 4 (1956), p. 77–80.

BUSINGER, J. A., 1956b
Warmeluchtverwarming in kassen. Meded. Dir. Tuinb. (1956), p. 145–150.

CANHAM, A. E., 1956
The electric lamp in British horticulture. Proc. XIV Int. Hort. Congress (1956).

CARMAN, P. C., 1956
Flow of gasses through porous media. Butterworths Scientific Publications, London.

CARSLAW, H. S. and J. C. JAEGER, 1950
Conduction of heat in solids. Clarendon Press, Oxford.

CHILDS, E. C. and N. COLLIS-GEORGE, 1950
The permeability of porous materials. Proc. Roy. Soc. London A 201 (1950), p. 392–405.

CHILDS, E. C., 1957
The physics of land drainage; vide Luthin (1957), p. 1–78.

CHILDS, E. C., 1960
Soil physics at Cambridge. Mem. 32 (1959/60). School of Agr., Univ. of Cambridge.

COLMAN, E. A. and T. M. HENDRIX, 1949
The fibre glass electrical soil moisture instrument. Soil Sci 67 (1949), p. 425.

COMM. PLANTENBESTRALING, 1951
Ned. St. Verl. 1951. Electrotechniek 29 (1951), p. 467–470.

CORPS OF ENGINEERS, 1949
Addendum no. 1, 1945–1947. Report on frost investigation 1944–1945. New England Division, Frost Effects Lab. (Oct. 1949).

CRONEY, D., T. D. COLEMAN and E. W. H. CURRER, 1951
The electrical resistance method of measuring soil moisture. Brit. J. Appl. Phys. 2 (1951), p. 85–91.

CSANADY, G. T., 1955
Disposal of dust particles from elevated sources. Austr. J. Phys. *8* (1955), p. 545.

DARCY, H., 1856
Les fontaines publiques de la ville de Dijon. Dalmont, Paris.

DEACON, E. L., 1950
Radiative heat transfer in the air near the ground. Austr. J. Sci. Res. A *3*(1950), p. 274–383.

DEE, R. W. R. and J. J. M. REESINK, 1951
Radiation measurements at Bandung. Meded. Landbouwhogeschool, Wageningen *51* (1951), p. 167–175

DINES, W. H. and L. H. G. DINES, 1927
Monthly mean values of radiation from various parts of the sky at Benson, Oxfordshire. Roy Met. Soc. Memoirs *2* (11) (1927).

DOETSCH, G., 1943
Theorie und Anwendung der Laplace Transformation. Die Grundlehren der Mathematischen Wissenschaften. Dover Publications, New York.

DUHAMEL, J. Ec., 1833
Polytech., Paris *14* (1833), Cah. 22.

DUIN, R. H. A. VAN and D. A. DE VRIES, 1954
A recording apparatus for measuring thermal conductivity and some results obtained with it in soil. Neth. J. Agr. Sci. *2* (1954), p. 168–175.

DUIN, R. H. A. VAN and D. W. SCHOLTE UBING, 1955
De invloed van het weer op de opbrengst van de aardappel. Landbouwk. Tijdschr. *67* (1955), p. 795–802.

DUIN, R. H. A. VAN, 1956
On the influence of tillage on conduction of heat, diffusion of air and infiltration of water in soil. Thesis Wageningen. Versl. Landbouwk. Onderz. *62* (7), 82 pp. (Dutch, English summary p. 1–10).

DZERDZEEVSKII, B. D., editor, 1957
Suchovei, their origin and the battle against them, 370 pp. Ed. Acad. of Sci. of the U.S.S.R., Moscow (Russian).

ECKEL, O., 1934
Messungen der Ausstrahlung und Gegenstrahlung auf der Kanzelhöhe. Met. Z. *51* (1934).

EDLEFSEN, N. E. and A. B. C. ANDERSON, 1943
The thermodynamics of soil moisture. Hilgardia *16* (1943), p. 31–299.

ELSASSER, W. M., 1942
Heat transfer by infrared radiation in the atmosphere. Harvard Met. Stud. *6* (1942).

EMANUELSSON, A., E. ERIKSSON and H. EGNER, 1954
Composition of atmospheric precipitation. Tellus *6* (1954), p. 261.

ENDE, J. VAN DER, 1955
De watervoorziening van tomaten (II). Meded. Dir. Tuinb. *18* (1955), p. 904–917.

EVELYN, J., 1661
Fumifugium.

FOURIER, J. B. J., 1822
Théorie analytique de la chaleur. Gauthier-Villars, Paris.

FRANK, P. und R. VON MISES, 1930
Die Differential- und Integralgleichungen der Mechanik und Physik. Vieweg & Sohn, Braunschweig. (Also published by Rosenberg, New York, 1943).

GAASTRA, P., 1958
Light energy conversion in field crops in comparison with the photosynthetic efficiency under laboratory conditions. Meded. Landbouwhogeschool, Wageningen 58 (4) (1958), p. 1–12

GADE, C., 1929
Einfluss von Fräse und Pflug auf Bodenzustand und Ertrag. Landw. Jahrbuch 70 (1929), p. 89–142.

GARDNER, W. and D. KIRKHAM, 1952
Determination of soil moisture by neutron scattering. Soil Sci. 73 (1952), p. 391.

GEIGER, R., 1961
Das Klima der bodennahen Luftschicht. F. Vieweg & Sohn, Braunschweig.

GERMING, A., 1956
Kunststof als materiaal ter vervanging van glas. Meded. Dir. Tuinb. 19 (1956), p. 141–145.

GIFFORD, F., 1959
Statistical properties of a fluctuating plume dispersion model, atmospheric diffusion and air pollution. Advances in Geophysics 6 (1959), p. 117.

GINSEL, L. A., 1943
Het doorlatingsvermogen van in Nederland voor kassen en bakken gebruikte ruiten. Rapport T.N.O (1943), T.A.–152.

Goss, J. R. and F. A. BROOKS, 1956
Constants for empirical expressions for downcoming atmospheric radiation under cloudless sky. J. Met. 13 (5) (1956), p. 482–488.

GRAY, H. E., 1947
The cause of cold spots in the greenhouse. New York State Flower Growers Inc. Bull. 26 (1947), p. 3.

GROEN, P., 1947
Verhandelingen Kon. Ned. Meteor. Inst. De Bilt, nr. 125. Meded. en Verhandelingen, Ser. B I, nr. 9 (1947).

GUGGENHEIM, E. A., 1950
Thermodynamics. North-Holland Publ. Co., Amsterdam.

GULIK, D. VAN., 1910
Iets over het gebruik van glas in broeikassen. Meded. v. d. R.H.L.T.B., deel III (1910). p. 108–118.

GUSTAFSSON, Y., 1946
Die Strömungsverhältnisse in gedrähntem Boden. Acta Agricult. Suecana, Stockholm 2 (1946), p. 1–157.

HALL, N. S., W. F. CHANDLER, C. H. M. VAN BAVEL, P. H. REID and J. H. ANDERSON, 1953
A tracer technique to measure growth and activity of plant root systems. North Carolina Agr. Exp. St. Tech. Bull. 101 (1953).

HAND, I. F., 1949
Atmospheric contamination over Boston, Mass., Am. Met. Soc. Bull. 30 (7) (1949), p. 252–254.

HANDBUCH DER KLIMATOLOGIE. Band I–V, 1938. Editors W. Köppen and R. Geiger, Borntraeger, Berlin.

HAURWITZ, B., 1934
Daytime radiation at Blue Hill Observatory in 1933 with application to turbidity in American air masses. Harvard Met. Stud. 1 (1934).

HAURWITZ, B., 1936
The daily temperature period for a linear variation of the Austausch coefficient. Royal Soc. of Canada, Transactions, 3rd Ser. Section III, *30* (May 1936), p. 1–8.

HELD, E. F. VAN DER, 1952
Evaporation of a free water surface into a stream of air. De Ingenieur *64* (1952), p. 89–94.

HELLMANN, G., 1915
Meteorol. Z. *32* (1915), p. 1.

HOARE, E. and L. G. MORRIS, 1955
Heating and ventilating of glasshouses. J. Inst. Brit. Agr. Eng. *12* (1955–1956), p. 7–40.

HOELPER, O., 1939
Registrierungen der Sonnen- und Himmelsstrahlung im Allgäu. Met. Z. *56* (1939), p. 333–342.

HOLLAENDER, A., editor, 1956
Radiation biology. McGraw-Hill, New York.

HOLLDACK, H. and W. VON NITSCH, 1926
Der Einflusz der Bodenbearbeitung auf den Flächenertrag der Kulturen. Ill. Landw. Z. *46* (1926), p. 163–164.

HOLMES, J. W., 1956
Measuring soil water content and evaporation by the neutron scattering method. Neth. J. Agr. Sci. *4* (1956), p. 30–34.

INST. GEOF. COIMBRA UNIV., 1940.

INST. MET. PHYS. GLOBE, 1953.

INST. V. TUINB. TECHNIEK: Jaarverslag 1951, p. 26; 1953, p. 15; 1954, p. 17; 1955.

INTERNATIONAL CRITICAL TABLES. Volumes I to VII. McGraw-Hill, New York, 1930.

JACKS, G. V., W. D. BRIND and R. SMITH, 1955
Technical communication no. 49 of the Commonwealth Bureau of Soil Science (1955), p. 87.

JACOBS, W. C., 1951
Aerobiology. Article in T. F. Malone, Compendium of Meteorology.

JAHNKE, E. and F. EMDE, 1945
Tables of functions with formulae and curves. Dover Publications, New York.

JUNGE, CHR. E. and P. E. GUSTAFSON, 1957
On the distribution of sea salt over the United States and removal by precipitation. Tellus *9* (1957), p. 164.

JUNGE, CHR. E., 1958
Atmospheric Chemistry, Advances in Geophysics *4* (1958).

JUUSELA, T., 1945
Untersuchungen über den Einfluss des Entwässerungsverfahrens auf den Wassergehalt des Bodens, den Bodenfrost und die Bodentemperatur. Acta Agr. Fenn. *59* (1945), p. 1–212.

KEEN, B. A., 1930
Studies in soil cultivation, V. Rotary cultivation. J. Agr. Sci. *20* (1930), 364–389.

KERSTEN, M. S., 1949
Thermal properties of soils. Bull. Univ. of Minnesota Inst. of Techn., Engn. Exp. Stat. Bull. *28* (1949).

KIEFER, P. J., 1941
The thermodynamic properties of water and water vapor. Monthly Weather Rev. *69* (1941), p. 329–331.

KIMBALL, H. H., 1918
Nocturnal radiation measurements. Month. Weather Rev. *46* (1918).
KIMBALL, H. H., 1924
Solar and sky radiation measurements. Month. Weather Rev. *52*, nr. 1 (1924), p. 42.
KIMBALL, H. H., 1927
Measurements of solar radiation intensity and determination of its depletion by the atmosphere. Month. Weather Rev. *55* (1927), p. 155–169.
KIRKHAM, D., 1957
The ponded water case; *vide* Luthin (1957), p. 139–181.
KIRKHAM, D., 1963
Chapter on soil physics. Handbook of Hydrology. McGraw-Hill (in press).
KLOEPPEL, R., 1930
Pflanzenbau *3* (1930), p. 465–493.
KÖHLER, H., 1932
Ein kurzes Studium des Austausches auf Grund des Potenzgesetzes. Beiträge zur Physik der freien Atmosphäre *19* (1932), p. 91–104.
KOHLRAUSCH, F., 1947
Praktische Physik. Mary S. Rosenberg, New York.
KOPECKI, J., 1914
Int. Mitt. Bodenk. *4* (1914), p. 138–180.
KÖPPEN, W. and R. GEIGER, editors, 1938
Handbuch der Klimatologie Band I–V. Borntraeger, Berlin.
KRAUSSE, M., 1931
Landw. Jahrbuch *73* (1931), p. 603–690.
KREUTZ, W., 1943
Beitrag zur Erforschung des Boden- und bodennahen Klimas im Emslandmoor in Anlehnung an Bedürfnisse der Praxis. J. f. Landwirtschaft *89* (1943), p. 81–112.
KREUTZ, W., 1949
Meteorologische Beobachtungen im Gewächshaus. Trowitz–Verlag, Holzwinden.
KRISCHER, O. and H. ROHNALTER, 1940
Wärmeleitung und Dampfdiffusion in feuchten Gütern. V.D.I. Forschungsheft *402* (1940).
KRISCHER, O., 1956
Die wissenschaftlichen Grundlagen der Trocknungstechnik. Springer–Verlag, Berlin.
KRONIG, R., 1959
Textbook of physics. Pergamon Press, New York.
LAICHTMAN, D. L., 1947
Transformation of an air mass under the influence of the underlying surface. Meteorologiia i Gidrologiia, no. 1 (1947).
LAICHTMAN, D. L. and CHUDNOVSKII, 1949
Physics of the atmosphere's ground layer. G.I.T.T.L., Moscow–Leningrad.
LAKE HEFNER STUDIES, 1952
Water-loss investigations. Vol. *1*, technical report. Washington, D.C., Geological Survey.
LAMBERT, J. H., 1760
Photometria. Augsburg.
LANDOLT·BÖRNSTEIN
Zahlenwerte und Funktionen. Teil I–V. Springer–Verlag, Berlin–Gottingen–Heidelberg, 1950–1957.

LANG, C., 1878
Über die Wärmekapazität der Bodenkonstituenten, Forschung Gebiete Agrikultur-Physik *1* (1878), p. 109.

LAWRENCE, W. J. C., 1948
Science and the glasshouse. Oliver and Boyd, Edinburgh–London.

LEEFLANG, K. W. H., 1938
De chemische samenstelling van de neerslag in Nederland. Chem. Weekblad *35* (1938), p. 658.

LEHENBAUER, P. A., 1914
Growth of maize seedlings in relation to temperature. Physiol. Res. *1* (1914) p. 247–288.

LETTAU, H., 1949
Geophys. Res. Pap., no. 1. Base Dir. Geophys. Res. Air Force. Cambridge Res. Lab. (1949).

LETTAU, H., 1952
Synthetische Klimatologie. Deutscher Wetterdienst in der U.S. Zone. Berichte, no. 38 (1952), p. 127–136.

LIN, C. C., 1955
The theory of hydrodynamic stability. Cambridge Univ. Press.

LORCH, J., 1959
Windbreaks and windbreak effects in the banana plantations of the Jordan Valley. Met. Notes, no. 17, Ser. A, Jerusalem (1959), p. 25.

LOWRY, PH. H., 1951
Microclimate factors in smoke pollution from tall stacks. Met. Monogr., Vol. *1*, nr. 4, Am. Met. Soc. (1951), p. 24.

LUCAS, D. H., 1958
The atmospheric pollution of cities. Int. J. Air Pollution *1* (1958), p. 71.

LUNELUND, H., 1931
Registrierung der Sonnen- und Himmelstrahlung in Helsingfors. Finska Vet. Soc. Helsinki, Comm. Phys. Math. *5* (18) (1931), p. 1–56.

LUTHIN, J. N., 1957
Drainage of agricultural lands. Agronomy, Vol. VII, Am. Soc. Agro. Madison, Wisconsin.

LYKOW, A. W., 1958
Transporterscheinungen in kapillarporösen Körpern. Akademie-Verlag, Berlin.

MACHE, H., 1910
Ueber die Verdunstungsgeschwindigkeit des Wassers in Wasserstoff und Luft. Math. Naturwiss. Sitz. Ber., Wien *119* (1910), p. 1399

MAKKINK, G. F., 1957
Testing the Penman formula by means of lysimeters. J. Inst. Water Eng., Vol. *11*, no. 3 (1957), p. 277–288.

MALONE, T. F., editor, 1951
Compendium of meteorology. Am. Met. Soc., Boston, Mass.

MARCIANO, J. J. and G. EARL HARBECK JR., 1952
Mass-transfer studies. Lake Hefner Studies Vol. 1, Technical Report *327* (1952), U.S. Navy Electronics Lab., San Diego 52, Cal.

MARCIANO, J. J. and G. EARL HARBECK JR., 1958
Water-loss investigations. Lake Mead Studies. Geological Survey Professional Paper *298*. U.S. Dept. of Commerce, Weather Bureau (1958).

MASON, B. J., 1957
The physics of clouds. Oxford Monographs on Met.
MAYILL, P. L., F. R. HOLDEN and CH. ACKLEY, 1956
Air pollution handbook, p. 5. McGraw-Hill, New York.
McADAMS, W. H., 1951
Heat transmission. Heating and cooling fluids inside tubes (2nd edition). McGraw-Hill London.
McCABE, L. C. 1952
Air pollution proceedings of the United States Technical Conference on air pollution. McGraw-Hill, New York.
McCABE, L. C., 1956
Air pollution. Air pollution handbook. McGraw-Hill, New York.
MEETHAM, A. R., 1950
Natural removal of pollution from atmosphere. Q. J. Roy. Met. Soc. 76 (1950).
MEETHAM, A. R., 1952
Atmospheric pollution, its origins and prevention. Pergamon Press Ltd., London.
METEOROLOGICAL ABSTRACTS AND BIBLIOGRAPHY. Malcolm Rigby, editor. Am. Met. Soc., Boston, Mass.
MIDDLETON, J. T., 1954
Response of plants to air pollution. Air pollution symposium, A.A.A.S., December 1954.
MILLER, E. E. and R. D. MILLER, 1956
Physical theory for capillary flow phenomena. J. Appl. Phys. 27 (4) (1956), p. 324–332.
MITSCHERLICH, E. A., 1954
Bodenkunde, Paul Parey, Berlin–Hamburg.
MONIN, A. S. and A. M. OBUKHOV, 1954
Basic laws of turbulent mixing in the atmosphere near the ground. Akad. Nauk S.S.S.R. Geof. Instit. Trudy 24 (151) (1954), p. 163–187.
MONTEITH, J. L., 1954
Error and accuracy in thermocouple psychometry. Proc. Phys. Soc. B 67 (1954), p. 217–226.
MOON, P., 1940
Proposed standard solar radiation curves for engineering use. J. Franklin Inst. Vol. 230, nr. 5 (1940), p. 583–617.
MORSE, P. M. and H. FESHBACH, 1953
Methods of theoretical physics. McGraw-Hill, New York.
MORRIS, L. G., J. D. POSTLETHWAITE, R. I. EDWARDS and F. E. NEALE, 1953
The dependence of the water requirements of glasshouse crops upon the total incoming solar radiation. Nat. Inst. Agr. Eng. (1953), Techn. Memo nr. 86.
MORRIS, L. G., J. D. POSTLETHWAITE and R. I. EDWARDS, 1954
Ventilation and the supply of carbon dioxide to a glasshouse tomato crop. Nat. Inst. Agr. Eng. (1954), Techn. Memo nr. 87
MORRIS, L. G. and F. E. NEALE, 1954
The infrared carbon dioxide gas analyzer and its use in glasshouse research. Nat. Inst. Agr. Eng. (1954), Techn. Memo nr. 99.
MOSBY, H., 1925
Scientific results 1 (17) (1918–1925).

MUSKAT, M., 1936
The flow of homogeneous fluids through porous media. McGraw-Hill (1936), New York. Reprinted Ann. Arbor Mich., J. W. Edwards (1946).

MUYZENBERG, E. W. B. VAN DEN, 1943
Overzicht van de historische ontwikkeling van de kassenbouw en de kasverwarming. Inst. Tuinbouwtechniek, Meded. 1 (1943).

MUYZENBERG, E. W. B. VAN DEN, 1948
Het licht in de kas. Meded. Dir. Tuinb. 11 (1948), p. 514–521.

MUYZENBERG, E. W. B. VAN DEN, 1951
De kas als kweekmilieu. Meded. Dir. Tuinb. 14 (1951), p. 691.

NAKAMURA, vide Tamura, T., 1905

NEIBURGER, M., 1949
Reflection, absorption and transmission of insolation by stratus cloud. J. Met. B (1949), p. 98–104.

NIELSEN, D. and E. R. PHILIPS, 1959
J. Am. Soc. of Agronomy (1959).

NITZSCH, W. VON, 1937
R.K.T.L. Schriften 70 (1937), p. 1–188.

OBUCHOV, A. M., 1946
Turbulence in an atmosphere with inhomogeneous temperature. Akademiia Nauk S.S.S.R., Instituta Teoreticheskoi Geofiziki, Trudy, Tom 1 (1946), p. 95–115 (Russian).

O'GARA, 1956
Air pollution handbook, Section 9.2.4. McGraw-Hill, New York, 1956a.

PAESCHKE W., 1937,
Beitr. Phys. für Atmos. 24 (1937), p. 163.

PALMEN, E. VON, 1934
Über die Temperaturverteilung in der Stratosphäre und ihren Einfluss auf die Dynamik des Wetters. Met. Zeitschr. 51 (1934), p. 17–24.

PASQUILL, F, 1962
Atmospheric diffusion. London.

PEERLKAMP, P. K., 1944
Bodemmeteorologische onderzoekingen te Wageningen. Meded. Landbouwhogeschool, Wageningen 47 (3) (1944), p. 1–96.

PENMAN, H. L., 1948
Natural evaporation from open water, bare soil and grass. Proc. Roy. Soc. London A 193 (1948), p. 120–145.

PENMAN, H. L., 1949
The dependence of transpiration on weather and soil conditions. J. Soil Science, Oxford 1, nr. 1 (1949), p. 74–89.

PENMAN, H. L., 1955
Humidity. The Institute of Physics, London.

PENMAN, H. L., 1956a
Estimating evaporation. Trans. Am. Geophys. Union 37 (1) (1956), p. 43–46.

PENMAN, H. L., 1956b
Evaporation: An introductory survey. Proc. informal meeting on physics in agr. Neth. J. Agr. Sci., Vol. 4, nr. 1 (1956), p. 9–29.

PHILIP, J. R., 1957a
The theory of infiltration. Soil Sci. *83* (1957), p. 345–357; *83* (1957), p. 435–448; *84* (1957), p. 97–182; *84* (1957), p. 257–264; *84* (1957), 329–339.

PHILIP, J. R., 1957b
Evaporation and moisture and heat fields in the soil. J. Met. *14* (4) (1957), p. 354–366.

PHILIP, J. R. and D. A. DE VRIES, 1957
Moisture movement in porous materials under temperature gradients. Trans. Am. Geophys. Union *38* (1957), p. 222–232.

PHILIP, J. R., 1958
Physics of water movement in porous solids. Special report *40*, Highway Research Board, Washington, D.C. (1958).

PHYSICS ABSTRACTS, edited and issued by the Inst. Elec. Eng., London.

PLANCK, M., 1900
Verhandl. deutsch. physik. Ges. *2*, p. 202–237.

PLANCK, M., 1901
Ann. Physik *4*, p. 553.

POPPENDIEK, H. F., 1952
A periodic heat transfer for an atmosphere in which the eddy diffusivity varies sinusoidally with time and linearly with height. J. Met. Vol. *9*, no. 5 (1952), p. 368–370.

PRANDTL, L., 1932
Meteorologische Anwendung der Ströhmungslehre. Beiträge zur Physik der freien Atmosphäre. Bjerknes–Festschrift *19* (1932), p. 188–202.

PRIESTLEY, C. H. B., 1954
Vertical heat transfer from impressed temperature fluctuations. Austr. J. Phys. Vol. *7* (1) (1954), p. 202–209.

PRIESTLEY, C. H. B., 1956
Convection from the earth's surface. Proc. Roy. Soc. London A *238* (1956), p. 287–304.

PRIESTLEY, C. H. B., 1957
The evolution of energy gain by the atmosphere through contact with the ground or ocean. Univ. of Chicago, Sci. Rep. nr. 2, Contract no. AF 19 (604) (1957), p. 2179.

PRIESTLEY, C. H. B., 1959
Turbulent transfer in the lower atmosphere. Chicago, Univ. of Chicago Press.

PROCEEDINGS INFORMAL MEETING ON PHYSICS IN AGRICULTURE in September 1955 at Wageningen, main subject evaporation. Special volume Neth. J. Agr. Sc. *4* (1) (1956).

PROCEEDINGS OF THE FIRST NATIONAL AIR POLLUTION SYMPOSIUM. Los Angeles (1951).

PROHASKA, F., 1943
Die Globalstrahlung in Davos. Beitr. Geoph. *59* (1943), p. 247–275.

RADIATION BIOLOGY, 1956
A. Hollaender, editor. McGraw-Hill, New York.

RAMAN, P. K., 1938
Measurement of the radiation from the sun and the sky at Poona in 1935. Mem. Met. Dept. India *26* (1938), p. 151–164.

RAMANATHAN, K. R. and B. N. DESAI, 1932
Nocturnal atmospheric radiation at Poona. Beitr. Geophys. *35* (1932).

RAMDAS, L. A., 1948
The physics of the bottom layers of the atmosphere. Proc. 35th Ind. Sci. Cong.: Part II, Presidential adresses (1948).

RAMDAS, L. A., 1951
Microclimatological investigations in India. Arch. Met., Geophys., Bioklim. Ser. B, *3* (1951), p. 147.

RAMDAS, L. A., 1953
Convective phenomena near a heated surface. Proc. Indian Acad. Sci. Ser. A, Bangalore, *37* (2) (1953), p. 304–317.

RAYLEIGH, LORD, 1911
Phil. Mag. *22* (1911), papers 6, 51, p. 381–396.

RAYLEIGH, LORD, 1916
On convection currents in a horizontal layer of fluid when the higher temperature is on the underside. Scientific Papers *6* (Cambridge Univ. Press), p. 432–446.

REESINK, J. J. M. and D. A. DE VRIES, 1942
The yearly and daily variation of daylicht in the Netherlands Meded. Landbouwhogeschool, Wageningen *46* (1) (1942), p. 1–24. (Dutch).

REPORT OF THE JOINT COMMITTEE ON SOIL TILTH. Am. Soc. Agro. and Am. Soc. Agr. Eng. (1945).

RICHARDS, L. A., 1931
Capillary conduction of liquids through porous media. Physics *1* (1931), p. 318–333.

RICHARDS, L. A., 1942
Soil moisture tensiometer materials and construction. Soil Sci. *53* (1942), p. 241.

RICHARDS, L. A., 1947
Pressure membrane apparatus, construction and use. Agr. Eng. *28* (1947), p. 451–454.

RICHARDS, L. A. and D. C. MOORE, 1952
Influence of capillary conductivity and depth of wetting on moisture retention in soil Trans. Am. Geophys. Union *33* (1952), p. 531–539.

RICHARDS, L. A. and C. H. WADLEIGH, 1952
Soil water and plant growth, chapter 3 in Soil physical conditions and plant growth. Vol. II. Agronomy. Acad. Press.

RICHARDS, L. A., 1958
Thermocouple for vapor pressure measurement in biological and soil systems for high humidity. Paper presented at the Western Society of Soil Science Meeting Logan. Utah.

RIDER, N. E., 1954
Eddy diffusion of momentum, water vapour and heat near the ground. Roy. Soc. London, Phil. Trans., Ser. A, *246* (918) (1954), p. 481–501.

RIMMER, W. B. and C. W. ALLEN, 1950
Mem. Comm. Obs. Mt. Stromlö *11* (1950).

ROBITZSCH, M., 1926
Strahlungsstudien Ergebnisse. Arbeiten Preuss. Aeronaut. Obs. *15* (1926).

ROODENBURG, J. W. H., 1948
De bruikbaarheid van verschillende lichtbronnen voor het bevorderen van de groei van kasplanten. Meded. Dir. Tuinb. *11* (1948), p. 522–528.

ROODENBURG, J. W. H., 1949
Nieuwe resultaten met toepassing van kunstmatige belichting. Meded. Dir. Tuinb. *12* (1949), p. 490–505.

ROODENBURG, J. W. H., 1952
Elektrische lichtbronnen voor plantenbestraling. Tuinbouwgids (1952), p. 216.

RUSSEL, M. B. *et al.*, 1959
Advances in Agronomy *11* (1959). Acad. Press, New York.

SAUBERER, F., private communication.

SCHARRINGA, M., 1956
Het klimaat in kassen en bakken. Tuinbouwgids (1956), p. 121.

SCHEIDEGGER, A. E., 1957
The physics of flow through porous media. Toronto Univ. Press.

SCHIELDRUP, P. H., 1952
Global radiation in Bergen. Årbok Univ. Bergen 1952, Naturvitensk. Rekke 9 (1952).

SCHIRMER, R., 1938
Die Diffusionszahl von Wasserdampf-Luftgemischen und die Verdampfungsgeschwindig-
keit. Z. V. D. I., Verfahrenstechnik 6 (1938).

SCHLICHTING, H., 1958
Grenzschicht Theorie. G. Braun. Karlsruhe.

SCHMIDT, F. H., 1957
On the diffusion of stack gases in the atmosphere. Meded. en Verh. Kon. Ned. Met.
Inst. 68 (1957).

SCHMIDT, F. H., 1960
On the dependence of the parameters in Sutton's diffusion formula. Beitr. Phys. Atm. 33
(1960), p. 112.

SCHMIDT, F. H. and J. H. BOER, 1963
Local circulation around an industrial area. Deutscher Wetterdienst, Proc. Meteorologen-
Tagung 1962 (in press).

SCHMIDT, W., 1918
Sitz. Ber. Akad. Wissensch., Wien 12 (1918), p. 1889.

SCHOLTE UBING, D. W., 1959
Studies on solar and net radiation and on evapotranspiration of grass. Thesis. Meded.
Landbouwhogeschool, Wageningen 59 (10) (1959), p. 1–93. (Dutch).

SCHOLTE UBING, D. W., 1961
Short wave and net radiation under glass as compared with radiation in the open. Neth.
J. Agr. Sci. 9 (3) (1961) p. 163–167.

SCHUBERT, J., 1930
Handbuch der Bodenlehre, Berlin.

SCHULZE, L., 1955
Lichteinstrahlung in glasgedeckte Gewächshäuser. Inst. für Technik im Gartenbau und
Landwirtschaft der Tech. Hochschule, Hannover

SCHULZE, R., 1953
Über ein Strahlungsmessgerät mit ultrarotdurchlässiger Windschutzhaube. Geofis. Pura
Appl. 24 (1953), p. 107–114.

SCHWIND, R., 1938
Der Einflusz von Grubber, Pflug, Klausingpflug und Fräse auf Wachstumsbedingungen
und Erträge unserer Kulturpflanzen. Landw. Jahrbuch 86 (1938), p. 928–988.

SEEMAN, J., 1952
Strahlungsverhältnisse in Gewächshäusern. Archiv. Met., Geophys., Bioklim., Ser B.
Band IV, Heft 2 (1952).

SEEMAN, J. und J. WELECZKA, 1954
Wärmeregelung senkt Heizungskosten. Technik im Gartenbau 1 (5) (1954).

SHAW, B. T. (1952), editor
Soil physical conditions and plant growth. Acad. Press, New York, 491 pp.

SHAW, W. N., 1930
Manual of meteorology. Cambridge (Eng.) Univ. Press, Vol. *3* (1930), p. 337–338.

SHEPPARD, P. A., 1947
The aerodynamic drag of the earth's surface and the value of von Kármán's constant in the lower atmosphere. Proc. Roy. Soc. London, Ser. A (1947), p. 208–222.

SHERLOCK, R. H. and E. A. STALKER, 1940
The control of gases in the wake of smokestacks. Mech. Eng. *62* (1940), p. 455.

SLATYER, R. O., 1957
The significance of the permanent wilting percentage in studies of plant and soil water relations. Botan. Rev. *23* (1957), p. 585–636.

SMITH, F. B., 1957
The diffusion of smoke from a continuous elevated point-source into a turbulent atmosphere. J. Fluid Mech. *2* (1957), p. 49.

SMITH, M. E., 1951
Meteorological factors in atmospheric pollution problems. Am. Ind. Hyg. Assoc. Quart. *12* (1951), p. 151.

SMITH, W. O. and H. G. BYERS, 1938
Proc. Soil Sci. Soc. Am. *3* (1938), p. 13–19.

SMITH, W. O., 1939
Proc. Soil. Sci. Soc. Am. *4* (1939), p. 72–74.

SMITH, W. O., 1942
The thermal conductivity of dry soil. Soil Sci. *53* (1942), p. 435–459.

SMITHSONIAN METEOROLOGICAL TABLES, 1951
Smithsonian Misc. Coll. Vol. *114*. Smithsonian Inst., Washington, D.C.

SMITHSONIAN PHYSICAL TABLES, 1954
Smithsonian Misc. Coll. Vol. *120*, Smithsonian Inst., Washington, D.C.

SPOELSTRA, P. A., 1954
De mogelijkheden van warmeluchtkachels in de tuinbouw. Meded. Dir. Tuinb. *17* (1954), p. 889.

STEFAN, J., 1879
Sitzungsber. Kais. Akad. Wiss., Wien. Math-naturwiss. Klasse *79*, p. 391.

STERK, M. J., 1956
On the time dependence of the eddy heat conductivity in the lower air layers from the ratio of the amplitudes of the diurnal and annual temperature waves at 200 and 10 cm. Neth. J. Agr. Sci., Vol. *4*, no. 1 (1956), p. 139–142.

STEWART, M. G., H. J. GALE and R. M. CROOKS, 1957
The atmospheric diffusion of gases discharged from the chimney of the Harwell pile (BEPO), Atomic Energy Res. Establ. HP/R 1452 (1957).

SUMMERHAYS, W. E., 1930
A determination of the coefficient of diffusion of water vapor. Proc. Phys. Soc. *42* (1930), p. 218–225.

SUOMI, V. E. and C. B. TANNER, 1958
Evapotranspiration estimates from heat budget measurements over a field crop. Trans. Am. Geophys. Union Vol. *39*, no. 2 (1958), p. 298–304.

SÜRING, F., 1929
From J. Keränen, Einführung in die Geophysik *2*. Springer–Verlag, Berlin.

Sutton, O. G. 1947
The theoretical distribution of airborne pollution from factory chimneys. Q. J. Roy. Met. Soc. *73* (1947), p. 426.

Sutton, O. G., 1953
Micrometeorology, a study of physical processes in the lowest layers of the earth's atmosphere. McGraw-Hill, London.

Sverdrup, H. U., 1937
On the evaporation from the oceans. J. Marine Res., Vol. *1*, no. 1 (1937), p. 3–14.

Swinbank, W. C., 1951
The measurement of vertical transfer of heat and water vapor by eddies in the lower atmosphere. J. Met. *8* (3) (1951), p. 135–145.

Swinbank, W. C., 1955
An experimental study of eddy transports in the lower atmosphere. Div. Met. Phys. Technical paper no. 2, Melbourne (1955).

Tamura, T., 1905
Observations of air temperature in Japan, Monthly Weather Rev. *33* (1905), p. 296–302 (this article quotes Nakamura's measurements).

Tanner, C. B., 1957
Factors affecting evaporation from plants and soils. J. Soil and Water conservation, *12* (1957), p. 221.

Tanner, C. B., 1960
Energy balance approach to evapotranspiration from crops. Proc. Soil. Sci. Am., *24* (1960), p. 1–9.

Tanner, C. B. and A. E. Peterson, 1960
Light transmission through corn to interseeded alfalfa. Agr. J. *52* (1960), p. 487–489.

Taylor, G. I., 1915
Eddy motion in the atmosphere. Roy. Soc. London, Phil. Trans., Ser. A *215* (1915), p. 1–26

Temperature, its Measurement and Control in Science and Industry.
Vol. *I* (1941), Vol. *II* (1955), edited by H. C. Wolve, under the auspices of Am. Inst. of Physics and the Bureau of Standards. Reinhold Publ. Corp.

Thornthwaite, C. W., 1948
An approach toward a rational classification of climate. The Geogr. Rev. *38* (1948), p. 55.

Timofeev, M. P., 1951
On methods for determining the heat balance components of the underlying surface. Study Central Geophys. Obs., *27* (89) (1951).

Townsend, A. A., 1958
The effects of radiative transfer on turbulent flow of a stratified fluid. J. Fluid Mech. *4* (1958), p. 361–375.

Ulrich, R., 1894
Untersuchungen über die Wärmekapazität der Bodenkonstituenten. Forschung Gebiete Agr.-Physik *17* (1894), p. 1.

U.S. Atomic Energy Commission, 1955
Meteorology and atomic energy, U.S. Atomic Energy Comm., Washington, D.C. (1955), p. 71.

Veihmeyer, F. J. and A. H. Hendrickson, 1949
Methods of measuring field capacity and permanent wilting percentage of soil. Soil Sci. *68* (1949), p. 75–94.

VERHOEVEN, B., 1953
Salt and moisture conditions in soils flooded with seawater. Thesis Wageningen.

VERYARD, R. G., 1958
Some climatological aspects of air pollution. Smokeless Air *106* (1958), p. 277.

VOLZ, F., 1954
Die Optik und Meteorologie der atmosphärischen Trübung. Ber. Deutschen Wetterdienstes *2* (1954), Nr. 13.

VOS, A. S., 1953
Methodes en instrumenten voor het meten van temperatuur en het gebruik van thermistors als nieuwe mogelijkheden ervoor. Chem. Weekbl. *49* (1953), p. 68–76.

VOS, J. C. DE, 1953
The emissivity of tungsten ribbon. Thesis Amsterdam.

VRIES, D. A. DE, 1952
Het warmtegeleidingsvermogen van grond. Thesis. Meded. Landbouwhogeschool, Wageningen *52* (1) (1952), p. 1–73.

VRIES, D. A. DE and C. T. DE WIT, 1954
Die thermischen Eigenschaften der Moorböden und die Beeinflussung der Nachtfrostgefahr dieser Böden durch eine Sanddecke. Met. Rundschau *7* (1954), p. 41–45.

VRIES, D. A. DE, 1955
Solar radiation at Wageningen. Meded. Landbouwhogeschool, Wageningen *55* (6) (1955), p. 277–304.

VRIES, D. A. DE, 1958a
Two years of solar radiation measurements at Deniliquin. Austr. Met. Mag. *22* (1958), p. 36–49.

VRIES, D. A. DE, 1958b
Simultaneous transfer of heat and moisture in porous media. Trans. Am. Geophys. Union *39* (1958), p. 909–916.

WADLEIGH, C. H., 1955
Soil moisture in relation to plant growth. Water, the yearbook of agriculture. The U.S. Dept. of Agriculture.

WARN, G. F., 1953
Drought and dust on the plains. Weatherwise *6* (1953), p. 67.

WARTENA, L., 1959
The climate and the evaporation from a lake in central Iraq. Thesis. Meded. Landbouwhogeschool, Wageningen *59* (9) (1959), p. 1–90. (Dutch).

WARTENA, L. and A. J. W. BORGHORST, 1961
The energy balance of an evaporation pan and the measurement of the reflectivity of its bottom. Q. J. Roy. Met. Soc. (1961), p. 245–249.

WASSINK, E. C., 1956
On the mechanism of photosynthesis, *vide* Radiation biology, Vol. III (1956), p. 293–342.

WENDELL HENSON, E., 1953
Atmospheric pollution in relation to microclimatology and micrometeorology: some problems. Proc. of the Toronto Met. Conference (1953), p. 240.

WENTCHKEWITCH, G. Z., 1958
Agrometeorology. Hydrometeor. Publ., Leningrad (Russian).

WESSELING, J. and W. R. VAN WIJK, 1955
Optimal depth of drainage. Neth. J. of Agr. Sci. *3* (1955), p. 106–126.

WESSELING, J., 1957
Some aspects of the water government in agricultural soils. Thesis Wageningen. Versl. Landbouwk. Onderz. *63* (5) (1957), p. 90.

WESSELING, J. and W. R. VAN WIJK, 1957
Soil physical conditions in relation to drain depth. Drainage of agricultural lands. Agronomy, Vol. VII (1957), Am. Soc. Agro. p. 461–504.

WEST, E. S., 1932
The effect of a soil mulch on temperature. Austr. Counc. Sci. Ind. Res. J. *5* (4) 1932, p. 236–246.

WEXLER, H., 1950
The great smoke pall – September 24–30, 1950. Weatherwise *3* (1950).

WIEN, W., 1896
Ann. Phys. *58*, p. 662

WILLET, H. C., 1944
Descriptive meteorology. Acad. Press, New York.

WIT, C. T. DE, 1953
A physical theory on placement of fertilizers. Thesis Wageningen. Versl. Landbouwk. Onderz. *59* (4) (1953), 71 pp.

WIT, C. T. DE, 1954
An oscillating psychrometer for micrometeorological purposes. Appl. Sci. Res. A *4* (1954), p. 120–126.

WIT, C. T. DE, 1958
Transpiration and crop yields. Versl. Landbouwk. Onderz. *64* (6) (1958).

WOOD, R. W., 1909
Note on the theory of the greenhouse. Phil. Mag. (1909), p. 319.

WÜST, G., 1920
Die Verdunstung auf dem Meere (German). Inst. für Meereskunde, Veröff. Berlin, A *6* (1920).

WIJK, W. R. VAN and C. T. DE WIT, 1951
A physical theory of fertilizer placement. Landbouwk. Tijdschrift *63* (1951), p. 764–775. (Dutch; English summary).

WIJK, W. R. VAN and D. A. DE VRIES, 1952
Weer en klimaat. F. Bohn, Haarlem.

WIJK, W. R. VAN and D. A. DE VRIES, 1954
Evapotranspiration. Neth. J. Agr. Sci. *2* (1954), p. 105–119.

WIJK, W. R. VAN and A. P. HIDDING, 1955
Onderzoek over de verandering van het klimaat achter windschermen. Landbouwk. Tijdschrift *67* (1955), p. 707–712.

WIJK, W. R. VAN, W. J. DERKSEN and H. GOEDKOOP HZN, 1959
On turbulent heat exchange in the air near the ground. Physica *25* (1959).

WIJK, W. R. VAN, W. E. LARSON and W. C. BURROWS, 1959
Soil temperature and the early growth of corn from mulched and unmulched soil. Proc. Soil Sci. Soc. Am. *23* (6) (1959), p. 428–434.

WIJK, W. R. VAN and J. DE WILDE, 1962
Proceedings of the Paris symposium 1960. Arid Zone Research *18*, Unesco, Paris (1962), p. 83–113.

ZUIDHOF, G. and D. A. DE VRIES, 1940
Radiation measurements at Wageningen. Meded. Landbouwhogeschool, Wageningen *44* (4) (1940), p. 1–18. (Dutch).

LIST OF TABLES

CH. 2. THE ATMOSPHERE AND THE SOIL

Composition of the atmosphere, 21
Physical properties of water-free air, 36
Physical properties of ice, 40
Physical properties of liquid water, 41
Physical properties of saturated water vapor, 42
Diffusion coefficient of water vapor in air, 42
Relative saturation vapor pressure at 15°C, 47
Hydraulic conductivity of saturated soil, 51
Hydraulic conductivity of unsaturated soil, 53
Particle size distribution of soils, 54

CH. 3. RADIATION

Depletion of solar radiation by atmospheric constituents, 79
Normal spectral irradiancy at sea level, 79
Short-wave radiation on horizontal surface, 80
Monthly average of daily total global radiation, 84
Values of α and β in equation (3.28), 84
Values of α in Ångström's linear regression equation, 86
Reflection factors of natural surfaces for total global radiation, 87
Absorption coefficient of solar radiation in water, 88
Reflection and transmission of leaves for short-wave radiation, 89
Absorption factors of natural surfaces for long wave radiation, 91
Net radiation loss of the earth's surface, 93
Values of a and b in Brunt's formula, 96
Values of constants a, b and γ in Ångström's formula, 96

CH. 4. PERODIC TEMPERATURE VARIATIONS IN A HOMOGENEOUS SOIL

Thermal properties of soil constituents at 20°C, 105
Average thermal properties of soils and snow, 110
Effect of roughness and wind velocity on the heat wave, 128, 129
Annual heat wave in the soil for different climates, 132
Scheme for calculation of first order Fourier coefficients, 136
Scheme for calculation of Fourier coefficients of soil temperature, 137
Average temperature, amplitudes and phase shifts, Fourier components, 139

CH. 5. GENERAL TEMPERATURE VARIATIONS IN A HOMOGENEOUS SOIL

Values of the error function, 146
Initial temperature as a function of depth in Iowa Silt Loam, 147
Calculation of transient term for Iowa Silt Loam, 148
Thermal diffusivity and damping depth for sand, clay and peat, 169
Thermal diffusivity for a sandy soil, 170
Diurnal temperatures in a sandy soil, 170

CH. 6. SINUSOIDAL TEMPERATURE VARIATION IN A LAYERED SOIL

Amplitude and phase in a soil consisting of two layers, 173
Thermal properties of a sandy soil after tilth, 183
Comparison of uncultivated and ploughed clay soil, 191
Measured and calculated data for the diurnal wave in a sandy soil, 193
Properties of sand and peat both at field capacity, 193
Change of pore volume after tilth, 196
Thermal properties of dry sand and of dry peat, 201
Thermal properties of snow and of dry humus, 204
Data pertaining to a peat soil covered with sand, 207

CH. 7. THERMAL PROPERTIES OF SOIL

Thermal properties and densities of some materials, 210
Specific heat values and densities of several soils, 212
Specific heat values and densities of several organic soils, 212
Specific heat values and densities of several soil minerals, 213
Experimental and computed values of the thermal conductivity, 231, 232, 234

CH. 8. TURBULENT TRANSFER IN AIR

Approximate values of apparent thermal diffusivity above Paris, 245
Evolution of heat flux as dependent on the underlying medium, 248
Representative values of z_0 and $\sqrt{(\tau_0/\varrho)}$ for natural surfaces, 252
Calculation of b for heat impulse, 263
Evapotranspiration and yields of agricultural crops, 272

CH. 9. THE GLASSHOUSE (GREENHOUSE) CLIMATE

Some characteristics of various types of glasshouses, 284
Typical daylight coefficient for a number of glasshouses, 287
Temperature observations during a cold spell in glasshouses, 296
The efficiency of various light sources in the spectral ranges, 308
Examples of usage of light sources in horticulture, 309
Comparative results of a ventilation experiment, 312
Comparison of evaporation in identical glasshouses, 314,315

CH. 10. ATMOSPHERIC POLLUTION

Quantity of chlorine as a function of distance from the coast, 321
Time concentration relationships for different degrees of injury, 328
Effect of relative humidity on sensitivity to SO_2, 329
The constant C as a function of H and n, 341
Maximum concentration of pollant at ground level, 342
Fall velocity of spherical particles, 346
Mean daily ground concentrations of SO_2 in the center of Londen, 353

SUBJECT INDEX

absorption coefficient, 64
– factors of leaves, 90
– in clouds, 79
–, water, 88
adiabatic expansion, 35
advective air, 245
aerosol, 319
agricultural engineering, 2
air circulation, 292
– mass, optical, 77
– pressure units, 22
albedo, 88
Angot's values, 76
atmosphere, composition, 20
–, pollution, 319
–, structure, 17
Austausch, 240, 244
barometric height, 33
Bénard cell, 32
black body, 65
bolometer, 99
Bouguer–Lambert's law, 64
Bowen's ratio, 241, 281
brightness, 90
Campbell–Stokes, 85, 99
candela, 90
carbon dioxide, 310, 317, 326
climate control, 293, 304, 318
clouds, absorption, 79
complex amplitude, 174, 207
– numbers, 111
condensation nuclei, 321, 324
conductivity, apparent thermal, 221
–, constant thermal, 244
–, hydraulic, 50
–, thermal, 103, 213, 214, 223
contact coefficient, 173, 259
Coriolis force, 23
crop yield, 7, 268
damping depth, 12, 109, 110, 169, 173, 257
Darcy's law, 49
daylight coefficient, 286, 295
density, 212, 213

dew point, 38
diffusion, pollution, 334
diffusivity, thermal, 107, 140, 169, 210
distribution, spores, 322
drainage, 13, 49
Duhamel's theorem, 259
dust, 320
– counter, 331
eddy velocity, 236
emittancy, 63
energy balance, 11, 114, 279
engineering, agricultural, 2
error function, 147
evaporation, 273, 281, 313
evapotranspiration, 270
exchange coefficient, 240, 250
–, molecular, 238
–, turbulent, 240
extinction coefficient, 65
fertilizer placement, 3
field capacity, 52, 182, 229
Fourier analysis, 133, 148, 191
frictional force, 30
friction velocity, 32
frost, penetration, 166
– point, 38
gases, noxious, 325, 327
Gibbs free energy, 48
glasshouse, 277
–, heating, 297
–, orientation, 295
–, plastic, 295
–, pollution, 294
–, types, 283
granular materials, 214
Grashof number, 32
greenhouse–effect, 277
growth curve, 205
heat balance, 274
– capacity, 211
– –, measurement, 163
– conduction, 103
– –, measurement, 163

– flux, 114, 177, 247, 288
– – ratio, 124, 258
– release, 118, 149, 151
– specific, 35, 110, 212, 213
– storage, 118, 149, 151
– wave, 128, 129, 132, 257
humidity, 37
–, effect on leaf damage, 329
– measurement, 57
ice, properties, 40
illumination, 90
impactor, 332
inertial force, 30
inversion, 18
ionosphere, 20
irradiancy, 63
isobar, 23
Kirchhoff's law, 65
Lambert's law, 67
Lamont's correction, 139, 144
Laplace transform, 156, 261
lapse rate, dry adiabatic, 18, 26, 36, 39, 348
– –, wet adiabatic, 28, 39
Lehenbauer's growth curve, 205
Liegean sphere, 331
light sources, 308
–, transmitted through crop, 102
lumen, 90
luminous intensity, 90
microclimate, 266
mixing length, 236, 251
– ratio, 38
moist air, density, 38
moisture movement, 218
– sorption curve, 229
mulch, 13, 171, 203, 267
night frost, 13, 125, 198
osmotic pressure, 45
ozone, 25
Penman's formula, 275, 313
permeability, saturated, 49
–, unsaturated, 51
phase constant, 113, 173
photodiodes, 99
photosynthesis, 70, 89, 307, 309
Planck's law, 68
plant radiation, 307

Poiseuille's law, 50
Poisson's law, 36
pollution, atmospheric, 319
–, diffusion, 334
–, fall velocity, 346
–, influence lapse rate, 347
– measurements, 330
–, particulate, 324, 326
pore space, 48, 183, 195
precipitation, 332
pressure head, 52
psychrometer, 57
– constant, 242, 281
pyrheliometer, 99
radiancy, 63
radiation, atmosperic, 92
– balance of the earth, 97
– influence on plants, 307
–, long wave, 74
– measurements, 99
–, net, 93, 285
–, net long wave, 185
–, short-wave, 74
–, terrestrial, 91
–, total global, 81, 99
–, total net, 100
Raoult's law, 45
Rayleigh number, 32
– scattering, 76
reflection factor, 65, 88
Reynolds number, 31
Richardson number, 31
Ringelmann chart, 331
roughness, 127
– height, 31, 251
– parameter, 31, 251
sea water droplets, 321
shearing stress, 30
shelterbelt, 254
smog, 319
snow properties, 110, 204
soil air, 49
– composition, 48
–, homogeneous, 103
–, layered, 171, 206
– moisture measurement, 59
– – tension, 52

– properties, 105, 110, 169, 183, 193, 195, 201, 204, 210
–, saturated, 49
– temperature, 10, 102, 171, 206
– texture, 48
–, unsaturated, 51
– water, 48
solar battery, 99
– constant, 73
– radiation, 73
solarimeter, 99
stability, dynamic, 29
–, hydrostatic, 25
stack height, 337, 343
Stephan–Boltzmann's law, 67
steradiancy, 63, 70, 71
stilb, 90
storage of heat, 118, 149, 151
stratosphere, 19
summer crop, 198
temperature, annual variation, 109, 112, 130, 187
–, diurnal variation, 109, 112, 183, 258
–, general variation, 144, 259
–, glasshouse, 279, 291, 305
– lapse rate, 18, 26, 28, 36, 39, 348
– measurement, 55
–, periodic variations, 102, 108, 171, 244, 254
–, potential, 25
–, radiant, 70
– regime, 121, 127
–, sinusoidal variation, 102, 108, 145, 171, 254
–, soil, 10, 144, 160, 180, 190

–, stratosphere, 23
–, surface, 102, 177
–, troposphere, 23
–, virtual, 39
tensiometer, 59
thawing, 166
thermistor, 56
thermocouple, 57
thermometer, 55
tilth, 10, 181
transient term, 144
transmission factor, 65
tropopause, 17
troposphere, 17
turbidity, 76
turbulence, 236, 347
Van 't Hoff's law, 46
vapor pressure, saturation, 42, 45
ventilation, 282, 296, 310
viscosity, dynamic, 30, 239
–, eddy, 240
–, kinematic, 31, 239
water, properties, 41
– requirement of crops, 267
– supply, 317
– vapor, properties, 42
Wien's displacement law, 67
wilting, 54
wind, 236
– function, 273, 274
– profile, 250, 274, 340
– screen, 254
window for radiation, 92
winter crop, 198
yield, 7, 268

AUTHOR INDEX

ACKLEY, CH., *vide* MAYILL, P. L.
ALBRECHT, F., 77, 131
ALISOW, B. P., 78, 87, 266
ALKALI, I. C. I., 84
ALLEN, C. W., *vide* RIMMER, W. B.
ANDERSON, A. B. C., *vide* EDLEFSEN, N. E.
ANDERSON, E. R., 95, 96
ANDERSON, J. H., *vide* HALL, N. S.
ANGOT, A., 75, 76, 244
ÅNGSTRÖM, A., 86, 87, 89, 95, 96, 99
ASKLÖF, S., 96
BADEN, W., 199
BARAD, M. L., 340, 348
BARNES, E. C., 332
BAVEL, C. H. M. VAN, 59
BEERS, N. R., *vide* BERRY Jr., F. A.
BELCHER, D. J., 59
BÉNARD, M., 32
BENER, P., 99
BERLIAND, O. S., 250
BERNHARDT, F., 78, 79, 80
BERRY, Jr., F. A., 81, 87
BEST, N., 24
BLACK, J. N., 78, 84, 85
BLANCHARD, D. C., 321
BLANEY, H. F., 272, 276
BOER, J. H., *vide* SCHMIDT, F. A.
BOLLAY, E., *vide* BERRY Jr., F. A.
BOLTZMANN, L., 67
BOLZ, H. M., 96
BONYTHON, C. W., *vide* BLACK, J. N.
BORGHORST, A. J. W., *vide* WARTENA, L.
BÖRNSTEIN, R., 89, 213
BOSANQUET, C. H., 336, 337, 339
BOUMAN, D. J., 352
BOUTARIC, A., 96
BOUYOUCOS, G. J., 60
BOWEN, I. S., 242, 280, 281, 284
BRACHT, J., 211, 212
BRAY, J. R., 326
BRIGGS, L. J., 271
BRIND, W. D., *vide* JACKS, G. V.
BROCKS, K., 20
BROOKS, F. A., 96, 252, 267
BROUWER, R., 70
BRUIJN, P. J., 72, 166
BRUINENBERG, A., 94

BRUNT, D., 32, 39, 40, 94, 95, 153
BUDYKO, M. I., 78, 243, 250, 266
BURGER, H. C., 214
BURROWS, W. C., 204
BUSINGER, J. A., 31, 289, 300, 304, 310, 313
BYERS, H. G., 217, 218
CANHAM, A. E., 309
CARMAN, P. C., 51
CARSLAW, H. S., 150, 154, 156, 259
CHANDLER, W. F., *vide* HALL, N. S.
CHILDS, E. C., 3, 49, 52, 54
CHUDNOVSKII, 267
COLEMAN, T. D., *vide* CRONEY, D.
COLLIS-GEORGE, N., 52, 54
COLMAN, E. A., 60
CRIDDLE, W. D., *vide* BLANEY, H. F.
CRONEY, D., 60
CROOKS, R. M., *vide* STEWART, M. G.
CSANADY, G. T., 346
CURRER, E. W. H., *vide* CRONEY, D.
CUYKENDALL, T. R., *vide* BELCHER, D. J.
DARCY, H., 49, 50
DEACON, E. L., 94
DEE, R. W. R., 82, 86
DERKSEN, W. J., *vide* WIJK, W. R. VAN
DESAI, B. N., 96
DINES, L. H. G., 96
DINES, W. H., 96
DOETSCH, G., 156, 162
DROSDOW, O. A., 78, 266
DUHAMEL, J. Ec., 154, 259
DUIN, R. H. A. VAN, 10, 11, 12, 181, 182, 188, 191, 192, 193, 269
DZERDZEEVSKII, B. D., 254, 266, 267, 276
ECKEL, O., 96
EDLEFSEN, N. E., 48
EDWARDS, R. I., *vide* MORRIS, L. G.
EGNER, H., *vide* EMANUELSSON, A.
ELSASSER, W. M., 94
EMANUELSSON, A., 322
ENDE, J. V. D., 317
ERIKSSON, E., *vide* EMANUELSSON, A.
EVELYN, J., 319
FALCKENBERG, G., 96
FESHBACH, H., 147
FRANK, P., 147
GAASTRA, P., 89

GABRIELSEN, 309
GADE, C., 191
GALE, H. J., *vide* STEWART, M. G.
GARDNER, W., 59
GEIGER, R., 19, 87, 89, 191, 266
GERMING, A., 295, 309
GIFFORD, F., 343
GINSEL, L. A., 294
GOEDKOOP HZN., H., *vide* WIJK, W. R. VAN
GOSS, J. R., 96
GRASHOF, 32
GRAY, H. E., 306
GROEN, P., 153
GUGGENHEIM, E. A., 45, 48
GULIK, D. VAN, 277
GUSTAFSON, P. E., *vide* JUNGE, CHR. E.
GUSTAFSSON, Y., 3, 49, 51
HALL, N. S., 205
HAND, I. F., 326
HARBECK, Jr., G. E., *vide* MARCIANO, J. J.
HAUGEN, D. A., *vide* BARAD, M. L.
HAURWITZ, B., 86, 250
HAVENS, R., *vide* BEST, N.
HELD, E. F. VAN DER, 58
HELLMANN, G., 252
HENDRICKSON, A. H., 182
HENDRIX, T. M., 60
HIDDING, A. P., *vide* WIJK, W. R. VAN
HOARE, E., 299, 311
HOELPER, O., 83
HOLDEN, F. R., *vide* MAYILL, P. L.
HOLLDACK, H., 191
HOLMES, J. W., 59
JACKS, G. V., 267
JACOBS, W. C., 323
JAEGER, J. C. *vide* CARSLAW, H. S.
JUNGE, CHR. E., 322, 324
JUUSELA, T., 199
KASTROW, 78
KEEN, B. A., 191
KEPNER, 252
KERSTEN, M. S., 211, 212, 217, 218, 230, 232, 233
KIEFER, P. J., 27
KIMBALL, H. H., 77, 79, 86, 91, 96
KIRCHHOFF, 65
KIRKHAM, D., 3, 49, 59

KLOEPPEL, R., 197
KÖHLER, H., 250
KOPECKI, J., 183
KÖPPEN, W., 363
KRAUSSE, M., 196
KREUTZ, W., 120, 199, 317
KRISCHER, O., 218, 219, 220, 222, 227
KRONIG, R., 77, 237
LA GOW, H., *vide* BEST, N.
LAICHTMAN, D. L., 250, 267
LAMBERT, J. H., 67
LAMONT, 140, 144
LANDOLT, 89, 213
LANG, C., 211, 212, 213
LARSON, W. E., 204
LAWRENCE, W. J. C., 294, 295
LEEFLANG, K. W. H., 321
LEHENBAUER, P. A., 205
LETTAU, H., 31, 245, 250
LIN, C. C., 31
LORCH, J., 253
LOWRY, PH. H., 343
LUCAS, D. H., 351
LUNELUND, H., 86
LUTHIN, J. N., 3, 14
LYKOW, A. W., 218
MACHE, H., 220
MAKKINK, G. F., 276
MALONE, T. F., 323
MARCIANO, J. J., 273
MASON, B. J., 321
MAYILL, B. L., 346
McADAMS, W. H., 288, 298
McCABE, L. C., 330
MEETHAM, A. R., 324, 333
MIDDLETON, J. T., 320
MILLER, E. E., 365
MILLER, R. D., *vide* MILLER, E. E.
MITSCHERLICH, E. A., 198
MONIN, A. S., 250
MONTEITH, J. L., 58
MOON, P., 79
MOORE, D. C., 53, 54
MORRIS, L. G., 299, 310, 311, 316, 317
MORSE, P. M., 147
MOSBY, H., 86
MUSKAT, M., 49

MUYZENBERG, E. W. B. VAN DEN, 278, 294
NAKAMURA, T., 139
NEALE, F. E., *vide* MORRIS, L. G.
NEIBURGER, M., 81
NEKRASSOV, 196
NEUMANN, F., 167
NIELSEN, D., 60
NITZSCH, W. VON, 191, 197
OBUCHOV, A. M., 31, 250
O'GARA, 327, 328, 329
PAESCHKE, W., 252
PALMEN, E. VON, 24
PASQUILL, F., 335
PEARSON, J. L., 336, 337, 339
PEERLKAMP, P. K., 136, 172
PENMAN, H. L., 58, 84, 97, 269, 270, 272, 274, 275, 282, 313, 316
PETERSON, A. E., 102
PHILIP, J. R., 3, 51, 52, 54, 95, 218, 220
PHILIPS, E. R., 60
PHILLIPS, H., 78, 79, 80
PLANCK, M., 68, 70, 92
POPPENDIECK, H. F., 243, 250
POSTLETHWAITE, J. D., *vide* MORRIS, L. G.
PRANDTL, L., 237
PRESCOTT, J. A., *vide* BLACK, J. N.
PRIESTLEY, C. H. B., 32, 241, 243, 247, 248
PROHASKA, F., 86
RAMAN, P. K., 82
RAMANATHAN, K. R., 96
RAMDAS, L. A., 19, 121, 242, 243
RAYLEIGH, LORD, 32, 150
REESINCK, J. J. M., 82, 86, 91
REID, P. H., *vide* HALL, N. S.
RENARD, 306
REYNOLDS, 29, 31, 50
RICHARDS, L. A., 53, 54, 59, 60
RICHARDSON, L. F., 31
RIDER, N. E., 241
RIMMER, W. B., 84
ROBITZSCH, M., 96
ROHNALTER, H., 219, 220, 222, 227
ROMANOVA, 254
ROODENBURG, J. W. H., 308, 309
RUBINSTEIN, E. S., 78, 266
RUSSEL, M. B., 368
SACK, H. S., *vide* BELCHER, D. J.

SAUBERER, F., 86
SCHARRINGA, M., 287
SCHEIDEGGER, A. E., 51
SCHIELDRUP, P. H., 83
SCHIRMER, R., 220
SCHLICHTING, H., 31
SCHMIDT, F. H., 339, 341, 346, 349, 352, 355
SCHMIDT, W., 191, 240, 244, 245, 246,
SCHOLTE-UBING, D. W., 87, 94, 100, 269, 276, 285
SCHUBERT, J., 170
SCHULZE, L., 286, 287, 295
SCHULZE, R., 101
SCHWIND, R., 191
SEEMAN, J., 294, 295, 318
SHANTZ, H. L., *vide* BRIGGS, L. J.
SHAW, B. T., 10
SHAW, W. N., 252
SHEPPARD, P. A., 252
SHERLOCK, R. H., 350
SLATYER, R. O., 54
SMITH, F. B., 338
SMITH, M. E., 349
SMITH, R., *vide* JACKS, G. V.
SMITH, W. O., 217, 218, 224
SPOELSTRA, P. A., 302
STALKER, E. A., 350
STEFAN, J., 67
STERK, M. J., 258
STEVENSON, 55, 58
STEWART, M. G., 350
SUMMERHAYS, W. E., 220
SUOMI, V. E., 276
SÜRING, F., 169
SUTTON, O. G., 19, 31, 32, 266, 336, 337, 338, 339, 340, 341, 343, 346, 348, 349, 350
SVERDRUP, H. U., 274
SWINBANK, W. C., 241, 243, 250
SWANSON, R. W., *vide* BAVEL, C. H. M. VAN
TAMURA, T., 139
TANNER, C. B., 102, 276
TAYLOR, G. I., 238, 244
THORNTHWAITE, C. W., 276
TIMOFEEV, M. P., 250
TOWNSEND, A. A., 33

TRYSELIUS, O., 86
ULRICH, R., 211, 212, 213
UNDERWOOD, N., *vide* BAVEL, C. H. M. VAN
VEIHMEYER, F. J., 182
VENEMA, 316
VERHOEVEN, B., 272
VERYARD, R. G., 326, 327
VITCHKII, 254
VOLZ, F., 77
VOS, A. S., 56
VOS, J. C., DE, 70
VRIES, D. A. DE, 18, 59, 83, 84, 85, 86, 87, 88,
    91, 97, 200, 201, 211, 212, 213, 218, 220,
    222, 223, 231, 276, 288, 316
WADLEIGH, C. H., 52
WARN, G. F., 320
WARTENA, L., 86, 95, 273
WASSINK, E. C., 89

WELECZKA, J., *vide* SEEMAN, J.
WENDELL HENSON, E., 322
WENTCHKEWITCH, G. Z., 372
WESSELING, J., 14, 15, 16, 272
WEST, E. S., 192, 193
WEXLER, H., 321
WHITTLE, 283
WIEN, W., 67
WIJK, W. R., VAN, 3, 14, 15, 18, 166, 204,
    254, 261, 267, 272, 276
WILDE, J. DE, *vide* WIJK, W. R. VAN
WILKINS, 353
WILLET, H. C., 97
WIT, C. T. DE, 3, 5, 6, 7, 8, 9, 58, 200, 201,
    211, 212, 270
WOOD, R. W., 277
WOODCOCK, A. H., *vide* BLANCHARD, D. C.
WÜST, G., 252
ZUIDHOF, G., 88